PENGU

CHOPPING DOWN

Linda Christmas was born in
journalist in 1966 and worked
and *The Times Educational Supplement* before joining the *Guardian*
in 1971 where she remained as a feature writer for eleven years.
Since 1982 she has been a freelance journalist writing for several
national daily newspapers and also for BBC2's *Newsnight*. She is
currently Senior Lecturer in Jornalism at City University, London.
Chopping Down the Cherry Trees is her second book. The first, *The
Ribbon and the Ragged Square*, a portrait of contemporary Australia,
is also published by Penguin.

CHOPPING DOWN
THE CHERRY TREES

A PORTRAIT OF BRITAIN IN THE EIGHTIES

LINDA CHRISTMAS

PENGUIN BOOKS

To Peter Carson

PENGUIN BOOKS

Published by the Penguin Group
Penguin Books Ltd, 27 Wrights Lane, London w8 5tz, England
Viking Penguin, a division of Penguin Books USA Inc.
375 Hudson Street, New York, New York 10014, USA
Penguin Books Australia Ltd, Ringwood, Victoria, Australia
Penguin Books Canada Ltd, 2801 John Street, Markham, Ontario, Canada, l3r 1b4
Penguin Books (NZ) Ltd, 182–190 Wairau Road, Auckland 10, New Zealand

Penguin Books Ltd, Registered Offices: Harmondsworth, Middlesex, England

First published by Viking 1990
Published in Penguin Books 1991
1 3 5 7 9 10 8 6 4 2

Printed in England by Clays Ltd, St Ives plc

Contents

Acknowledgements

I wish to thank warmly the hundreds of people I met on my journey around Great Britain and Northern Ireland; many gave me hours of their time and some generously allowed me to become part of their lives for several weeks.

I also wish to thank: John Higgins, for his constant support, and Alastair Hetherington, former editor of the *Guardian* and latterly Research Professor at Stirling University, for reading the manuscript and offering advice and guidance.

Preface

He wakes me before 7 a.m. at least one morning a week. In summer it is often nearer 6 a.m. His favourite day is Saturday, so often on Friday evenings I find myself wondering whether I have anything special to leave out for Squeak. I began by calling him the Squeaky Man, but that soon got shortened to Squeak. He acquired that nickname because it is the sound I associate with him: he opens the dustbin lid and it squeaks in response. For several weeks I watched him from a window two floors above. His appearance is striking. He is tall and well built, aged around fifty, and he wears dark-rimmed glasses, the kind that were fashionable in the seventies. His dark hair is slicked back carefully, but no arrangement can conceal the bald patch. He wears a Guernsey sweater and fawn trousers in summer and in winter a fawn-coloured raincoat. His movements are slow and deliberate. He carefully lifts everything from the two bins, sorts through the lot, putting selected items into plastic bags he has brought with him, and packs the discards back so neatly that I end up with model dustbins. He is looking for food, wine and copies of the *Daily Telegraph*. He rejects the *Mail*, *Times*, *Guardian* and *Independent* and takes only the *Telegraph*. He is equally fussy about food. He likes sausages and chocolate biscuits but shuns brie and yoghurt. When he comes across a wine bottle he puts it to his lips and twists it expertly to catch the last remaining drops. He then peruses the label on the bottle.

After watching Squeak for several weeks, I raced down stairs one morning and tried to talk to him. Although we were a mere six feet apart, he ignored me and, picking up his plastic bags, walked slowly away.

I called: 'I only want to help. Maybe I could put aside the things you want, to save you going through the bins.' He continued to walk. The position of his head said it all; it was held high. I decided to leave him his dignity.

Squeak puzzles me. Is he the stigma of the eighties? In fifteen years of living in the same north London square no one has dabbled in my dustbins before. We hear much of the London homeless, those who are sleeping in cardboard boxes. The media dwell on the young people who say they come to the capital looking for jobs; but of older men we know little. We don't even know exact numbers, all we know is that they appear to have grown. The Salvation Army and the University of Surrey are working together to assess the numbers and the causes and to try to discover alternative accommodation. It's shocking to feel that in this rich country there are thousands of Squeaks, homeless, living in squats, rummaging in dustbins for bits and pieces. But it is not the only shocking statistic: there is growing violence and there is massive unemployment. And of these three, it was unemployment that first turned my thoughts to writing this book.

In 1986 3 million people, 11 per cent of the working population, were unemployed. The figure was so horrific that comedians made tasteless jokes: 'In 1972 we had 1 million unemployed and it was suggested they be put to work sweeping up the leaves. Now there are 3 million – that's enough to catch the bloody leaves!' In the autumn of 1986 there was a symbolic march of the unemployed from Jarrow to London: a handful of men chose to draw attention to the plight of the north-east of England by retracing the steps of Depression victims. Their march ended in Trafalgar Square one sunny autumn Sunday. I went along expecting huge crowds and emotional speeches. The speeches were loud and the crowd was thin; I walked around with ease listening to the foreign tongues of tourists. Where was the voice of the unemployed? What was happening? The rich were getting richer, the poor were getting poorer, there were many more of them and yet there was no anger. Were the unemployed of the north unable to make the journey south? Were the unemployed in the south too cowed to care? Were the employed too complacent to show their concern?

What was going on? We heard so much of divisions; of a growing north–south divide; of Scotland disowning the ways of Conservative-voting England; of Northern Ireland 'loyalists' doubting their allegiance to a country that had dumped an unpalatable 'Agreement' on them.

That the eighties are an age of transition is beyond doubt. Mrs Margaret Thatcher became Prime Minister in 1979; she inherited the leadership of a country that had once been a great industrial power and a great world power and had for several decades been lamenting the decline from that pinnacle. It had lost the recipe for its earlier success and seemed incapable of finding another. There had been much talk, endless talk, about the reasons for this decline, and yet no one seemed capable of halting the debilitating drift, let alone reversing the situation. The nation appeared mentally to have put on its slippers and seemed content to sit by the fire and recall its prestige-laden past; the nation seemed weary, satisfied to bumble along, muddle through, watching the embers die and having enough energy only to spring to life through yet another strike, yet another fight in the age-old battle between management and labour.

Mrs Thatcher had other ideas. She had a recipe, a potion for waking us up. She ordered us to adopt a new attitude; she began by inviting change and demanding changes in a country that seems to loathe every word. Like a boy-scout she found a couple of sticks, which was about all we had in the national cupboard, and, rubbing them together, she let sparks fly as she lit fire after fire. Monumental fires, like the Falklands War and the year-long miners' strike; massive fires, like the privatization of industries that had been cossetted for forty years. In turn these lit mini fires; the phone boxes are no longer red; the buses have shrunk in size. As she set about whipping us into action there were shrieks and gasps from every corner. She wanted us to become entrepreneurs rather than passive employees; she wanted us to own our own homes; she wanted us to own shares as well as cars. She wanted us to stop looking to national and local government to solve our problems and instead mould our own lives and make our own decisions. As well as kicking us, she kicked our institutions too, whether they were museums no one visited or the health service that everyone used. Each was prodded out of its cobwebbed corner and called to account. Doctors raised their voices in protest, the schools were in a ferment of change, the universities were limping, lawyers whimpered. The government was poking its nose into everything. And Mrs Thatcher was being called all sorts of names: a few described her as the greatest peacetime leader, but most of the titles were derogatory, from the Iron Lady to Empress of all the Finchleys. In my circle of friends it became impossible to say anything kind; to attempt to do so was a worse social solecism than belching. To attempt to point out that much Thatcher-baiting had its roots in impotence – an impotence caused by there being no effective opposition of any name, or any colour – was to invite derision.

The seed that was sown with the unemployment figures was watered by confusion, and fertilized by unconstructive antagonism towards the one person who refused to sit around and 'talk' and instead took action. Rather than curse the darkness I decided to light a candle and make a journey through the UK and see what picture would emerge once I had left egotistical London, where everything is seen not just through a southern prism, but through a tiny lens of Westminster and Whitehall; where the so-called opinion formers begin with 'policy' and end with 'people'. I'd make a journey starting at the most northerly point, working my way south back to London. I'd up-end Britain and put London in its place and set about refuting the charge that we southerners know nothing about things north of Finchley, an accusation which for the most part is true. My task was to look and listen and learn about a country that I had taken for granted. At the age of eighteen I had discovered the joys of travel, but my fascination had been with other countries, other societies, other ways of doing things. I knew our 'relatives' passing well: I had made a dozen trips to America in the seventies and spent a year in Australia in the early eighties. I had visited several countries where British influence had been profound – Malaysia, Sri Lanka, India – but I had also visited those countries whose visions were radically different from our own: Russia, Albania, Cuba and North Korea. Now I wanted to discover the United Kingdom of Great Britain and Northern Ireland.

My path from north to south would zigzag from coast to coast. Every time I hit the west coast, I would head to the east, and vice versa. That seemed a good way of covering as much ground as possible and guaranteed the inclusion of many big cities, which are, after all, where most people live. And on this journey I would pay much attention to areas often ignored, to Shetland and Orkney, to Scotland, to Northern Ireland and Wales. Nowhere was included by chance; I deliberately chose to visit Glasgow rather than Edinburgh and Liverpool rather than Manchester. I played with the map for hours before buying my ticket north, assigning issues that were uppermost in my mind to the areas with which they were most suited. Some marriages were obvious: oil and nuclear power in Scotland, race relations in Bradford. But education, for example, is a worry to us all. I chose to look at a school in Newcastle because in the north-east there are special factors – there is no tradition of higher education in the area. Son followed father out of school as early as possible and into jobs that demanded good muscles rather than trained minds. Such jobs are vanishing; new ones demand qualifications and therefore a change in attitude towards education. Newcastle's battle is the country's fight writ large. I chose to look at lawyers in Bristol because the city has a reputation for legal innovations; I chose to visit the University of East Anglia because it was a 'new' university with a lowish profile and a lot to say.

My aim in each place was to carve out a piece of a jigsaw, which, when fitted together, would form a picture, a mosaic of modern Britain.

My luggage was minimal. I had no political baggage. My allegiance belongs to he who deserves it most on election day. But perhaps it's just as well if I open my bag at the beginning of my journey and try to prove the point. In 1959 I was my school's Labour candidate, which wasn't as grand as it sounds. It meant that there was one debate between three candidates, Labour, Tory and Liberal. My school was in Eastbourne, the safest of Tory seats, and I lost soundly. In 1964 I eagerly used my first vote for Labour. Apart from anything else I wanted to see for myself what a Labour government was all about. The Tories had been in power for thirteen years: I knew nothing else. I voted Labour again in 1966. In 1968 I married a Conservative candidate, Norman Fowler (who was later to spend ten years as a minister in Mrs Thatcher's cabinet), and through three elections remained loyal to that cause. By the late seventies I was divorced and a passionate floating voter. In 1979 I voted for Mrs Thatcher; in 1983 I was in Australia and did not vote and in 1987 I voted for the Liberal/Social Democrat Alliance. I remain deeply interested in politics, but uncommitted; my allegiance to Labour during the sixties had proved disappointing; that decade showed just how far Labour had moved from its basic principles. In the seventies their performance was worse; it was a time of conflict and confusion and economic decline. My allegiance to the Conservative party had brought the only heartfelt political row of my life. My decision to become a floating voter was deliberate. I'm not a wishy-washy Don't Know; I do know. I know that no party has all the answers and I know that political parties change and I reserve the right to change too.

I took with me two special small items: an unusual attitude towards change: others may fear it but I find it fascinating. I believe it releases hidden energy in individuals and in countries. And I took a message from Dr Johnson: 'The use of travelling is to regulate imagination by reality and instead of thinking how things might be, to see them as they are.' I wanted to see things 'as they are', but I knew I could not refrain from thinking how they might be.

Chapter 1

Shetland and the Gift of Oil

That day no fish flew over the lighthouse. It was too calm. As I stood happily marooned on a rock at the northernmost tip of Britain, staring at the seals as they sunbathed and squinting at the sea a hundred feet below, revealing, as it slapped against the rocks, an underskirt of turquoise frilled with white lace, I longed to swap this beguiling midsummer idyll for the wildness of winter; for a fish flying over the lighthouse.

They say that there are times when the sea has no trouble scaling these rocks and that such is the height and impact of the waves that fish have been hurled over the roof and on to the courtyard. Such a visual memento would have been more appropriate than this mendacious impression, this soothing sight of sleeping seals. Lighthouses were not born of picnicking puffins, nor of fulmars fancying themselves in the sun, nor of almost nightless summers with print still legible at midnight. They were born of elemental fury to guide ships through swirling seas on stormy nights when rearing cliffs and broken rocks and hidden reefs threaten sailors.

The sea swells all around this kingdom; nowhere is far from its shore. The sea, citizens are told from earliest schooldays, is of the greatest importance; it dominates our history, providing a natural defence, a source of wealth and fortune and adding imagination and the spirit of adventure to our characters. The catalogue of its blessings is seemingly endless. All of which would be true if we limited our thinking to *recent* history. For something like 1,500 years the most the sea offered was a source of food. Other than that it allowed us to be constantly conquered; it provided a pathway for the Romans, the Danes, the Saxons and the Normans to sail in and settle. The sea did not make Britain great; she became great only when she decided to conquer the sea. She got a taste of success with the defeat of the Spanish Armada that gale-ridden summer some 400 years ago, and she built upon the success until Britannia Ruled the Waves. And here I was sitting among the sea pinks in a pose that would have pleased Millais, and wanting another gale-ridden summer so that fish could fly over the lighthouse.

These thoughts dissolved into a shiver as a voice called to me from the lighthouse. At least it was chilly. The July day might yield only a few hours of darkness, but the temperature up here on a rock called Muckle Flugga, one mile north of the island of Unst, itself the most northerly of the Shetland Islands, was not concerned to match such fluctuations. It couldn't be bothered to go below zero or rise above $15°$. That day, just past midsummer, it hovered around $13°$.

'Come and see the most northerly geraniums,' called Walter Gammach, principal lighthouse keeper. I glanced up at him from a spot halfway between the courtyard and the sea. He looked the part dressed in a black roll-neck sweater and dark trousers, with a greying beard, balding head and missing teeth making him seem older than his fifty years. We'd met that morning a mile from Muckle Flugga, across the sea, at the shore station. Drizzle drained the colour from the landscape but Walter's spirits were in fine form either because he had just had a month on shore, or because he was about to go off-shore for a month. While we waited for the helicopter to effect the shift change, he chattered away to me and to everything else in sight.

'Fire extinguisher . . . I must put you out for the chopper. Marge, away you go to the fridge, and you too, bread.' All the time he fretted over the arrival of the helicopter and kept phoning for an update on its progress. 'Haloo, any update on the chopper? Ay, get me Dave. Dave, any update? Aha, aha. Refuelling is it, aha. Tip me off when it leaves, will you? Ay, it's been hectic these past weeks. My brother died a week past yesterday, and I've been running to Aberdeen. Ay, much obliged, bye for noo.'

In fact, his four years at Muckle Flugga had been marred by family problems which he rattled off complete with dates that were etched on his memory. 'I came here on 8 November 1982. On 11 December my mother died. Then on 27 December my father died. Eighteen months later my sister died and this past week my brother. I just managed to see him. I'm on the lightkeepers' committee now. I was voted in. It is part of the TGWU and I have to go to Aberdeen for meetings from time to time. Fortunate that. I knew my brother was ill and thought it was cancer, but didn't want to rush down and alarm him. The committee meeting gave me a good opportunity. I was just in time. No, this has not been a lucky station.'

And professionally it's been a quiet rock. A light bulb blowing is the limit of excitement. Anyway, he's not the sort to make much of disasters. He told me of one, some years back in Orkney. 'I was trying to put over the weather report and I couldn't get through on the phone. So I thought I'd have a wash down instead. There were no facilities there, only a basin for water. I'd just started and only had a towel around my waist when I saw a flash. I thought it was the weather people ringing me but it turned out to be the coastguard at Kirkwall. A Greek ship had run aground while on autopilot, and it wasn't at all sure where it was. We asked it to light flares from which we could work out its position. The ship turned over in the end and five died.'

The phone rang and Dave gave us the news that the chopper was on its way. Walter clambered into his orange-coloured safety suit and we assembled outside to watch the bright red modern miracle whirl into view and land on a sixpence. 'Close your eyes as it comes into land . . . it blows dust and grit everywhere.' Everything began to happen at double speed. The pilot warned me of the bumps as we headed down the firth. There were no bumps and the journey was much too short; it was over in four minutes. A few more minutes and the couple going on duty had off-loaded the stores, the two going off duty had jumped aboard and the helicopter disappeared, away for its fortnightly visit to the next lighthouse.

Leaving the men to unpack and settle in, I took advantage of the momentary appearance of the sun and strolled to sea-level to tease the seals, who slid off the rock at the very sight of me, swam a few strokes into the sea and then turned their cheeky faces towards me to get a better look at the intruder who had dared disturb their siesta. And I'd gone down to count the steps, 243 new steps. The old ones, hewn out of rocks when the lighthouse was built in 1854, were wonky and abandoned. Something else was new too.

The home of the most northerly geranium, Walter's room, was in a block built in 1969, alongside the lighthouse in a space saved by electrification. Walter's room was the size of the average hotel's single room: more spacious than I'd imagined. There were two other similar rooms – it takes three to man a lighthouse around the clock – a large kitchen-dining room and a lounge with a television, much watched even though the reception was poor. The lounge was tidy, basically furnished with a few decidedly male frills, including the statutory picture of a topless girl which stood alongside a pertinent message:

> He who works and does his best
> Gets the shit like all the rest.

Someone had written 'censored' through the word 'shit'. A previous keeper had provided, as evidence of his hobby, paintings of daffodils and of poppies, and a cartoon featuring a Russian submarine. 'There are plenty of those around here,' said Walter, walking towards the door, eager to whisk me away from all this space and show me the lighthouse and the way things used to be: circular, cosy and cramped; tiny spaces, piled on top of each other with vertical steps as links. Machinery dominated the ground level, above that a cell in which to eat, above that a crow's-nest in which to sleep and, at the very top, the light itself, its importance underscored by the gleaming brass rails adorning the vertical stairs.

'We don't touch those because we've got to polish them, but it's OK . . . go on, you cling to them.' I hauled myself up to admire the ancient device that had been such an essential navigational aid to sailors down the centuries – a light bulb around which revolved a prism of glass. Walter put the light on just for a minute to show me how it worked. It seemed such a simple invention, but it was a huge engineering leap from the days when mariners were lucky to catch a glow, provided accidentally from the shore, when men made salt and had to keep coal fires burning around the clock. Trinity House, the organization that provides lighthouses for England and Wales, came into being in 1565, but Scotland did not acquire its Northern Lighthouse Board until 1786. Now there are 140 lighthouses. One by one they are being automated. This reflects perfectly our changing world. With modern sophisticated technology, merchant ships from oil tankers to container vessels no longer need lighthouses to warn them off the rocks. Smaller boats still need the winking light bulb but they do not need it to be guarded around the clock by three men. What could be more labour intensive and out of keeping with the spirit of New Britain? The lighthouse, picturesque and shrouded in romantic imagery, may remain, but the lighthouse-keeper's job has a limited future.

Walter did not seem bothered. He described how in his twenty-eight years on the job he had moved around the Board's lighthouses, spending four years each in Orkney, the Hebrides, Shetland and so on. Each cameo ended with the same lines: 'That's automatic now and the lightkeeper's home is a chalet let to holiday-makers.' He said it with a broad Aberdeen accent, without a trace of sentiment, nor a Luddite whine about the passing of a way of life. He gave me the impression he'd drifted into the service and would drift out again.

'I sometimes think I joined for the uniform. I'd been in the RAF and when I came out at twenty-two I hadn't much in mind and thought I'd give it a try. Now we don't wear the uniform more than once a year, when we get all brushed up and bonny for the annual inspection. Sometimes I think about coming out. I'd be quite happy driving a taxi in Lerwick.

'Come on, let's go and do the weather report and then we'll have lunch.' Making the weather report every three hours seemed a complicated business to me. I remember the wind speed was around 14 knots and that the sea state was 4. 'Small waves, becoming larger, fairly frequent white horses.' The rating goes to 12 which denotes a wind speed over 56 knots and chaotic sea conditions.

At lunch I would meet Tom. I'd already met Jim Leask at the shore station. He'd been a baker once, then a lighthouse keeper for seventeen years. He talked well of the life and claimed that no basic qualifications were needed apart from an interest in ships and the sea and a handyman's ability to be a plumber, painter, joiner and electrician. Any major problems – a malfunctioning engine for example – and they'd phone Edinburgh. By evening an engineer would arrive by helicopter. 'Oh yes, and a very strict medical. They look at everything, including your teeth. They don't want you to get on the rock on Monday and ask to come off on Tuesday with a toothache!

'The only time it's hard is when things go wrong at home and your wife is left with the kiddies to sort things out. My wife copes well. Her dad was in the Air Ministry and was sent to different airfields as a wireless operator, so she got used to men being away. My father was a whaler and spent half the year in the South Atlantic. We are well used to men on the move. It beats being in a factory. You even have more time for your kids in the end. When you are on shore you can give them all your attention.

'The secret is to pace yourself during the twenty-eight days on the rock, and to switch off from worries on the other side. In this job you must be self-reliant and a contented sort. If you need to go out a lot then you are in the wrong job. Even on shore we live quietly. The job's not well paid, but you get a free house, no bills, no rates and 60 per cent of the furniture provided. My wife doesn't know the price of a duvet cover, she gets them through the Board.' And on retirement? 'Those who haven't got a house of their own put their names down for a council property. There's no problem.'

Walter had told me about Tom. 'I said you were coming and that he had to get cleaned up. Tom isn't happy with soap and water. He's a bachelor, a crofter, born on Unst.'

Tom, a large silent man, had trousers that were a touch grubby, but his shirt and sweater suggested that he had received Walter's message. He was the cook. At 1 p.m. he presented us with soup and mince and tatties. It's always the same on change-over day. We chatted about hobbies; lighthouse men are famous for their hobbies. Jim's is fly-tying, making the neat little feathery things that go on the end of lines to attract fish. The library sends boxes of books and since Walter's son works in the library they have no trouble with special requests. No trouble with anything. Fresh water was the only item they had to treat with care. It has to be brought from the shore station by boat, twelve barrels at a time, and then winched up from sea-level, three barrels at a time. When the weather is bad it can be weeks, maybe seven weeks, before the boat can make the journey.

I munched my mince and listened to these steady, reliable men making light of their isolation, alternately being good companions and working as a team and then slipping away each to his own room, and wondered what it was really like to be a threesome, holed up, parted from the rest of the world for twenty-eight days at a time. I'll never know. I requested permission to stay on the lighthouse, but the Northern Lighthouse Board had said no. Accommodation was the problem. The three men said it was no such thing; no one slept in the bunks in the lighthouse and I could have had the lot to myself. But arrangements had been made for Ali the boatman to sail the mile across the sea and take me off. I hoped the weather would detain him, but of course it didn't.

Tom stayed at the top in the courtyard and waved. Jim and Walter followed me down the steps again to help anchor the little boat to the vertical steps. As the boat slipped away it afforded a splendid view of the white tower on the rock with its biscuit-coloured bricks framing the slit windows, designed as it happens by David and Thomas Stevenson. Their father Robert was one of Britain's greatest lighthouse builders. One year in 1814 he asked his schoolfriend Walter Scott to accompany him on his annual six-week tour of inspection. This enabled Scott to write a dull little book called *Northern Lights* and, more importantly, to acquire the knowledge he wove into *The Pirate*. Thomas Stevenson's son went even further to link lighthouses and literature. His name was Robert Louis Stevenson.

It was raining again and Ali presented me with oilskins, which I snuggled into as I sank back and watched for the last time the puffins flirting, flying and flitting across the water, their bills providing a dash of orange to match my oilskins; a splash of colour in a scene that had otherwise been painted from the same grey shade-card. I was chilled but exhilarated by my half-hour journey back to the shore station.

The little boat dumped me on the shore by the lighthouse base. It had taken me three days, one tube train, two aeroplanes, three ferries, four buses, one taxi and one helicopter to reach Muckle Flugga. And now I had another problem: how to bridge the six-mile gap to my hotel. Ali's wife is the local driver, but she was away on another mission. It was raining, which ruled out walking. And then, while shedding my oilskins, I saw a car a few yards away attempting a three-point turn. 'He's a stranger, that's for sure,' said Ali. 'Ask him where he is going.' I did and he gave me a lift. The stranger was a first-time visitor from Aberdeen, an asbestos expert who'd been called to the RAF station to provide an estimate for the removal of the stuff, once of great value, but now considered to be a health hazard. 'It'll cost them plenty. This place is so remote. There's nothing here. Where are the shops?' He had driven past the only store without recognizing it.

'The charms of Unst are not immediately apparent, are they?' I was about to disagree when I realized that my mind was full of coastal beauty, grand cliffs and sheer precipices; of voes and firths, of fulmars, puffins and seals. He had seen none of this and, as I looked around the flat land offering nothing but peat and boulders and sheep, I found myself agreeing. There are no trees. Oh what a glorious thing is a tree, but here they have all been chopped down centuries ago, and now they won't grow. If a shoot escapes the mouths of passing sheep, it soon suffers at the hands of the wind and the salt-ridden air.

I returned to Hagdale Lodge with my mind a great deal easier than it had been when I first arrived. It is not as grand as its name suggests; indeed, it is a former construction camp tarted up to resemble a one-storey motel. But the decision to stay there had been simple enough; there are only two hotels on Unst and they are both owned by the same person. One phone call reserves a room in either. My phone call from London was greeted by a moment's silence and then the message that they were full up, permanently full up with oilies (oil-rig workers), and no longer took casual guests. I asked the receptionist for the phone numbers of other places I might try. 'It won't be easy. Most of the bed and breakfasts are full up with oilies too. Look, call back in a day or two and I'll see what I can find.'

I called back; a room had been found, but it came with a warning: 'You realize that it is all *men* up here, don't you, and that you are going to be here over a weekend and it can be rowdy?' After I'd flown to Lerwick I had to stay overnight before catching the clutch of ferries and buses that would enable me to reach Unst. I stayed at an isolated pub on the Island of Bressay, four minutes by ferry from Lerwick. I was the only guest and the owner, who had recently moved from Unst, told me that he didn't think it a good idea for me to stay at Hagdale, for much the same reasons as the receptionist.

It is a sad fact that nowadays a woman travelling alone cannot afford to ignore such warnings. So I didn't ignore them, I mulled them over, faltered and found myself inside the Tourist Office asking for alternative accommodation. I left with two phone numbers written on a piece of paper, and as I shoved this in my coat pocket I felt ashamed by what appeared to be a loss of nerve *and* a new inclination to lean on the opinions of others. My confidence returned as I recalled other occasions in my life when timid, unadventurous souls had described my plans as 'unwise'. Some are wise and some are otherwise. The manager of Hagdale Lodge met me. With great charm he told me that he had given me a room as far away from the bar as possible and advised me against using the showers. 'There are three in a row and the chances are that two men will be using the others. There's a bathroom next door.'

The oilies turned out to be helicopter pilots. There was only a handful of construction workers around; *they* are responsible for the oilies' poor image. The helicopter pilots were the best of company. They wore blue sweaters with 'Treasure Finder' stripped across the shoulder. That's the name of an accommodation rig, moored in the ocean alongside the oilfield. The pilots had loved living on the rig and didn't much care for Hagdale or the local b. & bs. But now that oil prices were sinking they'd had to move as part of a cost-cutting exercise. Another pound-trimming scheme had been to centre them on Unst; they used to fly from Sumburgh, near Lerwick, but the charges had increased and forced them northwards.

The Saturday night noise was minimal; a number of the pilots had been invited to a local dance given by the sailing club to celebrate the day's regatta. The noisiest moment was provided by a chap who felt a blow on the bagpipes would liven up the munching of deep-fried haddock. I felt as though I were in a foreign country. I was. Up here 'going south' meant going to Edinburgh and Edinburgh was in a foreign country called Scotland. The Shetland Isles may just admit that they are part of Britain, but they are not, they argue, part of Scotland. This was stated to me time and again and puzzled me at first, since I'd always considered the islands to be part of Scotland. But it isn't as simple as that. The Picts, part of a loose federation of related tribes, were the original settlers. They managed to avoid invasion by the Scots, only to be swamped by the Vikings in the eighth century. The Vikings stayed until 1468, when a marriage settlement muddled things. The daughter of King Christian of Denmark and Norway wanted to marry James III of Scotland. King Christian promised a handsome dowry, but when the time came he found himself strapped for cash and instead pledged the lands of Orkney and Shetland. He intended to redeem the pledge once his fortunes improved, but they never did. Neither group of islands liked being handed to Scotland on a plate, and worse was to come. Scottish landowners bought up tracts of lands. Some of the owners proved to be bad landlords. They gave crofters a hard time and in the end cleared them off the best land. The Clearances have left the deepest scars on the islanders.

They still don't trust the Scots, and it's one of the reasons why in 1979 they voted against the devolution of power from London to a Scottish Assembly. They feared that they would be ignored in favour of Strathclyde, the most populous region of Scotland. Faced with the choice of being ignored by Edinburgh or ignored by Westminster, they chose Westminster.

The next day I left early to catch the bus for my journey southward. The morning was mournful. It must have been contemplating either the loss of June which had been, as indeed it is supposed to be, flaming, or the fact that it knew what I had yet to discover: that the next two months were going to be miserable: so chilly that I came to bless the invention of the thermal vest; so chilly that at times I lay in the bath at night until I felt warm enough to go to bed. And wet. My memory depicts me either carrying or huddled inside a voluminous hooded black raincoat, attempting a poor imitation of the French Lieutenant's Woman. The British have a reputation for going on about the weather. They have no reason for doing so since it is mostly predictable, rarely startling or surprising. We exaggerate its importance; it is not unusual enough to warrant the attention we give it. What do we really know about heat or cold? We've had the odd drought, and the odd hurricane, and we manage a bit of flooding now and again; and here and there a few gale-force winds and heavy rain (and where would romantic fiction be without them?). Yet we consider the weather to be a valid topic of conversation. It isn't; it is merely a socially acceptable conversational comma – or barrier. We use it as a filler behind which we hide either from those with whom we do not wish to communicate, or from those with whom we do, but for the moment need to pause while we reorganize our thoughts and think of something more interesting to say.

To a writer, however, the weather has another function. It is a paintbrush that changes the appearance and the mood of the picture before us. And on Unst that July morning the sky was sullen and the landscape melancholic, which is easy enough to achieve in a landscape without trees and with only a sparse and occasional covering of heather. The paintbrush had daubed subtle, sad shades on the scene, making bright splashes grab the eye and seem incongruous. Time and again my eyes caught blue plastic sacks by the roadside. I asked the elderly woman in front of me what they were.

'Peat,' she answered. 'Peat waiting to be transported from the moors to home.' And then she told me how she'd been visiting relatives and had been out many a time cutting the peats. She said it with pride and no doubt at home they would be hearing about it too. The coming of oil has not made peat a thing of the past. Indeed, it is now considered a fashionable way of getting exercise: it's damned hard work, but worth it for the feeling of well-being and for the endless supply of free fuel. The elderly woman described how it is done. First the heather or moss has to be removed from the surface and laid to one side; then slabs of peat, longer and thinner than a brick, are sliced away and laid upon the ground to dry. For a more thorough airing, they are then lifted up and stacked like rifles to form a pyramid. Finally the heather or moss is laid back on the lower surface. The process scars the landscape a little. It is not obvious from the bus, but when walking it becomes clear that the moors are criss-crossed with ditches of varying depths.

Peat cutting is no more a thing of the past than is knitting, although when oil first came knitting and many other things were put on one side while women went off to do the chores of construction workers. Sixteen-year-old girls could be seen leaving school at 4 p.m. and stepping into waiting buses to spend a few hours at the terminal making beds for money that was way beyond their teenage dreams. Others abandoned school altogether because, for once, work was plentiful. Such a traumatic dislocation of traditional patterns has given rise to its own local literature.

When I moved from the bus to the ferry, I found a corner away from the cacophony of portable transistors and raced through a volume called *Thin Wealth*, by Robert Alan Jamieson, which takes a vicious and vivid stab at the illusion of progress provided by oil and the negative influence of 'soothmoothers' (incomers) in search of a fast buck. The author worked at the terminal, so he clearly saw much of the downside: the rise in illegitimacy; of drunkenness, of fecklessness, of loss of neighbourliness, of family tensions born of higher expectations, of wives nagging husbands to give up the sea and settle for a steady job at Sullom Voe. Jamieson does not balance this with the improvements to the standard of living, the new roads, school, the leisure centre, the homes that now have bathrooms and are well insulated against the cold. The elderly have benefited much. There are many of them, some 14 per cent of the 24,000 population. The islands now boast the best sheltered housing in the UK, and each household with an elderly or disabled person gets a £200 bonus at Christmas; the disabled have Volvo cars with hand controls instead of invalid cars which are no good in high winds and which have no room for families to take outings together. Village halls have been revamped, churches have received attention. The list is long.

Shetlanders argue, however, that they were not in bad shape when the oil came: fishing was going particularly well. The population may have dwindled to 17,000 but that meant that the faint hearts had left for softer beds and the ambitious had followed job opportunities, leaving behind people content with their lot. Their rugged life made them self-reliant and interdependent; they needed each other and they looked out for one another. The picture that is painted of the pre-oil years gives meaning to those hollow phrases: 'quality of life' and 'standard of living'; their standard of living was poor, but the quality of life was exceptional. It was once remarked that the islands had few pubs, and the answer came back: who needs pubs when you can walk through anyone's door and have a drink?

Oil put Goliath among the Davids, but the Davids were sensible enough to know that oil needed Shetland more than Shetland needed oil. This started as a mere slogan, but it is now deeply entrenched into the communities' thinking. They knew that the oil companies did not have the technical ability to bring oil to the mainland of Scotland at an economic price. The oil had to come ashore in Shetland, and that put the Islands Council in the strongest of positions. They made the most of it.

They were lucky to have had Ian Clarke around at the time. As treasurer he came to Shetland from Scotland in 1968 at the age of twenty-nine. By 1974 he was chief executive and under his guidance the Council made the rules for the coming of oil; they were bold rules, good rules and much applauded. The key was participation. Clarke and the Council wanted to have an on-going say in the development and a direct influence over it. To this end they bought the land where the terminal was to be sited, thus remaining the landlord; they insisted that the oil companies get together and use one terminal; that the SIC was to be the Port Authority, in order to monitor the oil companies. And in return for leasing the land, building the port and the camp for construction workers, the oil companies had to pay a 'disturbance allowance', based on the tonnage of oil passing through the port, which would be invested in local industries so that they would be able to sustain the island's prosperity once the oil had gone. The investment has been impressive. Through grants or loans, the islands have new fishing boats, new fish-processing plants, harbours have been improved, a farm-salmon-fishing industry started and a fisheries training centre. Farmers have been able to buy lime and fertilizers to enrich the soil and they have been encouraged to increase their stock of beef cattle to improve the balance between sheep and beef. There have been new hotels built to encourage tourism and the knitters have had training and a joint marketing company set up.

But there are problems, not all is golden. The SIC claim that the oil companies over-estimated the throughput of oil and that they have never received the amounts they expected; they now want compensation for lost millions. And that, alas, is not the only serious argument: there's another about the cost of jetties; another about water charges; and another about the size of rent payable. All these are in the hands of lawyers and are destined for the courts. It seems such a pity: such a pity that agreements lauded by so many are later found to contain loopholes that people cannot sit down and resolve without the aid of the courts and of expensive lawyers.

Ian Clarke thinks it's a pity too. He's in Glasgow now, a chief executive of Clyde Cable Vision, and I sought him out one evening, eager to discover what he felt about the squabbles.

Clarke is not a man given to false modesty: 'I have no doubt that what was achieved in Shetland was one of the major successes of the century. If I had to do it over again, I'd change nothing of fundamental importance. No one could have foreseen all the problems that would arise. All I can say now is that the SIC must be happy to abdicate the decision-making to lawyers.'

He thinks well of the oil companies. Indeed, he must, for he went to work for BNOC when he first left Shetland. 'The oil companies are always being criticized for not looking after the community, but the community has to look after its own interests. The oil companies should of course behave like good citizens, but they are there to act in the best interests of shareholders. In dealing with that industry one must be wide awake; they can afford the best minds in the world. By and large they are open and honest and you'll never hear me criticize them for being underhanded.'

If there are quarrels now at least they do not spill over into one area of negotiations. Everyone praises the way in which the environment was considered. The mechanics of bringing oil ashore do not interest me, and my visit to Sullom Voe was to discover how the environment had been safeguarded rather than sacrificed.

I saw it before the ferry docked; it peeped over the brow of the hills: a solitary flame, the symbol of modern Shetland. Sullom Voe had been a sea-plane base during the war, after which it was deserted, leaving behind a few dilapidated jetties and the odd ruin of a building. The terminal had been created from scratch, its architects given the luxury of a blank sheet of paper; the result is not unpleasant. The flame might be visible for miles, but nothing else is allowed to dominate the skyline. Everything is single storey, except the power station which is painted green like the storage tanks, so they can blend into the background.

Oil is an environmental headache. It is messy stuff and the thought of a tanker running aground on a wild night and threatening the coastline with its contents hardly bears contemplation. The tankers are not allowed to sail within ten miles of the coast unless they are about to enter the harbour. They can, however, still have accidents inside the harbour. They had a mighty accident inside the harbour at 11.30 p.m. on 30 December 1978, when a ship collided with the jetty and 1,200 tons of oil spewed into the sea. It seems that a tug towing the tanker caught fire and had to let go of the tow rope. Something like that. Captain Flett told me about it in the most amusing way. He's an honest man and willingly admitted that this accident was a blessing, a catalyst for the introduction of some of the stiffest rules going. It is all to do with the ballast, or rather, the disposal of ballast. Empty tankers have partly to fill their cargo holds with water to give them enough weight to remain below the water, and inevitably the water becomes oil-smeared. On coming into port they need to get rid of this before taking oil on board. They do this by dumping it in ballast holds, a costly and time consuming business. The port charges £100 per 1,000 tons and a tanker might have to discharge 10,000 tons; this could take up to twelve hours. Naughty tanker masters have been known to save time and money by getting rid of the stuff as they sail along. Captain Flett knows. He was once a tanker master. The poacher's ways of cutting corners are handy ammunition to the gamekeeper. The port thus has tight regulations and spot checks, and stiff penalties for those who break the rules. The checks are carried out by small aircraft that twice a day go spotting for tell-tale oil slicks.

I asked if I might fly with the anti-pollution squad; a phone call speedily settled it, but Captain Bray and his spotter Bobby Sandison were less than pleased to see me. 'You another passenger? Want a nice view of the islands do you? Happens all the time when the sun comes out. There are another two somewhere. I wonder whose friends they are.' He was most ungracious; I felt like turning away. The captain managed to answer a few questions before tuning in the radio to the cricket. He'd found only one slick but he firmly believed in the deterrent value of the flights and he sneered at the boats who thought the oil companies were paying for the flights; they are in fact paid for from harbour charges. 'We don't advertise that much, ships might get uppity if they knew!' Spotting a slick is an easy business from the air – the rainbow effect is unmissable. We headed north-west out to sea before turning southwards, flying low over a Greek tanker to make sure he had seen us.

After some minutes, Bobby Sandison noticed a blot on the seascape; it clearly was not oil, but it looked interesting enough for the plane to dip for closer inspection. Sandison saw birds pecking away and jumped to the conclusion it must be a fish. But anyone could see it was too big for a fish. Binoculars revealed the answer. 'It's a dead sheep. How the hell did it get there? Must have fallen off a cliff and been swept out to sea.' That mystery solved, we went on in search of oil. The only spot we found was trailing behind a pleasure boat and it didn't bother Captain Bray and so we returned to base.

I took a taxi from the airstrip to the ferry where I knew there would be a bus to Lerwick. The driver had once been a roofing contractor in New York, but his wife got so homesick for Shetland that he brought her home and now they lead simple, self-sufficient lives, rearing sheep, planting and reaping. We were so busy talking, I missed the bus. It pulled in and out of its allotted place without either of us noticing. That's because it did not look like a bus; it was an unmarked mini-van. 'You weren't to know that, but I should have done,' said the taxi driver. 'Look, I've got a friend who runs the garage down the road, and he usually knocks off about five and heads for Lerwick. I'm sure he will give you a lift.'

'I'd never leave a woman stranded,' said the garage man, 'but the last chap I gave a lift to was sick all over the place. Get in.' We didn't bother with introductions. I sat in the back while he and a colleague chatted in dialect as the car sped towards Lerwick. This had once been a single track with passing places, but oil had provided a race track. As we neared Lerwick the two apologized for talking in dialect and returned to the subject of drink and drunken passengers. 'There's a good little pub by the ferry. They are open from 8 a.m. until 11 p.m. You'll see some sights in there.'

Alcohol abuse is a problem for these islands. A survey in 1979 revealed that one in ten men had problems with drink which showed up in their health, their work or their family relationships. Oil money has been used to fund programmes to tell the community of the perils of drink, through schools, through helping employers identify the problems. There are even special day centres where people can meet to talk without being tempted to drink. No one can blame the coming of oil; it has always been a badge of manhood around here to be seen with a bottle bulging out of a back pocket.

While waiting for the ferry to take me back to my pub, the Maryfield on the Isle of Bressay, I met Jonathan Wills, who lives on the island. He asked me home to tea, which is the kind of spontaneous gesture that delights this Londoner and I accepted with relish, even though I'd had a long day and felt travel-weary and talked out. Jonathan Wills is well known in Shetland. He's been a boatman, a crofter, a warden of a sanctuary island, Labour candidate, writer of children's books, manager of the local radio station and editor of the *Shetland Times*. He tried leaving the islands to seek fame and fortune, but soon headed back. He said that at the end of the eighteen-hour journey by boat from Aberdeen, grown men have been known to cry at the sight of the Bressay lighthouse and Lerwick harbour. He knows and loves the islands well, but he can be very critical. That night he was in the mood to kick the oil companies out, tell them to go to hell and come back only when they had sorted out all the squabbles. He has an inclination to see the oil companies as wicked giants taking advantage of little islanders. He can also be hard on the islanders. Some of the new industries, started on oil money, try to hire non-union labour at low wages, with one lavatory between a workforce of forty. There was, I felt, a tendency to exaggerate; to find one bad egg and then be suspicious of the whole box. After a while he conceded that Shetland had gained substantially from oil. The future looked bright: talented residents no longer had to leave in search of work, everyone had a wider outlook brought about by the infusion of outsiders and yet the very same infusion has also made them more aware of being Shetlanders and had given rise to a new interest in their own culture, their music and their language.

We went peat cutting at 10.30 p.m. It was completely light as we parked the car by the television mast and walked across the moors. My pathetic attempts to try my hand were made easier by the description provided by the elderly woman on the bus that morning. 'It's a lovely way to end an evening,' said Jonathan, as we humped three sacks to the car, stopping to ease our backs and to allow ourselves to be thoroughly sentimental about the view of the harbour, where two Polish ships were anchored. Jonathan said they did a nice line in contraband, swapping watches and cameras for mail-order catalogues to take home to their wives, who could then copy the fashions. When we'd finished being sentimental about the view, we became sentimental about the sunset, forcing ourselves to ignore the arctic edge on the July breeze. We came across a host of yellow iris and by falling to our knees we could line them up with the horizon and allow the red rays to peep through. It was a photographer's dream.

Walking back across the moors we had our final discussion on oil and oil revenues. Whatever the hiccups and whatever the social problems, at least the islanders can see where the money has been spent and that some of it has been invested in the future – for the day when the oil runs out. Looking at Britain as a whole, this cannot be said.

Tony Benn was minister of energy in the mid-1970s when the oil began to come ashore, but by the time the money began to roll into the Exchequer he was no longer in office and now claims that his successors have misused the funds – 'The greatest act of treachery to the national interest in the twentieth century.' Well, have they, or is this left-wing hyperbole, or what? The answer is not simple; economists disagree. Some argue that the Thatcher government has blown the money funding the dole queues and on an orgy of consumer-spending on imported goods; others say that the money has been used to erode trade-union power, which has helped to make industry leaner and fitter and to build up assets abroad, both of which will pave the way for years of steady economic growth.

Taxation of oil companies alone has yielded billions of pounds for the Chancellor to play with. The Labour party argue that they would have put this money in a fund for investment in industry – just like Shetland – to help manufacturing get on its feet, so that it would be able to pay the country's bills when the oil money runs out. The Conservative government chose not to have such an earmarked fund, and instead put the billions into the general budget. They don't seem unduly worried that manufacturing now accounts for a mere 20 per cent of our economic base, compared to 30 per cent in Germany and Japan, and they don't seem unduly worried as they watch our bill for manufactured imports growing. They argue that we ought to be glad to see the back of old-fashioned, overmanned, uncompetitive industry and that new industries are taking the place of manufacturing; service industries such as banking, insurance and tourism. This is true and has accounted for a hefty rise in 'invisible earnings' to help offset our trade balance. None the less the Labour party has a point: we should be putting more money into research and development to discover new products, new things for Britain to sell in the world market. Industry's record is pathetic; research suggests that only 1,000 of Britain's 80,000 manufacturing companies invests in research and development. It's hard to get the true picture: such figures are not published in annual reports.

Let me repeat a story, a story that I read somewhere which well illustrates the problems of our age. It is the tale of two cameras. Once upon a time in 1952, the Brownie 127 was born and sold in millions over the next twelve years. During that time there was one model change. In 1979 the Japanese company Canon brought out a market leader and by 1987 there had been five changes of model. The company, during this time, had spent 10 per cent of its turnover on R. & D. to make sure it maintained its leading position. The moral is that change is more rapid and that you can't have a winner and then sit back. A winner this year is obsolete next year.

All these arguments about poor investment in research and development are nothing new. It's well established that the British are no slouches when it comes to pure scientific research, but leave much to be desired when it comes to applying the knowledge to producing marketable products. But it doesn't have to be like this. I have every sympathy with those who say that at least some of the oil money should have been earmarked to boost this kind of development rather than let it swill around the economy and hope that the private sector will become rich enough to allow itself to think long term rather than short term. The next century will see the worth of Tony Benn's remarks. Either that or Mrs Thatcher will confound her critics once more.

Chapter 2

Orkney and the Atomic Devil

Orkney is different. It's only fifty miles from the southern tip of the Shetland Islands to the northern tip of the Orkney Islands, but the difference was immediately apparent, especially as I had had to fly, which minimized the distance and maximized the contrast. I wanted to idle away a day on the ferry – I'd become fond of travelling by ferry between Shetland Islands – but on that Saturday in July it had decided to take a day off to play in the local regatta. Orkney, then, is farms, farms and more farms; fertile land as far as the eye can see. A neat geological twist arranged that. The landscape is softer, the hills are heather-topped and there is a profusion of long-stemmed buttercups. Trees are almost as rare as in Shetland, but at least Orkney is making an effort to encourage them to grow, planting them where houses offer shelter – which is something of a role reversal for a tree. The people of the islands have grown so used to their treeless habitat that when they go south they have been known to comment that the trees get in the way of the view. And the view is of farmland. At times, after the more rugged shapes and peaty black tones of Shetland, Orkney's farmland seemed like an urban child's view of country life as depicted upon cereal packets. The colours are clear, the yards clean and uncluttered and cows, in pretty shades of light beige, of reddish brown and of startling black and white, are gentle and contented.

Outsiders often speak of Orkney and Shetland in one breath, but it is Orkney that has the higher profile and it is Orkney that appears to have greater confidence. Maybe this is because under Nordic rule Orkney was the more important; maybe it is because in the two World Wars, Orkney played the bigger role; maybe it is because for thirty-two years its famed member of Parliament, Jo Grimond, chose to make his home there. Lord Grimond, as he now is, still has his home not far from Kirkwall. The 1983 general election was fought without him, and many wondered what would happen to the vote of 40,000 people (for both island groups) over whom he'd held sway for so long. The new Liberal candidate, an Edinburgh lawyer, James Wallace, won safely against the Tories, the Labour party and the Scottish National Party. The Liberals are entrenched. It was Gladstone, having deserted the Tories and become Liberal prime minister, who passed the Crofters Act in 1886 which changed the life of so many tenant farmers. I'd have thought that a hundred years would dim memories and diminish loyalties, but this is not the case; besides, the Liberal party's knack of putting down deep roots at a local level more than offsets the shorter memories of younger voters.

Eric Linklater, one of Orkney's best-known writers, adds to the list of differences between these two groups of communities by claiming that the people of Shetland are more outgoing than the men of Orkney, who by comparison seem shy and less loquacious. I did not find this to be so, but this may be because a lucky chance led me to be invited to stay with Linklater's widow, Marjorie, at her house in the centre of Kirkwall. A wonderful bonus which not only meant that I was cossetted and looked after like a daughter, but also enabled me to feel enveloped by the community, rather than an outsider looking in from the vantage point of the local pub. It also led me to look at things that otherwise I would have missed.

I am, for example, not much moved by ancient history, by enlightened guesswork that enables men to describe the lifestyle of thousands of years ago. I have a tough enough time trying to digest the vast layer-cake of history – prehistory I'm happy to leave to archaeologists. Orkney is an archaeologist's paradise. Perhaps, then, it was appropriate that within hours of arriving I found myself seventeen miles outside Kirkwall, walking along the cliff edge towards the Broch of Gurness, the best preserved of some hundred brochs that litter these islands and the north of Scotland. Broch is said to come from the Norse word for castle. At any rate, a broch is a circular stone tower, beehive shaped, with vastly thick walls, encircled on three sides (the fourth is the sea) by ramparts and ditches. The story goes that in times of attack people holed up inside the broch. Who built these brochs and who the inhabitants were hiding from is anyone's guess.

It seems likely that they were built by the Picts, the 'painted people', to keep out foreign intruders, or indeed other Picts, since they were a war-like people who might well have had to fight over the most fertile bits of land. But who knows? The pamphlet provided by the Department of Ancient Monuments of Scotland is a masterpiece of dullness, and does less to excite the imagination than merely standing there on the cliff top and allowing one's mind to marvel at how learned men can make so much of a pile of stones.

Having braved a world said to be at the junction of history and prehistory, I ventured even further back, and with Marjorie visited the Ibsister Chambered Tomb of South Ronaldsay. Once again I was on a cliff edge overlooking the sea. The tomb was a burial chamber, but not for whole bodies. The dead were left on the cliff for the birds to pick the flesh, and then an assortment of bones were placed in the tomb. The discovery was made on farmland owned by the Simison family, and it is Ronald Simison who shows visitors around. Instead of handing out unreadable documents, he stands in the conservatory of his home, amid the geraniums and his wife's sewing-machine and, handing around fragments of bone, weaves stories that hold the most reluctant listener spellbound. He is obsessed with his treasures and relates their history – which he has taught himself – in a simple and passionate way that is the antithesis of the academic approach. Clutching a variety of skulls said to be 5,000 years old, he rattles through a complete family history. 'This skull belongs to a man of about 5 feet 7 . . . and this to a woman of about 5 feet 3 . . . if you look here you will see she had trouble with her wisdom teeth . . . this male ankle bone shows wear and tear – they were always scaling cliffs for birds and eggs.' It was a delightful presentation; an antiques roadshow without the price tags.

On the drive to and from Orkney mainland, the road runs through the water like a ridge across an eastern paddy field. That road rockets us back into recent history, for it was built on the top of the Churchill barrier; the barrier which Sir Winston Churchill, as first Lord of the Admiralty, ordered to be built at the outbreak of the Second World War to seal off the eastern approach to Scapa Flow. In both World Wars Scapa Flow was an important base for the British home fleet, its purpose not just to protect our shores but to block the Atlantic from the Germans. Much happened here to delight military historians, and relics of both wars remain below the sea to entertain divers. At the end of the First World War seventy German ships were herded into this expanse of water encircled by the islands where they sat waiting for the terms of the peace treaty. The German navy had been told to scuttle their ships rather than allow them to fall into enemy hands and a German admiral, tired of waiting, or fearing that war might break out again, one day, one lunchtime in June 1919, gave the signal for his ships to be sunk and one by one they went down, watched by a party of schoolchildren on a day's outing to view the spoils of victory. Everyone in Orkney knows the story and tells it to every visitor.

Scapa Flow was also the site of Lord Kitchener's last hours. He came in June 1916 *en route* for Russia, and no sooner had his boat, the *Hampshire*, headed out from the Flow in vile weather than it was struck by a mine. Or so it is said. There's a bleak, blank memorial to him at Marwick Head; a walk provides a lovely view of birds squabbling over nesting places on the ridges below. Both Shetland and Orkney, it can be argued, had good wars. Being garrisoned meant that there were men to feed and money to be made and many memories. A primary school headmaster in Shetland told me that in the first class he taught after the last war there were any number of illegitimate children who did not know their fathers. He was making the point that the war and the coming of oil had produced some similar problems.

Oil coming to Orkney caused problems, but the impact was not so great as in Shetland, mainly because the quantities involved are smaller and because it was possible to restrict the flurry of activity to the Island of Flotta, away from the main centres of population. They had their quota of White Settlers, as outsiders are called because of their colonial we-know-best attitudes. Orcadians were anxious lest traditional occupations be jettisoned in favour of high earnings from the oil fall. But on the whole the Orkney Council handled the affair in a lower key and did not become so involved. They did not become partners in the venture and they did not step in and buy the land – so somewhere, it is rumoured, there is a Flotta millionaire, a man who made a killing selling his land.

And they lost a little too. Once it had been possible to leave your car unlocked and if anything went wrong in the community the police could find the culprit by calling at a dozen houses. Neither is possible now. As with Shetland, millions of pounds have been poured into other industries, into farm machinery and buildings, into fish farming, into knitwear and into an abattoir. Before oil the slaughterhouse employed two people to keep full the shelves of local butchers and the rest was shipped south alive; there is more money to be made shipping south dead. But despite this, and tourism, oatcakes and a rather splendid whisky called Highland Park, the Orkney Islands have an unemployment rate of 10 per cent. It is no longer possible to go south in search of work and no longer fashionable to emigrate in shoals to Canada and Australia; the unemployment figures are no longer masked by exodus. But none of this is new; oil brought a few gifts, but Orkney remains a farming community, its products prized. That's why they mind so much about Dounreay.

The word refers to a clump of buildings on the other side of the Pentland Firth, seven miles from Orkney. The clump has been there since 1959. It was built by the Atomic Energy Authority and its full title is the Dounreay Nuclear Power Development Establishment and its task has been to develop a fast reactor system. Orcadians see it as a threat.

A non-fast or thermal reactor uses uranium, a naturally occurring metal found, like oil and coal, in the earth's crust. But as with oil and coal there is a limit to the economical supply of uranium and so scientists have been seeking a way of cutting down on the amounts used. The answer lies in plutonium, which is created when uranium is burnt in a reactor and which can be extracted by reprocessing the spent fuel. If plutonium is placed in a fast reactor and surrounded by uranium or spent fuel, then while the reactor is busy producing energy it will also obligingly convert some of the surrounding uranium into additional plutonium. The new supply can then be surrounded once again and the cycle repeated. A fast reactor is said to provide fifty to sixty times more energy from uranium than a thermal reactor.

In 1962 Dounreay became the first experimental fast reactor in the world to produce electricity. The amount was small, enough to satisfy a town of some 10,000 people. The time came then to build a larger fast reactor, and by 1976 such a reactor had produced enough power to satisfy the needs of a city the size of Aberdeen.

The reactor's basic job is to test technology so that one day a full-scale commercial fast reactor can be built. On the site there is also a reprocessing plant, a small one especially designed to handle fast-reactor waste. But there are plans afoot for a much larger plant and a public inquiry was being held in Thurso (where Dounreay is sited) to decide whether or not to give outline planning permission for this creature whose full name is the European Demonstration Fast Reactor Reprocessing Plant.

Britain claims to have the lead in fast-reactor technology, but other countries are also steaming ahead with similar projects. In 1984 a group of countries – Belgium, France, Italy, West Germany and the UK – decided to collaborate; to pool knowledge and speed up the process of designing a fast reactor that would be able to produce electricity at a price that could compete with thermal reactors. Under this joint development programme it was agreed that three fast reactors would be built – in France, West Germany and Britain – together with one single fuel-reprocessing plant to service them. The British nuclear industry would like to claim the prize, but then so would France, which is geographically more centrally located. The decision has yet to be made; meanwhile outline planning permission is an essential step.

Orkney says No. Orkney has said No before, when uranium was

found in the islands. Marjorie Linklater was in the forefront of the lengthy fight to stop exploration. No one panicked at first; the thought of a few holes, a little exploratory drilling, seemed harmless enough and landowners signed on the dotted line without much hesitation. And then someone read the small print and discovered that they had also signed away their territorial rights; that the South of Scotland Electricity Board had the rights to acquire the land, should it be considered in the national interest to extract any uranium found. Just the jolt needed to awaken indignation and self-interest. A campaign against uranium exploration was supported by 99 per cent of Orkney residents.

That was in the mid-1970s, but once a community has been politicized it is that much easier to mobilize, particularly when the expansion of Dounreay revives many of the same fears. It may not directly affect the landscape (as uranium mining would have done), but it activates all the old arguments about the effects on man, on agriculture and on fisheries. And so it should. Chernobyl taught us that. On 26 April 1986, an accident occurred in the number four reactor at a nuclear power plant in the Ukraine in the Soviet Union. Contamination spread far beyond Soviet boundaries and once more alerted the world's attention to the dangers of fiddling with nuclear power.

'You'll not find anyone to defend Dounreay,' said Marjorie, as I left to spend a Sunday with two farmers, one laird-like and the other not.

'Are you going for lunch?' she queried, surprised to see me trouserless and neatly skirted.

'I assume so. I was asked for one o'clock.'

She laughed. 'Your English assumptions are not much use up here! Were you actually asked for lunch?'

By this time I couldn't remember the details, just the time; the rest hadn't seemed to matter too much.

'Perhaps we should phone and check.'

'No,' I said emphatically. 'Let's treat it as an adventure and see what happens!' I was embarrassed. I hadn't given a thought to farm duties dovetailing into church demands and driving out Sunday lunch, nor had I considered that Orcadians are not much given to middle-class conventions of inviting non-family to share meals.

Eoin Scott took me straight into the kitchen and offered me a glass of wine. His father left the room as soon as he had said hello and his mother remained seated at the table, eating slices of juicy bacon. The room bore no resemblance to the fantasy farmhouses of Sunday newspaper supplements; it was functional, unfussed by designer frills and messy with the business of living. Marjorie was right; there was no mention of lunch. I accepted an invitation to walk around the farm and admire the tree plantation, spruce, sycamore and horse chestnut, which Eoin is tenderly nurturing, and the new barns that will allow the cattle (and cattle owner) to have a cosier winter.

Eoin's views on nuclear power are straightforward and all too reasonable. 'I am not against it, but I am against the industry. No one trusts it any more. Dounreay has been there for years and it seemed to bother no one, and we thought it was safe and it is only during this public inquiry that we have heard about leaks and other things we didn't know about – slack practices and so on. The industry needs to get its house in order, clear up the matter of waste and of safety. I watched the lamb prices in Scotland and in Wales fall by two thirds as a result of the Chernobyl accident, but in an odd way I think it may have helped our cause. It may result in the plans being modified and additional safeguards added.'

He didn't much rate the campaign's chances of getting Dounreay phased out altogether.

'No, I don't think we can succeed. The Tories want a nuclear industry, and where better to put it than in the north of Scotland? I'm cynical about the government's attitude to peripheral areas like Orkney. They either use us for their own ends or they ignore us. Thatcher's government promised to improve the subsidy we get to cover the cost of transport so that we are better able to compete on prices, but nothing has been done.'

Hugh Halcro-Johnson's house looked grand from outside but lacked grandeur inside. It was both unlived in and uncared for. The house and the land had been in his family for 250 years, but Hugh's English wife, Erica, didn't care for Orkney. She'd married Hugh when he was export manager of Alcan, but when he decided he'd had enough and wanted to return to Orkney to help his ageing father and eventually take over the land and the farm, she liked it not. She stays in Oxfordshire, ostensibly for the sake of her children's education, and returns to Orkney now and then and fills up the freezer. Hugh copes with the help of a microwave oven. We ate rock cakes and drank tea. It was 4 p.m., and I'd definitely been asked for tea.

The Halcro is Norse and the Johnson is Scots and Hugh is proud of the combination. He's all too aware of the reputation of lairds in the past, but is not in the least defensive. 'There were good landlords and bad landlords, but you never hear about the good ones, do you? It's true that my grandfather gave the orders rather than did the work, but he was interested in the farm and invested in it and did not just live off the tenants. The crofting legislation penalized the good. That's all it did . . . The bad ones left, leaving the good ones with legislation that tied their hands. It's way out of date now, and constantly abused, but it is such a powerful, emotive subject that no one will do anything about it.

'Let me tell you about one croft nearby. It has forty acres and is owned by a woman whose husband is a coastguard, and they live in Kirkwall and not in the croft. They rent out the land to the local farmer and the croft itself they rent out each summer for charges way in excess of what they have to pay. Of course it isn't a croft anymore, not in the real sense, but just you try getting it de-registered! It's costly and a nightmare and this is not an isolated example of abuse.'

He talked at length and with feeling about the perils of crofting legislation and reduced me to laughter in the end. 'You've spent half an hour or more reviling a masterpiece of *Liberal* legislation,' I said. He looked at me and was silent. Then he laughed too and suggested we move into his study, which was smaller and warmer. The joke was that Hugh Halcro-Johnson had hoped to take over from Jo Grimond, but the selection committee preferred an Edinburgh lawyer. He'd have loved to have been the islands' MP; it would have solved his wife's problems too.

I sensed that he was tempted to sell up and go south, but the thought of leaving the land that had been in his family for so long was a wrench. Besides, he made a model gentleman-farmer, good-humoured and a good organizer. There are forty-eight milk producers in Orkney and he is their chairman; they have problems over EEC-imposed milk quotas, which are stifling the cheese industry. He's been running to Brussels to see if he can get a rule or two changed. He had 50 cows and 80 beef cattle on just over 300 acres and 200 breeding ewes on a further 500 acres of moorland. Part of the latter has been designated a Site of Special Scientific Interest, which means that he has been given a grant to fence it and has promised that he won't plough it up for grass for very greedy sheep. He's conservation minded; his forefathers were conservation minded also and that is why there is so much wildlife around. To help him in his labours he has a female herdsperson, as he put it, and a farm labourer and his son. Three generations of that family have worked for three generations of his family. That sort of thing is getting rare; most farms in Orkney are small enough to depend solely on family help.

We chatted until the phone rang at 7 p.m. Marjorie had tracked me down, dying to know if I'd had lunch and whether I'd be home for supper. Dressed crab was being prepared; no microwave could compete with that, so Hugh came too and I could boast that I had introduced two old Orkney families; they had never met.

In the car he dismissed Dounreay sharply. 'In the past people were afraid of aluminium; they said it caused premature senility or something. People are always afraid of new things. In the 1950s and 1960s we were really proud of Dounreay, but the position has changed. It was put there as an experiment; right, the experiment has been successful – the thing is said to be safe. Fine. Then put it in Finchley. One whisper of trouble from Dounreay and our reputation as a food producing island has had it. "Made in Orkney – subject to radiation, but well below the limit" – it sounds a great advertisement.'

The clean Orkney argument is powerful. There are many others, equally powerful: they aren't difficult to find when the substances being discussed, uranium and plutonium, are equally well known for the devastation they caused at Hiroshima and Nagasaki. Orkney is the home of the Campaign against Dounreay Expansion, an umbrella group coordinating the work of other organizations throughout the Highlands and Islands. I talked with several of them and was much impressed by their depth of understanding of nuclear technology, which enabled them to make pointed criticisms. They see before them the distinct possibility that Dounreay will become a nuclear park. If plans to build a demonstration reprocessing plant proceed, who knows what could follow. They do not believe that the world in the twenty-first century faces serious energy problems; they consider that to be a scare cooked up by the nuclear industry to keep itself in business. They do not believe that fast-reactor technology can economically produce electricity, arguing that the industry's claim to produce fifty to sixty times the electricity from the same amount of uranium as a thermal reactor is nonsense and that Dounreay has many problems that it keeps hidden from the world. And as for the thought of spent uranium from Europe arriving at a port in northern Scotland and then going by road or rail to Dounreay ... and as for the thought of newly minted plutonium being flown out of Thurso ... and as for the thought of emissions into the atmosphere and the sea ...

My mind was choking; my vision clouded by Raymond Briggs's sad little couple saying goodnight to each other for the last time at the end of his brilliant anti-nuclear book, *When the Wind Blows*. The time had come for me to hear the other side of the case. The planning inquiry being held in Thurso was about to take a summer break. I would hop on the ferry and at least catch the mood and the main characters.

Thurso is a dull place. The surrounding land may be of interest to wildlife enthusiasts, but at a glance it is flat and vacant. Thurso, the most northerly town on the mainland of Britain, owes its existence to a sheltered bay which once provided safe anchorage for trading vessels. The harbour is hardly used now, the ferry sails into nearby Scrabster. In the nineteenth century Thurso owed its prosperity to paving stones; Caithness flagstones were quarried locally and shipped throughout Britain and to the continent. Concrete killed all that. Both World Wars found Thurso useful as a ferry point for troops going to Orkney – and then there was nothing. The population shrank to 3,000. It is now 10,000. Dounreay made the difference. The town is totally dependent upon it as a source of employment. A casual walk through the streets shows the strength of support for the establishment; there are stickers everywhere welcoming expansion.

The place is fairly prosperous; the shops in the pedestrian precinct are packed with functional rather than luxury goods: there is a large Woolworth, a small bookshop, a popular fish-and-chip bar and an excellent off-licence selling a surprisingly large selection of whiskies from the Highlands and Islands. Thomas Carlyle passed by one day and stopped to say hallo to the baker, Robert Dick, an amateur botanist whose house merits a plaque since he helped to identify many a plant in the area. The hotels are humming, their rooms filled – since April, when the inquiry started – with barristers from Edinburgh, top personnel from the UKAEA and official shorthand-writers from Sheffield who fly up on Mondays and return on Fridays (at the expense of the Scottish Office).

The planning inquiry was being held in the Town Hall, spruced up with new curtains and extra heating. It contains a large public room with a stage. The recorder sat on the stage, flanked by shorthand-writers. The body of the hall was reserved for legal representatives of both sides, the day's line-up of objectors, the public and the press. There were very few of the latter. Fleet Street had chosen to ignore the inquiry for the most part, but local press and local radio had soaked up every word.

Howie Firth from Radio Orkney relished it all. He'd sat there day in and day out and each morning regaled his listeners with what seemed to me an incomprehensible account of the proceedings. He was now so involved that his reports were like a nuclear Archers – if you listened daily you were gripped, but if you tuned in from time to time you were lost. Howie could discuss emission levels with the best of them. And he was by no means the only person to have started with zero knowledge and quickly acquired a decent layman's understanding. There were three women who could trump him.

The three women had come to dominate the inquiry. At least one was present every day. Sometimes they would arrive with rucksacks, full of nappies, and their children – they had nine between them – and set up a crèche. One day one brought along a goat that she was bottle-feeding. They asked questions and cross-examined witnesses and did their darndest to take on the nuclear industry. They had impressed everyone with their command of the areas in which they had chosen to specialize. Frances looked after safety and the environment; Penny medical matters and Lorraine transportation.

I heard much gossip about the three women. Frances McKie lived in Orkney, had three children and was eight months pregnant with the fourth, and was also about to move house. She was also just about to collapse according to her colleagues who had dispatched her to stay with her father until her child was born, leaving her husband to take care of the move. No one would give me her phone number. 'She'd insist on meeting you and that's just what we don't want her to do.'

The shorthand-writers told me about Lorraine Mann. They were glowing in their praise for her ability to cross-examine and this is high praise indeed from those who have to sit through every word and are able to make comparisons with Edinburgh lawyers. I read the transcriptions and saw what they meant. Lorraine lived miles away, at Fearn near Invergordon. Our timetables did not permit us to meet, but the phone confirmed the view of the transcripts and of the shorthand-writers. Lorraine claims to have cried herself to sleep throughout the Cuban Missile Crisis of the early 1960s. She was eleven. As soon as she could, she joined CND and became local chairman. She also became a primary-school teacher, got married and had three children.

'If I lived in Edinburgh or London I wouldn't ever have become involved. But up here if you want something done you've got to do it yourself. When the inquiry revealed that Invergordon was the preferred port, I *had* to do something. Greenpeace didn't seem to want to know, they said they had no money. Friends of the Earth stayed away. They have more important concerns in the south, and the north of Scotland didn't seem to matter. I *had* to do something.'

Doing something meant total immersion until she felt ready to hassle officials on the perils of moving spent fuel by road from Invergordon to Dounreay. Her model was childhood admiration for Perry Mason and the transcripts show how adept she became at drawing people out and getting them to admit what she wanted them to admit. Her coup concerned the sodium flask. She told me about it with evident delight. If I understand correctly, spent fuel is moved around in either wet (water-filled) flasks or dry (nitrogen-filled) flasks. And then there is sodium; sodium is hazardous because of the danger of fire. Lorraine's coup was to get someone called Brown from the BNFL to admit he has seen designs for sodium flasks.

The word sodium resounds around Dounreay. They talk of the Day of the Sodium Explosion. God knows what happened; it's all a muddle. Two ageing crofters tried to tell the inquiry about it. One described how he saw a mushroom cloud which darkened the sky and hovered from noon to four o'clock and how he received a phone call from Dounreay telling him to move his stock. But where to, he asked himself. The other explained that on the day of the explosion he had cut his cheek, shaving or something. It healed, leaving what looked like a wart, but which turned out to be cancerous and had to be cut out. Twice. The surgeon told him (he said) that it might have been wind-borne spores that caused it. His sheep also turned pink. He went to feed them the day after the explosion and they had turned *pink*. The director of Dounreay said it was a small explosion in a waste shaft and that it had been caused by sodium which should not have been there. No radiation was involved, he added, and the cloud was nothing other than washing powder. Washing powder! Tell that to the crofter with the pink sheep! They did and he replied, 'If they can't control washing soda one wonders how they are ever going to control radioactive waste. My old granny never blew the roof off the house with washing soda.'

Penny Boyle is the third woman. Slight and quietly spoken, she too had been a member of CND and Amnesty. She and her husband are going to live in New Zealand if the reprocessing plant is built. She had already moved from England to Glasgow and from Glasgow to Thurso in pursuit of a life on the land with goats. She acknowledges that some folk are critical of such an incomer pronouncing so loudly, but, she adds, it is incomers who seem to care more, because they have chosen to live there.

Her task that day was to soothe six women who had come eighty miles from Durness, near Cape Wrath, to present their objections. They live and work at Balnakeil Craft Village, east of Cape Wrath, a craggy finger sticking out into the north Atlantic, a place they consider to be the edge of the world as well as one of the last unspoiled places. They are potters and weavers and knitters and makers of leather goods and so forth, which they sell in the summer to tourists. One by one they announced that they felt privileged to live in such a place and that the expansion of Dounreay would ruin it all; would drive away tourists and their source of income as well as threaten their way of life. Their submissions were short and well prepared. They read them out, their voices breaking with emotion. Their fears were received in silence.

Then Ishbel McDonald began to talk of picking winkles with her children; of collecting seaweed as fertilizer for her garden; of drying the stuff to eat; of her children playing on the sand. The tears fell and she paused, hoping the tears would pause, but they continued to fall.

'We know that radioactive waste is discharged into the sea from Dounreay; the doses are small and we are told not to worry, but it is cumulative, no one knows what will happen. I was present in the coffee shop in Balnakeil Craft Village several weeks ago when someone who described himself as a government official involved in the monitoring of radioactive waste – up here to take part in this inquiry – expressed his concern, having seen the cows on the beach eating the stalks of the tangles. This, he said, was not monitored. In how many different ways does radioactivity enter the food chain?

'The Irish Sea is now known to be the most irradiated sea in the world due to the discharges from the reprocessing plant at Windscale. Leukaemia clusters are to be found in the vicinity of Windscale. Leukaemia clusters are to be found near Thurso. Living where we do we are likely to receive emissions from both, depending on the prevailing winds and currents.'

When she finished, a young man clapped.

There were no questions. The recorder pointed out that this was because most of the points had been made elsewhere in other forms on other days. The six women from Durness left the room in search of cups of coffee, and the chance to gossip away their fears that their views had carried little weight.

I wandered outside to the empty Co-op shop being rented by UKAEA and BNFL to put their case. It was a smart office manned by about thirty people, whose main task was to furnish the QC representing them and to act as an information centre for the public. There was a book for visitors to sign. I glanced down at the entries: 'Go for it,' signed Edinburgh; 'Keep it up,' Harrogate; 'Let's hope,' Thurso; 'Good Luck,' Glasgow.

Peter Davis headed this operation. He's normally based at the northern division of the AEA at Risley, where he is UK programme manager for electricity renewal technologies, which includes research into wind and wave power as well as nuclear. Wave power he sees as a long shot, more expensive, 'the laws of physics are against you'. Hydro is the best alternative, but most of the potential for that has already been exploited. Wind has its problems. 'The span of the windmill is the main problem. The Germans have a windmill that is a hundred metres in diameter, which is much too big; the Americans have another at eighty, but that seems too big; at the moment forty metres seems to work, but that produces only one megawatt of power and to be meaningful you need to be able to produce three. Even then that would mean a small place like Orkney would need seven windmills. What a blot on the landscape! I suppose in the long run wind might be useful for third-world islands, but it doesn't seem much of an answer to Britain's needs.' And he admitted without hesitation that the research into alternative methods of energy was 'political'; the government had to be seen to be doing it to appease environmentalists.

I asked him how he thought the inquiry was going. 'Slower than we thought, but we're pretty happy on the whole. All we are seeking is outline planning permission and these objectors want a full safety assessment, which we can't give them because we haven't done the designs. I do wish these people wouldn't keep asking questions when they are not qualified to judge the answers!'

There was no point in asking further questions. I was spending the whole of the following day at Dounreay, and there would be plenty of time for detailed conversation.

As I left the office, a young man called to me. It was the same young man who had clapped when Ishbel McDonald had presented her weepy evidence.

'Penny said you were looking for me.'

'No, I don't think so. Who are you?'

'Kevin Sinclair. I used to work at Dounreay and I have some stories.' I hesitated; the name meant nothing, I hadn't been looking for him and he had the irritatingly fashionable habit of pushing his coat sleeves up his arms. However I suggested a quick drink. Kevin is best described as an inquiry 'groupie'. He was unemployed and happy to be helpful to strangers, particularly female strangers. He told me his story. He had lived in Thurso since he was four and his father had worked as an electrician in the reprocessing plant from 1962 until 1967, when he received an unscheduled dose of radiation while changing a light bulb. A couple of years ago, twenty years later, he died. He had a blocked bowel and on the operating table they discovered that he was riddled with cancer.

'You can't prove anything; you can't prove that it was that dose of radiation that caused cancer.'

Anyway, the incident did not stop Kevin working there. There wasn't much choice: his passion is lead soldiers and his ambition is to run a military museum, but on the way to that dream he spent four years working for a sub-contractor whose task it was to do general work around the place, cutting grass, putting up scaffolding and so forth. Kevin was critical of the attitudes towards safety and illustrated this with many a story of careless moments. His conclusion was that the stuff may be safe if carefully handled, but people are dangerous, or at least the general workers employed by the sub-contractors are. He'd seen a play recently that had chilled him.

'It was called *Braham Seer*, about the great visionary who predicted all sorts of things that have come true. He predicted the Highland clearances and the advent of the railways and he saw that one day the sea from the east would meet the sea from the west – which must be a reference to the Caledonian canal. And there's one prediction left; he foresaw that there would be a disaster so great that the Highlands would become uninhabitable and the land blackened.'

My day at Dounreay was carefully planned. I didn't just want the tourist tour of the reactor, I wanted to talk to the people about why they worked there, why the dangers seemed so convincing to outsiders, and yet were wholly acceptable to those inside. And I particularly wanted to talk to new entrants – those who had chosen a career in the nuclear industry at a time when public awareness, public fears were heightened. Peter Bates wasn't young. He had joined the industry in 1961, at a time when the world was no longer innocent of the devastating effects of nuclear power, but, none the less, pretended innocence towards nuclear energy by refusing to make the connection. After twenty-five years in the industry, Peter Bates has no qualms. 'I have faith in the industry and have dismissed any doubts easily. If you understand what is happening it is that much easier. There are areas in the plant where the risk of exposure to high levels of radiation is high, but there are strict rules and regulations which if followed give no cause for alarm. We are allotted a certain "dose" each year and if anyone is getting close to the limit then they are not allowed to work in a risk area. It's all worked out.'

He is philosophical about the Chernobyl disaster. He can see ways of turning the accident to the industry's long-term advantage. 'The Russians have let the nuclear industry down badly, but I must admit we will get a lot of useful information out of that accident. It may sound callous, but in the end that information will be invaluable. After Nagasaki and Hiroshima the benefit to medical science was enormous. We learned so much about high-level exposure. And now Chernobyl will give us data on intermediate-level exposure. In ten years from now we will have filled an important gap in our knowledge. We are learning all the time. The people in the industry are exposed to low levels, so we are also learning the implications of that and all this in the end will breed security and confidence.'

'Meanwhile, what about the possibility of another accident?'

'Dounreay is not Chernobyl. We had to work very hard to dream up an accident scenario. There are so many checks in the system that for an accident to happen it would mean a multi-coincidence which by the laws of probability will never happen.'

Kathryn Cartwright took me through the reprocessing plant, thoughtfully answering a multitude of questions. Such was her skill I felt sure I understood the process. By the following morning, I knew that I did not, but that didn't matter. What mattered was that she managed to convey some of her own excitement about nuclear science. Kathy is twenty-five and comes from Newcastle via Bath University where she read chemical engineering; reprocessing is a chemical engineering problem. When she went to Bath she was offered sponsorship by British Steel and by the Atomic Energy Authority. She turned down British Steel because the industry was in the doldrums and she could see no future in it. A E A sponsorship is not binding on either side, but during the sandwich course Kathy came to Dounreay and liked it.

'I liked the fact that there are hardly any people up here. I like camping and outdoor life and I'm not interested in discos and visiting Marks and Spencer on Saturday. I also found that I liked the people and that they accepted me because I'm not one of those who come up here to sneer at the locals who dig peat and eat herring.'

Kathy took me 'over the barrier'. The barrier is indeed a barrier. To get over it you sit on top and swing your legs to the other side. The other side is a weird place, eerily empty, spotlessly clean, blindingly white and silent except for the ever present clip-clop, clip-clop of the surveillance system.

I must have spent two hours understanding and not understanding. Two hours listening to Kathy's explanation and commitment to the industry, sensing her belief in its future, querying her figures on the problems in store in the next century if we do not embrace nuclear energy, grappling with her confidence that Dounreay was safe and so too were other plants if they were properly managed, trying to let her knowledge and her youthfulness allay my prejudice. I left at the end of a shift and stood at the gates as the plant's 2,000 workers streamed into cars and buses for the journey home. I watched them and wondered whether they were all fools, blinded by propaganda and the need for money, blinded so that they no longer feared what they were doing to the world and to themselves. I wondered whether in twenty years' time they would die like Kevin's father.

I pictured a man from Mars arriving on Earth and looking at Dounreay, and not just Dounreay, for the dilemmas posed here are echoed around the country where a dozen nuclear power stations are sited, and wondered what he would make of it all.

There is Sellafield. Everyone has heard of Sellafield. It used to be called Windscale, but it became so firmly entrenched in the public's mind as a place to fear that the name was changed. Since the 1970s the media has been full of tales of how much junk is allowed into the sea, of poor management and poor safety. Finally the Nuclear Installations Inspectorate issued an ultimatum giving the place twelve months to clean itself up or be closed down.

On the opposite coast, there is Sizewell. Everyone has heard of Sizewell. It was the subject of an inquiry that lasted 340 days and cost the participants £20 million and produced a report 3,000 pages long, containing 16 million words which all boil down to one word … YES. Yes, to the building of Britain's first pressurized water reactor (that's a nuclear power station with a new method of keeping the reactor core cool. The first stations used carbon dioxide, later ones were gas cooled). Public anxiety resulted in the inquiry and Sir Frank Layfield pronounced that it was safe, that it was in the national interest and that the benefits would outweigh the risks.

Then there are shallow graves. A Marsman's journey would invariably involve a visit to a proposed waste-disposal site. Since 1949 Britain has been dumping low and intermediate-level waste at sea, in concrete and steel packaging, but this has stopped and an alternative is needed. (High-level waste is stored at the plant site in tanks above the ground where it can be monitored.) One answer seems to be to dump the stuff in the ground, low-level waste in shallow, concrete-lined graves and intermediate-level waste in deeper concrete-lined graves. In 1983 the government named the first of two possible sites, Billingham in Cleveland and Elstow in Bedfordshire. A long and frantic and at times hysterical fight was waged by local inhabitants, until the government could take no more and announced three more potential candidates: Bradwell in Essex, Fulbeck in Lincolnshire and South Killingholm, Humberside. All that did was move the battlefield. The issue remains unresolved.

The issue of planning permission for Dounreay's EDRP is also unresolved. No decision has been announced. The Conservative government is running down fast-reactor funding and has cut Dounreay's research budget from £10 million to £2 million. It is doing this not to demonstrate a lack of commitment to nuclear future, but to prepare the electricity industry for privatization. Such research is too costly to attract the short-term interests of shareholders. The government believes that faster breeder technology will not be needed commercially for thirty to forty years and is therefore content to leave the whole issue on the back burner. The Japanese believe it will be needed within twenty-five years and are steaming ahead. If we are committed to nuclear-produced power, I find it hard to argue against keeping our end up in the fast reactor race. If the French win the contract, the plant will still be too close for comfort.

Kevin was waiting for me at my hotel. He invited me to dine on lobster at his cottage some miles outside Thurso. Being unemployed, the £30 rent for the cottage was paid for by the local social security department, and he had £29 a week to live on. This did not run to lobster, surely? He had caught it himself. Being unemployed, he was also adept at catching lifts.

'Let me show you. Everyone does it around here. If I stand by the roadside someone will stop within five minutes. You couldn't do it because no one knows you, but everyone knows me.' It took seven minutes for a van to drive up and give us a ride to within walking distance of the cottage where we dined on lobster and homemade apple pie.

I wanted to see the lobster pots. We walked over the fields to the sea, stopping to admire oyster catchers stalking gracefully across layers of slate assembled to resemble a *mille-feuille*. We silently sat on a rock to soak in the beauty and the stillness of a chilly summer evening and I recalled a day several years before which had followed the same pattern; which had begun with nuclear talk at a uranium mine in northern Australia and had ended amid the beauty of Kakadu National Park. That day marked the beginning of my nuclear education, which has continued ever since; even so I remain a floating thinker. I am all too aware of the fuss men make about progress; of how they fussed about the Industrial Revolution; of how Macaulay wrote: 'We are told that our age has invented atrocities beyond the imagination of our fathers; that society has been brought into a state compared with which extermination would be a blessing.' Are we simply saying the same again? Or this time have we gone too far?

Sitting on that rock I thought of Rosie Bertell, a bespectacled, grey-haired nun with a PhD and years of research into the causes of leukaemia. She says forget the ultimate accident, we are all being slowly poisoned anyway. Uranium mining and weapons testing have raised the 'natural' background radiation levels and that this is harmful and will in time damage the entire gene pool. Will she go down in history as a hysteric or as a heroine?

Chapter 3

The Highlands and Dundee: Heavenly Beauty and Nationalist Fervour

A glimpse of beauty that evening at Scarfskerry, of lobster pots and craggy rocks, made me greedy for more. I wanted to find the real Highlands. The Highlands of my imagination were soaked in a sentimental haze supplied by Walter Scott's bestseller prose, and I already sensed that I would find little of this biscuit-tin culture, of bagpipes, kilts and swirling mists, but I might well find remnants of the isolated, hard Highland life, and descendants of that intriguing clan system with its weird hierarchical array of chiefs, tacksmen, tenants and sub-tenants, tough men given to fighting rather than farming.

Until a couple of hundred years ago, the English regarded this part of the country of little value and best ignored. And then in 1745 the Highlanders (or rather some of them) decided upon a final fling against the House of Hanover. After the skirmish, London decided to tame the Highlands, to attempt integration and the destruction of the separateness of the Highland way of life. Even so, for several decades few, apart from government officials, attempted the journey northwards.

It came as a surprise to discover that when Dr Johnson published his account of travels through the Highlands in 1775, the place was considered as exotic as the North Pole. Cobbett came much later, in 1832, and only briefly reached the foothills, but that didn't stop him pontificating in his *Tour of Scotland*. One glimpse and he felt able to sum up, though this may have been easier because he was interested only in two things – food and the land as potential for growing food. Starving in the army had made him a food bore. He saw oats and cattle and sheep and was well pleased. 'All that we have heard about the barrenness of the Highlands of Scotland has been a most monstrous exaggeration,' said he, with an equal amount of exaggeration. The Highlands can be barren. There is much granite and hard sandstone;

there are mountains running to the sea's edge where small communities cling within the entrance to a sea loch, offering a natural harbour for fishing and crofting. I was heading for such a community, Kinlochbervie, on the north-west coast.

From this point my journey took shape. I decided that in the interests of a comprehensive inquiry I would ricochet from coast to coast, from east to west and from west to east. Every time I arrived on one coast I would plan a route that returned me to the other, and in so doing would zigzag my way through Britain. In Thurso I was close to the east coast and thus I would head westwards. I'd heard much about the beauty of this coast. And I'd read an account of the westward road by Edwin Muir who, in the 1930s, had been commissioned to do for Scotland what J. B. Priestley had done for England. Most of the time during this section of his Scottish journey, he seemed obsessed with his car, which was always going wrong, but in between he did convey to me an impression of strangeness and, to use his words, a heavenly beauty.

Without a car I was in difficulty. I didn't believe it at first. There was a road, therefore there had to be a bus, a mail bus even; I was in no hurry and could wait a day or two. But the bus went as far as Bettyhill, leaving a gap far too wide to bridge by taxi. I quizzed the hotel receptionist; I went to the bus station and to the tourist office, but the answer was *no*. I even telephoned Thurso companies with connections to the fishing community at Kinlochbervie, and indeed found one that would have helped with a lift had it not been the holiday season. 'Sorry, pet, we just can't help this week.'

So I gave up, or rather gave in and abandoned the coast road and planned to reach KLB (as it is known locally) via a deep V, taking the train which runs down the east coast before moving inland to Lairg, at the point of the V, and from there I'd move northwards by bus. The train left at 6 a.m., and since it clearly scorns a close relationship with the bus, it leaves the traveller with a four-hour hiatus at Lairg, lengthening the journey to eleven hours. But in the end it was not necessary. The Barr family, strangers, mere voices on the telephone, suggested they meet me at Lairg. I protested. I felt inadequate. I had long since given up doing the two-hour round trip to meet folk at Heathrow (which seemed the nearest equivalent). It wasn't that I minded the driving, it was that I minded the airport. But then Lairg railway station was hardly in the same league. I accepted and once again felt cossetted.

The railway journey, apart from going in the wrong direction, was pleasant enough; the train was slow and full. I shared a compartment with two young Scots, unapproachable since they had blocked off contact by clamping on ear-phones, through which pop music seeped, and three French teenagers, one reading Katherine Mansfield, another reading Evelyn Waugh and the third eating crisps and biscuits. I accepted his offer of a biscuit just to be friendly and we chatted about where we were heading in that clipped Pinteresque dialogue which inevitably afflicts two people who are not at home in each other's language.

We hit the coast at Helmsdale and the sight was lovely, with sweeping apricot-coloured beaches, the sun winking at the water and not a soul in sight. I moved to the corridor for a better view and immediately found myself in conversation with an Australian Catholic primary-school teacher who was whizzing around Britain on an eight-day rail pass costing a mere £74. He was using it to the fullest extent, which meant that he hardly stopped for breath in each place, but none the less seemed happy with the view from the railway tracks and human contact supplied by fellow passengers.

I tried to get my thoughts together on KLB, which took no time at all since I knew little about the place, except the importance of fishing and the fact that Brian Friel, the Northern Irish playwright, had set part of his most unusual play, *The Faith Healer*, there. The station at Lairg was predictably tiny. Three people left the train. The other two, an elderly couple, were met by a lady in a large car.

'Are you all right?' she called to me. 'Can I give you a lift into the village?'

I explained that I was being met, but having misread the timetable I was a little earlier than I'd said and was happy enough to wait. Imagine that happening at Heathrow.

Sara, the Barrs' twenty-one-year-old daughter, arrived and we set off to find the Highlands. She drove very fast, which made me nervous for a while, until I realized just how well she knew these roads, every bend, every passing place on the single track. Then I relaxed and allowed myself to be swamped by the landscape, which was stunning. There were green fields, and darker green wooded hills, and in the distance mountains shading from blue to grey, and there was clear water and stone cottages. But merely to list them is like listing the ingredients of a recipe with no understanding of the final mouthwatering dish. The views were so lovely that I kept asking if we could stop for a moment so that I could imprint the scene on my memory. I felt I was being tiresome, but Sara assured me that it was flattering when a visitor responds to your native country, a place which you have long since taken for granted. Sara's parents, Robin and Jennifer Barr, own

22,000 acres of Sutherland, from KLB to Cape Wrath. Jennifer's father, Robert Neilson, bought the land after the war. He'd been a stockbroker but had no desire to return to that life. Sutherland then was a depressed place, the kind of place which gets featured in television films because it seems poor but at the same time has values and a style of living that makes a mockery of that four-letter word.

Colonel Neilson, when he arrived, pondered what he might do to improve the lot of Kinlochbervie, and of the crofters on his estate. The weather provided the answer. One day fishermen from the east coast were forced to find shelter in the loch and Neilson asked them what it would take to persuade them to land their catch in KLB on a regular basis. Ice and transport came the answer. Ice and transport ought to be possible, he thought, and enlisted the help of the forerunner to the Highlands and Islands Development Board and of his neighbour, the Duke of Westminster. If it hadn't been for Colonel Neilson, the story goes, there would be no fishing industry at KLB, but there is and it is thriving and ever expanding.

A new harbour was being built: a grand scheme costing £4 million, grant aided, including a chunk from the European regional fund, the money to be spent on a new fish market, a major dredging exercise to enable the harbour to accommodate up to eighty boats, perhaps a fish-processing plant and a repair yard. Fishing provides the crofters with a much-needed source of income; the two go well together. After all, it was what the better landlords had in mind when they cleared the Highlands for sheep. Before sheep there was poverty; moving families to the coast to make way for sheep meant they had a better chance, through fishing, of improving their lot. But that kind of thinking is rarely acknowledged; to most people there was nothing good about the idea of the Clearances. Today, however, men readily acknowledge that having a piece of land with, say, forty ewes and a few cattle, cannot provide a living, but fishing means they can stay close to the land they love and on which their families have lived for as long as anyone cares to remember. In the past the crofters would have to travel, going away for a season to fish; now they go to sea for less than a week at a time. There are some moans: the dual life keeps many busy and prevents them from devoting as many hours to the all-important business of being neighbourly, a pastime that acts like glue, attaching people to each other in an undissoluble way.

KLB is imbued with the best aspects of Coronation Street, the EastEnders, Ambridge or even Peyton Place. Everyone knows everyone; everyone gossips about everyone. Sometimes this sounds malicious, but it is a shallow kind of malice, the kind that makes men fight of a night outside the pub and embrace the next day. Such closeness can of course be claustrophobic, but I wasn't around long enough to feel that. I was around long enough to be entranced and much amused. Much of this was the Barr influence. I had intended to stay at a local hotel, but was invited to stay at their home, and anyway by the time the car turned the final hill for the descent into KLB, I already knew many a character by name and I already knew that the bothy vied with the local hotel as the centre of village life.

Sara had been at the bothy the night before until the wee small hours. It's at the bottom of her garden, so to speak: a wooden hut with space at one end for bunk beds, a sitting area in the middle and kitchen quarters just inside the door. The salmon fishermen live there in the season (from mid-May until mid-August) and when they are on land the door is always open. The bothy was my first port of call, and there I met Pete and Andy, who own the boat, and Willie and TC, who are helpers. The group have had a licence from the Westminster estate to fish in the same waters for ten years, and they wouldn't reveal how much it costs. They were cagey too on how much money they made, but said it supported the group for the season, after which they split up and go on the dole or to Thurso in search of work. Pete and Andy were most forthcoming on the subject of farmed salmon, which is all the rage; a new industry, heavily backed by the Highlands and Islands Development Board since it brings employment. There are around 200 farms producing around 20,000 tonnes of salmon, which could well rise to 50,000 tonnes by the early 1990s. Big business, and all too many under the umbrella of multinational companies like Unilever. Such farms are not universally popular, facing claims that they blight lochs and damage the tourist trade. For the salmon fishermen in the bothy at KLB there are other problems. Farmed salmon hardly bears comparison with wild salmon, but the market, which is mainly in the south, is too ignorant to know the difference; mostly they do not even know whether they are buying wild or farmed versions. The bothy boys know; they can tell at a glance; farmed salmon lack the blue-grey sheen on their skins; their fins are wimpish (they can after all only swim in a limited circle) and their meat is greyish because they have been fed on fish pellets rather than the prawns and shrimps that give wild salmon its distinctive colour. Farm salmon they claim is artificially coloured. They invited me to go out with them the following morning in the hope that we would net a stray farmed creature, one that had got away, and I could then see the difference myself.

Meanwhile we all arranged to meet in the pub later that evening for, being Friday, it would give me a chance to see the community at play.

This did not mean a cosy chat or two in a comfortable chair; it meant standing at the bar for some considerable time failing to keep pace with the quantities of beer and scotch being consumed. Sara warned me not to spend too much time talking to any one man; it would worry the women. 'The Black Widow' already had a reputation for being a snake after the men. I began with Willie. At the bothy he'd said very little; kept his nose in the newspaper and looked up only once: 'How many Ts in Rotterdam?' he ventured, needing help with his crossword. He was chatty in the pub. He told me how he had been living in Thurso with Angie, and together they had a son who died of leukaemia. 'We'd split up before it was diagnosed, but once we knew how serious it was we got back together for his sake. He used to play on the beach at Dounreay, but you can't prove it was that which caused his illness.'

'Look,' said Maureen, who runs the shop and who lives in a caravan with Ben. 'Look, there's the Black Widow. Can I introduce you?' The Black Widow earned her name from the colour of her hair rather than the colour of her skin; her dress tended to be black and as elegant and as time-consuming as her make up. We got on well. She'd worked in the wardrobe of the Scottish Opera before going to Canada, but she had become bored with city life and felt that KLB might be a good place to bring up her son. She thought she might stay: I thought she might not. 'Did you notice how she kept putting her hand on TC's shoulder? She's possessive,' Maureen whispered. 'He walked her home the other night after a party, but as he left the bothy he yelled to us that he'd be back within half an hour, just to make the point that he didn't intend to linger.'

'Yes,' said TC. 'I kissed her good night and then kicked the fuck out of the cat when I got home.'

I met Muriel. She has a daughter of fourteen who had just returned from her first visit south, where she had strawberries and cream. Muriel's brother had been banned from the pub for his behaviour. I met Sally, who had a mysterious background, aristocratic in some way, drug-related in another, who now ran a craft shop on the harbour side. Sara's mother sometimes knitted jumpers to sell in the shop. Sara, Gordonstoun-educated and with a degree, was hoping for a career in the film industry. One day, since she is an only child, she will be the landowner, but despite the difference in background, her ability to merge with the locals was matchless. It was either that or being lonely. By the end of a long evening, submerged in local gossip, I felt I had the makings of a soap opera to rival *Brookside*, one that would certainly overturn the legacy of *Dr Finlay's Casebook*.

The next morning, Saturday, the weather was poor, windy and wet, but the salmon boat had no option but to brave the swell. There's a rule that the leader net must be lifted from noon on Saturday until 6 a.m. on Monday, in order to give the fish a free weekend. If the weather precludes the net being lifted then the estate manager has to be notified, otherwise the fishermen risk being fined. We thought it worth trying to get the nets up, so donned oilskins and boots and clambered aboard the fibreglass all-purpose boat. It wasn't designed for salmon fishing, and once we started slamming against the waves, it seemed rather small and inadequate. TC sang at the top of his voice. My eyes closed against the rain and the spray which was annoying since I had wanted to enjoy the view from the loch, but whichever way I twisted and turned so that my back could take the pounding, leaving my eyes open, I still found my vision blurred. I decided it was best to keep my eyes shut until the boat stopped behaving like a roller-coaster and paused by the nets. The hauling up of nets is work for fit men, who place their toes under a piece of wood in order to anchor their feet in the hope of not tripping overboard. The first net yielded one salmon. The second net saw thirty-four plump, streamlined beauties plummet to the deck, showering us with scales, with tiny silver flakes like confetti. There they squirmed and lashed about in a futile attempt to regain their freedom.

'Mind the eyes,' yelled Andy as TC went for the kill. There's a knack to clubbing salmon so that there is no trace of the death blow; bruises and damaged eyes cause instant devaluation. I didn't think it worth trying my hand.

'Here we go – a perfect farm job,' Andy called to me with contempt in his voice. And he was right. Seeing the two side by side, the differences are marked: the dullish, brownish colour cannot compete with the heavy blue-grey of the wild creature, the shape was less streamlined and the fins were indeed feeble through lack of use. The sky grew darker and the wind increased, which prompted a brief debate about turning back, but we decided to go for one more net and a final attempt to reach the leader. The waves seemed to get bigger and the boat smaller, but it never occurred to me that we were in any way at risk. Afterwards Andy revealed that he had been apprehensive and that his decision to go for another net had not been wise. We didn't reach the leader. Instead we belted for the shore, cold and uncomfortable and clinging to the rail for fear of being tipped into the sea.

A morning of salmon fishing was followed by an afternoon witnessing an important local social event: the opening of new buildings at the Seamen's Mission by Anne, Duchess of Westminster. The weather spoiled her appearance; she wore the statutory big hat and pearls, but her dress was protected by a blue windcheater, which is not an elegant garment. The Seamen's Mission provides a home from home for fishermen from the east coast; while the catch is being unloaded and auctioned, they can have a shower, a meal and a game of snooker. The duchess thought it was all 'charming'. 'Isn't that *charming*. I really am most impressed,' she said in the gravelly voice of a heavy smoker. The fish market where the catch is auctioned had been turned into a fair, with stalls selling lobster and cakes and Christmas cards. Some boats were offering rides around the loch, others invited the nosey to crawl all over them. I crawled all over one which was old, cramped, uncomfortable and grubby. I then bought lots of cakes and went to the bothy to see if the salmon boys had thawed out.

During the next couple of days I turned my attention to white fish and learned about the growth in pair trawling and the difference in nets and of plans for the future and stories from the past; of the days when the Barr family first arrived, when the road from Lairg was mere gravel and there was no electricity and no running water. In those days the family owned and ran the local hotel and had three sheep. Now they've sold the hotel and have 300 sheep. Jennifer Barr loves the sheep. She'd had to bottle feed four of them. One morning I offered to help and found myself in a wrestling match with a sturdy, greedy little creature, quite determined to knock me over in an attempt to gobble more than his share. While he walked on my feet and butted me, I took mild pleasure in knowing something he had yet to learn. This was to be his last bottle; within twenty-four hours he'd be crying and bleating and longing for his bottle, angry that he'd been apparently forgotten, not realizing that he'd been kicked out into the world to fend for himself. The noise was pathetic, but sheep are surprisingly quick on the up-take; after two days he and his three chums got the message.

I left K L B one evening at 8.30, along with thirty tonnes of haddock and whiting in a lorry that was fifty-two feet long. I'd cadged a ride with Edwin, who was going through to Inverness (where I wanted to be), *en route* for Aviemore, where another driver would be taking the catch to Edinburgh. He seemed delighted to have a passenger. 'It's good to have company and I'm happy to be a taxi driver. You've got to be around here, the transport is so bad. I'm always giving rides. One day recently the boss rang me and asked me to take *three* people . . . turned out to be a wedding party, bride, groom and best man. They drank all the way and I had to pour them out of the lorry. They invited me to the wedding, but I couldn't turn up in a boiler-suit could I?'

Edwin had been driving this route for three years. He was born on the west coast and now lived in Lairg. For ten years, between 1959 and 1969, he was a policeman in Dundee.

'Nine or ten of us left at the same time. We were all disillusioned. It was the poorest-paid job in Britain then. I got £17 a week to take home. It's the kind of job that makes you cynical, and Dundee is not much of a place, but it is full of contrast, lots of unemployment and a big university. I was glad to get out.'

At first he worked in a garage changing clutches and brakes, and then he began to drive.

'It was the oil. There was a lot of money to be made driving for the oil people when all the construction was going on. I'd work fourteen hours a day, seven days a week for two years.' And with the money he bought his own lorry and began doing the beef run to London, driving illegally long hours until the day he fell asleep at the wheel and woke up in hospital with a ruptured spleen.

'Look, a deer,' I said, which was an obvious remark, but it was the first I'd seen.

'Yes, we're on Westminster land now. One man owns all this. It isn't right in my view. There's no farming done, it is one great park for shooting and fishing. He comes up here once a year for a month and that's all. There's money for you.'

'But it does create employment, doesn't it?'

'Not much.'

'But it must bring money to the area?'

'Not much.'

They say Queen Victoria is to blame. She read Walter Scott, fell in love with the area and bought Balmoral. This encouraged the rich to use the area as a playground. The Arabs own estates now, and so do the Dutch. The Arabs use their lands infrequently, flying up in their helicopters, leaving the place in the hands of agents much of the time. It doesn't promote good relations between the landowners and the rest, but then absentee landlords never do.

The village of Achferry is pretty. The Westminsters have decreed that all houses shall be whitewashed and have black-painted window-frames and doors. Everything is black and white, even the telephone box.

Edwin was bothered by the road. 'Look out of your window. You've got about three inches to spare on your side and I've got about the same on my side. We could do with a better road.' If the road was unsuitable for such huge lorries, it was also one of the most beautiful routes. We passed only one other vehicle, another fish lorry, and paused for a chat. I think Dr Johnson might have recognized it. He complained that the roads of Scotland 'afford little diversion to the traveller, who seldom sees himself either encountered or overtaken'. If it bothered him, it delighted me. The feeling of space and of emptiness was a bonus and a revelation. When you think of the size of the British mainland and of the size of the population, it seems inconceivable that there would be any empty space.

'They are still putting in a lot of trees around here,' said Edwin. 'Tax dodge, and it must be a good one with all those pop stars putting money in.'

They are indeed putting in a lot of trees, mainly in eastern Sutherland and Caithness. And it has caused much controversy. The rationale goes way back to the First World War, when Britain needed to replace depleted timber reserves. The Forestry Commission could be said to be the first nationalized industry, and many are surprised that it was not one of the first to be privatized. Rich sportsmen as well as pop stars have attracted much publicity for taking advantage of tax concessions for afforestation programmes. These have now ceased, but other grants have been introduced. And rows over what is planted and where continue. We need trees, of that there is no doubt, not to ensure an adequate supply of props for the trenches, but to reduce our import bill for timber heading for the pulp mills. This area is planted not with indigenous Scots pine, but with imported spruce, which is upsetting the wildlife and causing consternation among conservationists. This message has finally reached the right ears and in future the planting of broad-leaved deciduous trees is to be promoted on grasslands and arable lands. The greenshank and the golden plover will be pleased to see fewer foreign pines.

It was dark by the time we reached Inverness, three hours later. My first view was of thousands of street lights. How odd they looked. I hadn't seen such a sight in weeks; there had been a handful lighting KLB, but this array signalled a city – albeit a small city of 40,000. I'd happily forgotten about cities.

Edwin pulled into an industrial estate on the edge of Inverness where he was to deliver his first load of fish. From Highland Haulage he phoned for a taxi to take me to my boarding house. It was 11.45 and I was anxious. I'd phoned to say that I would be late, but the owner had sounded none too pleased. 'We'd better wait up for you,' he said. 'We don't want you ringing the bell and waking the rest.' He was waiting to receive my apologies. The sheets on my bed were made of nylon and a sign said that baths could only be taken between 6 p.m. and 10 p.m.

Inverness, at the mouth of the Ness, is called the capital of the

Highlands. It is *the* service centre, the trading centre and the headquarters of the summer tourist traffic. There are no shortages of bed-and-breakfast houses; people make their money in the summer and have a quiet winter. The city has doubled its population in the last twenty years. The coming of oil caused that, and now, with oil on the retreat, there is unemployment; but in the summer it is well concealed by the tourist. The Labour party tried hard in the 1960s to direct industry to the area. The result was an aluminium smelter at Invergordon and a pulp mill at Fort William. Both have now closed. To have had the two for ten years was better than not having the two at all, but thinking on regional policy has changed. It's no longer considered wise to bring in industry, garlanded with all manner of grants and tax incentives, for once all the incentives run out, such industries flounder. Much better to encourage smaller industries to grow from local needs so they have a better chance of taking root; much better for the locals to find their own solutions, than have vote-catching temporary expedients placed on their doorsteps. For all that, the busiest place in town was the tourist office, followed by Marks and Spencer. That's a landmark. M. and S. dithered about putting a store in Inverness, and have been amazed, so I was told, by its success. The unit sale, the amount each person spends on a visit, is said to be extraordinarily high. From miles around folk travel once a month to Inverness for all their needs. I wasn't interested in tourist Inverness, and vowed to ignore Loch Ness and its monster: it's more biscuit-tin culture. But then I heard the legend of the loch and liked it; it explains how the loch came into being.

Once upon a time in that neighbourhood there lived a holy man who somehow managed to have access to clear spring water and, being a generous man, he offered the water free to others, stipulating that they must place a wooden lid on the top of the well after drawing water. A mother came with her baby and while she was filling her jug she saw an adder creeping towards her child. She grabbed her offspring and ran, forgetting to put the lid back. The water rose and trickled out of the well and did not stop until the loch was formed.

My purpose in stopping in Inverness was of course to glimpse the Highland capital, but also to glimpse the descendants of the clan chiefs whose names are woven consistently throughout the tapestry of Scottish history. Commander Mackintosh is now the Mackintosh of Mackintosh. He lives a handful of miles outside Inverness, at Moy, in an elegant but modest house on a modest estate. He is a modest man, delightful company, and with a line in self-deprecation that is decidedly un-Scottish. He went to Dartmouth at the age of thirteen and, following in the footsteps of his father, became a naval officer. His father unexpectedly inherited the estate in 1938 and left it in the hands of a lawyer while he got on with the business of fighting Hitler. It was a vast estate then, but much land was sold; it now consists of 11,000 acres, the majority of which is moorland.

Commander Mackintosh debunked the mystery of the clan-system over tea in his paper-crowded study.

'There is nothing mysterious about tribes or the tribal system. The key to the Highlands is communication. Before 1720 there were no roads, so it was difficult if not impossible to get in and out. Farming was at subsistence level, so people starved or stole from the next person. Land in those days meant only one thing – food. We fought over food. And of course as soon as the roads came the clan system began to crumble.' Being a Scottish landowner took more than a few sips of tea to explain. 'I find it difficult to justify. If you want to take the view that land ownership is unfair, I find that statement hard to refute. When I was in the navy, it was so much easier. The navy was very much respected and I felt the approval of my fellow men. When I became a landowner, I immediately felt the difference. I became public enemy number one. When I first decided to stand for the local council my friends all told me not to bother. You'll never get in, they said; they won't vote for a landowner. Well, I stood and I won and since 1974 I've been unopposed. Even so there are only two landowners on a council of fifty-two.'

He sounded very defensive, more defensive than I'd have expected. 'I am defensive. Landowners in the Highlands have a very bad reputation and the Clearances are a big part of it. I've argued with historians about the Clearances. The Highlands before the Clearances had a greater population than it could accommodate and it was to the advantage of many to be moved or to be given a passage to the colonies. It was either that or penury. It was to the advantage of many. One day a Rolls-Royce full of Americans drew up outside here. They'd all come to trace their ancestors and I told them they were lucky. They'd done well by leaving.'

I mentioned that I was much surprised at the number of times the subject of the Clearances had come up in conversation since the day I set foot in the Shetland Islands, and that all landowners seemed to take much the same defensive view. And I also told him about my most recent encounter with the opposite view. I had been wandering around a churchyard near Cape Wrath looking at the graves when an elderly man in a cloth cap and raincoat began to talk to me. He didn't look at me; he kept his gaze fixed in the middle distance while he talked in a soft voice about the 'wicked factors' and how they waited until the most able men were away at war and then began to clear the land. He never mentioned the landowner, but used the phrase 'wicked factor' over and again. He came from the Isle of Lewis. The Clearances, it seems, refuse to become 'history'; they remain a raw living memory.

'In my youth we never talked of these things, but maybe that is because we were taught very little Scottish history. Nowadays all children learn about those times and talk about them. There's still a lot of resentment in the Highlands. The Clearances may be in the past, but on another level we don't think we get our share. There are primary schools with outside loos. We seem too far away; no one is interested – except those who are looking for a playground. "Incomer" is a nasty word and "White Settler" is even worse, but those of us who work the land resent them. We resent them out of fear; we feel vulnerable. We had to tear down the Victorian mansion because it was just too much to keep up. We put up this house in its place in the 1950s. I'm not particularly chauvinistic, because I've lived in the south, but when we struggle, we do resent those who use the land as a plaything.'

He made the life sound so hard that I shocked him by suggesting that he might sell. 'It's inconceivable. My family have been here for 600 years. Owning land in the Highlands is a luxury; it's a struggle, but we get by. And it's so different from being a landowner in, say, Wiltshire. There is a much greater spirit of egalitarianism in the Highlands, which is why English Tories always say that Scottish Tories are so much farther to the left. We have a different attitude to class. We all know each other. We mix with each other because we are interdependent.

'Once a year the Mackintosh of Mackintosh plays host to the clan. It's a world gathering to which several hundred come at a time. They are mostly Americans looking for the land they left behind. It sounds a touch ludicrous, I know, but it is harmless enough. To please them I have placed a collection of treasures, of clan memorabilia, in a hut in the garden. There's a bed in which Bonnie Prince Charlie slept. Come and have a look.' I went and looked at the wall hangings, the newspaper clippings, the swords and the bed. And then we walked back over a beautiful lawn, pausing to admire the view.

They speak ill of Dundee; 'they' being anyone of any note who has passed through and then felt obliged to comment upon the fact. Dr Johnson came and went and found nothing to remember; Queen Victoria declared: 'The situation of the town is very fine, but the town itself is not so.' James Cameron shared the same view, but expressed it more eloquently. He ribbed the place for being blessed with a site which should have encouraged a city of grandeur but instead gave rise to an absence of grace so complete that it was almost a thing of wonder. Dundee, climbing the hillside above the River Tay, had the makings of a kind of Naples, but instead 'had the air of a place that from the beginning of time had reconciled itself to an intrinsic ugliness'. Cameron lived there in the late 1920s, filling up glue pots on a magazine, improbably titled *Red Star Weekly*, for working girls who liked gory stories. The magazine was owned by D. C. Thomson, who was more famous for *Beano* and *Dandy*. Cameron was amused that what he insisted was one of the most alcoholic towns in the nation persisted in returning the only prohibitionist Member of Parliament. 'Endlessly voted for by the distracted wives in a hapless effort to keep the dole money from the pubs.' That prohibitionist, a Mr Scrymgeour, also had the distinction of unseating Winston Churchill, who as a Liberal represented Dundee from 1908 to 1922. When he deserted the Liberals he was dumped.

And it was another MP that was taking me once more eastward – Gordon Wilson, the Member for Dundee East, was one of only two Scottish Nationalists in the House of Commons (the other represented the Western Isles), and a chat with such a rare specimen was a powerful magnet. At the station in Inverness I had a choice; I could travel via Aberdeen or via Aviemore and Perth. I chose the latter because it sounded prettier. Dundee is a place with a past. It was once the centre of the jute and flax industry; 30,000 tons of the stuff once came into the port from India in a fleet solely devoted to the trade, and many factories in Bengal were owned by Dundee merchants. The industry employed 50,000 people producing rough sacking, carpets and linen. The city was also famed for jams, for marmalade and of course for comics.

In those days, towards the end of the nineteenth century, critics might argue the place was so engrossed in getting rich that it didn't bother about how it looked. The jute barons, and they included the Grimond family, achieved much, but the city was full of slums and poverty and violence – Saturday-night brawling was commonplace. Now, of course, Dundee is neither so busy nor so rich. Unemployment had reached 17 per cent among a population of 180,000 which is one of the reasons why the sensitive Liberal party chose to have its conference there in 1985. I attended as a sketch writer for *The Times*. The town was brimful and delighted to be on the lucrative conference circuit. At the best hotel, the Angus, they were singing to the sound of the tills ringing.

'I'm sorry, lovely,' said the barmaid, 'but the manager has said that all drinks served have to be doubles while the conference is on.' On my last day I decided to make a dash for the plane from Edinburgh to London, and asked a taxi driver if he fancied the run. He looked as though he had won the pools. 'Oh, I'd be happy to be out of Dundee for the afternoon. Let's go.' He told me in that hour his entire life story, a story of poverty in Glasgow and unemployment in Dundee. He also told me how he bridged the gap between his income and his needs with a life of petty crime. He picked up deals in pubs and always wore boots several sizes too large in case he left footprints behind. 'Why should I gaze in shop windows at things I can't afford to buy? There are always ways of getting them. Wouldn't you do the same?' I wondered if I might find him again on this, my second visit.

Outside Dundee station, I turned left and found a bed and break-fast hotel called The Bruce. At £9.50 a night it's the kind of stop that long-distance coach drivers use and sure enough it took me less than half an hour to find myself discussing the run to London. One driver said that it had become so boring he bit his fingernails for something to do; another discussed the cowboys who drive for twenty hours at a stretch and give the rest a bad name. As well as coach drivers, the hotel was seething with RAF cadets on a course. Since no meals were served they'd been out to collect fish and chips. I decided I needed a walk.

It was only 7.30, but the centre of the town was already alive with loudmouthed youths yelling at girls in their weekend best. I watched them and began to count the number of times the girls eased their blouses back over their shoulders, an action that was not done out of modesty, to cover an inch of cleavage. It was done for comfort: their garments were badly cut and slipped and slithered instead of staying put. Their shoes were similarly cheap; I checked by looking in shop windows, which had abandoned window-dressing skills for un-imaginative racks. Several of the shops were empty and plastered with stickers claiming that the royal family were parasites: 'What have they got that we haven't got?' they asked, and invited me to a public meeting to discuss the answer. Excellent, I thought, I'll go – only to discover that the anti-royalist heat had been dissipated the previous evening. Disappointed, I wandered instead to look at the new leisure centre; if a place is poor and struggling, it will have a large leisure centre built with guilt-appeasing grants. I thought about going in and then headed instead for a pizza parlour with mock Tiffany lamps, and more young girls adjusting their blouses. It was quiet and welcoming and neatly segregated into booths for smokers and non-smokers.

On the way back to The Bruce I stopped at the Job Centre and looked at the vacancies in the window: 'Housekeeper required, 23 plus, accommodation available, must be good cook, honest, reliable and of excellent appearance.' 'Door-to-door salesman required for bread rolls and dairy products.' 'Kitchen designer, commission only.' None of the ads mentioned money.

Gordon Wilson's office was uglier and scruffier than anything else I had seen in Dundee. The staircase leading from the street was dust covered; the ladies' room was locked; 'Oh, don't worry about that use the Gents.' I did, and it was stomach turning. Wilson's waiting room displayed dirty ashtrays and I was offered coffee in a cup so cracked I didn't dare drink out of it. I sat under a poster saying, 'England is too much trouble', and opposite a poster saying, 'Gordon Wilson works and cares', and another saying, 'It's time for self-government.'

Wilson is an unprepossessing, dull man with what seemed to me to be a total lack of political fire. Maybe a morning surgery listening to the complaints of his constituents had doused the fire and left him longing to get home to a round of golf or whatever it is MPs do with their spare time. He gave me a brief sketch of Dundee problems from nineteenth-century prosperity based on the sea to the coming of American companies like Timex and National Cash Register, both in the doldrums, having been overtaken by technological advance. The worst, however, was over, I was assured. 'In 1980 the use of the buses in towns dropped 20 per cent as factories closed, but things are picking up now. There are signs of recovery.' The most visible sign being the Wellgate Shopping Centre, a three-storey complex housing British Home Stores and Tesco, and undoubtedly responsible for some of the empty shops I'd seen the previous day in another part of town. We then turned to Scottish nationalism. He was interesting on the build-up of enthusiasm for the party during the early 1970s, which sprang inevitably from dissatisfaction with other parties and other policies; a build-up that offered the SNP 30 per cent of the vote in the election of October 1974, but which had evaporated by the time the referendum on devolution and the setting up of a Scottish Assembly came before the electorate in 1979. On that occasion 64 per cent turned out to vote and of that percentage 33 said yes and 31 said no. The bill demanded that at least 40 per cent had to be in favour; the mission failed and after that the SNP support crumbled further. The bill, said Gordon Wilson, had been a mess, and so complicated that all too few understood what it entailed and all too many found clauses over which to squabble, and reasons not to bother to vote.

That 64 per cent is a sad figure; it means that 36 per cent couldn't be bothered to vote on something as important as who makes the rules that govern them. On the whole, however, it is safe to assume that abstainers are in favour of the status quo, in other words that they were saying no to devolution. The closeness of the other figures is just as interesting: it reveals that those who bothered to vote were equally divided. A fine example of the Scottish personality – both realistic and romantic. The realists were saying no and the romantics were saying yes. Before the referendum most of us in the south thought that Scotland would vote for devolution; they kept saying they would. Allan Massie, a Scottish writer, tried to explain in an essay published in the *Spectator*. 'We may all be Jacobites and nationalists in our hearts, but a lot of Scots reserve sentimentality for whisky sessions and, when sober, don't like to let bread fall jam-side to the floor.' I accept Massie's theory, but Gordon Wilson believes that if there were another vote tomorrow it would be *for* devolution. The reason for the change is Mrs Thatcher. 'We feel that Scotland has been taken to the cleaners over oil, and we know that Mrs Thatcher is anti-Scotland. She treats us with contempt and has no sympathy for the fact that our best people are still having to leave Scotland in search of opportunities. This has been the pattern for centuries and it cannot go on much longer. If Scotland ran its own affairs such men would stay.'

I did not feel comfortable in Gordon Wilson's presence. Try as I did I could not establish a rapport with him. I felt unwelcome. He answered my questions briefly and quietly and did not seem to relish discussion. We bored each other. Looking back I can see that the tone for our meeting was set within the first few minutes and that it had been impossible to change it. During those early minutes his secretary had knocked on the door and said that a constituent was outside waiting to see him.

'Let him wait. He's late.'

I said that I didn't mind giving way to the constituent as our conversation might take some time.

'Let him wait. He's late.'

Gordon Wilson lost his seat to Labour in the election of 11 June 1987. He is now president of the SNP. The SNP won an important by-election at Govan in 1988; the result represented a 33 per cent swing against Labour. Most people, and especially the Labour party, like to see this as a mighty vote against the Thatcher government: a mighty roar of protest by a left-wing country against right-wing rule from London. The poll tax or community charge was the biggest single issue. This is the Conservative party's new alternative to rates. Instead of a charge on *property* to raise money for local services, *individuals* will have to pay, via flat-rate levy. The poll tax appears to have few admirers: many more people will have to pay it than pay rates. In fact, everyone over the age of eighteen will pay something, even those on social security will have to find 20 per cent of the bill. All this is part of Mrs Thatcher's attack on high-spending local authorities and also part of her campaign for citizens to feel involved and concerned about what is happening around them. More people paying the tax will mean more people who care about the quality of the local services, and more voices to complain if payment for those services is considered too high. The tax is said to be more costly to collect than rates (people move around, buildings don't), and those eligible for charges will be taken from the electoral roll. It is argued that to avoid paying people will not register to vote. The new system will cover England and Wales from 1990, but in Scotland the change came a year earlier. The able SNP candidate, Jim Sillars, latched on to the unpopularity of all this and used it as a focus for Scottish frustration in general. It helped to win the by-election. This victory may goad many to reconsider the virtues of devolution: I don't think it means that Scots want independence. The SNP argues otherwise. They have discovered the EEC. They were against the EEC at the time of the 1979 devolution debate. Now the EEC looks attractive.

If Scotland could get from Europe the kind of financial support it gets from London, it might well tempt the Scots to thumb their noses at London. I find the SNP change of heart over the EEC both cynical and opportunistic, but I also feel that the English have been far too superior in their dealings with Scotland and Wales. On these travels I came to value the Celtic fringe; to value the countryside for its beauty; to value the people for the contribution they make to the nation's life; to value the colour and sparkle that they add to the words Great Britain. England alone would be a dull lump. Our loss would be Europe's gain and it would serve us right.

I had intended to ask Wilson to show me his Dundee, the place in which he lived and worked. I'd discussed this idea with his secretary and she had said that he'd probably be delighted. In the end I didn't bother to ask him. I didn't think he'd say yes, and if he had, I feared the hours would be arid. I went instead to the Angus Hotel for a cup of tea and to ponder what to do next. I thought about the taxi driver I'd met on my previous visit and how I'd left in a hurry. In an instant, I decided to do the same again and within the hour I was back at the railway station waiting for the train to Glasgow.

There are too many stairs at Dundee Station and as I struggled with my luggage I failed to see the ticket office. When I discovered that I'd have to climb the stairs once more in order to get a ticket I asked a young woman if she would keep an eye on the luggage while I raced to the kiosk. Helen was the Manageress of Richards shops in Dundee. Actually she works in Aberdeen, but her shop there was being refitted, so she'd been moved to Dundee for a while and was living at the Angus. 'It's been rather boring. I don't feel safe out at night on my own, so I just go back to the hotel each evening and as I hate eating on my own I have something sent up to my room.'

The previous evening had been different. She invited her assistant Manageress to join her for dinner. 'All evening we were being eyed by two Arabs at the next table. I told my assistant to enjoy it, after all she's not very happy with her husband at the moment. In the end the Arabs came over and asked us to settle a bet. They thought my assistant was Italian . . . well she's South African and of course after that opening they invited us to join them for a drink.' Helen drank vodka and orange with her Arab until 1.30. He was here to buy property. He wanted an estate. I envied her the meeting. I'd have enjoyed talking to an Arab who wanted to buy a Scottish estate.

We'd been so busy with our chat that I hadn't noticed the station fill up with police. Once I did notice, I wanted to know why. A young officer said, 'There's a train coming in from Montrose, and there's a lot of trouble from football supporters, so you stand right back away from the track and be careful.'

The train came in. There was no trouble; a score or more of chastened youths got off. I looked out of the carriage window to ensure I missed nothing and both Helen and the young policeman waved to me as the train pulled out.

Chapter 4

Glasgow's Miles Better

Glasgow shares a problem with Dundee; it too is derided and has a dubious image; it too provokes a dismissive wrinkling of the nose from those who have never set foot in the place. Such people see the city as synonymous with drunken football fans, impenetrable accents, a foul-mouthed comedian called Billy Connolly and poverty in a place called the Gorbals. Arriving at the station my expectations were a little on the low side, but then, to be fair, they invariably are when heading into a strange, large city. Large cities present obstacles; they can be difficult to prise open. Beyond the tedious round of tourist monuments and the visual exploration of the delights and dilemmas of buildings, buildings and more buildings, they can seem as closed as any Masonic lodge. It's not that people are unwelcoming; it is easy enough to arrange formal interviews, but rarely is one invited into homes, and never, never is one invited to hitchhike towards a lobster! However, within days I'd fallen in like with Glasgow; a Glasgow that was anxious to explain itself; a Glasgow that was anxious that I should understand that it desired to change its image. It no longer wants to be the feared thug, the bullyboy, the ignorant, the victim. It wants to be well-dressed and charming and cultured, the victor.

How did Glasgow get such a dubious image? If one goes far enough back, to the early part of the eighteenth century, there are some attractive descriptions to be found; descriptions of handsome streets, of kitchen- and flower-gardens, of orchards and cornfields. Daniel Defoe passing through in 1727 described Glasgow glowingly; ''Tis one of the cleanliest, most beautiful and best built cities in Great Britain.' Nearby there was a pretty country village called Gorbals.

The slide came with prosperity and prosperity came with the Union with England in 1707, when Scotland was allowed to trade with Virginia and did so with relish, outwitting both London and Bristol to become the centre of the tobacco trade. The tobacco era did not diminish Glasgow. The wealthy merchants added buildings of beauty. It was the ending of tobacco (with the American War of Independence) and the coming of steam, iron and coal, of cotton, engineering and shipbuilding, that turned Glasgow into an industrial city, bringing in its wake too many people too quickly. By 1842 Glasgow was labelled the filthiest and the unhealthiest of British cities. The mud was flung and it stuck.

Now, many cities suffered from the impact of the Industrial Revolution; many cities found themselves throwing up homes to house the industrial slaves that rushed from the countryside in search of wages. In Glasgow they rushed from the north and west of Scotland and from Ireland to escape rural desolation and famine. A three-storey tenement, offering a room and a kitchen or just a room, was a pitiable existence, but arguably better than rural starvation. The central point is that while other cities got their slums – and Dickens and Mayhew graphically described those in London – Glasgow seems to have got more than its share, and the image of the Gorbals stays in the mind, refusing to budge. Why? The answer is painfully simple. Glasgow has been ill-served by its writers. Glasgow writers painted over and over again a vision of nastiness that was so vivid it became indelible. Writers on the whole do not like to dabble in moderation; it is easier to grab attention if balance is ignored and extremes are explored. Think of Dallas. Dallas is synonymous with wealth and oil barons, with the ruthless rich and the square-shouldered, well-groomed women who cling to them. It is seen as a city of stylish dirty tricks; full of Ewing family clones and of millionaires, more per head than any city in the world. How many people know or care that Dallas houses thousands of blacks and Hispanics living in festering slums? That's what writers have done to Dallas. They've done the opposite with Glasgow.

On the train I'd dipped once more into Edwin Muir's *Scottish Journey*, written in the 1930s. He devoted sixty pages to Glasgow, most of them describing his appalling experiences in 1901 when he was dragged, aged fourteen, by his parents from an idyllic but poor Orkney into the slums of Glasgow. The experience turned Muir into a committed socialist. He has nothing good to say of 'industrialism', nor of capitalism, which to him was sanctioned greed such as the world had never seen before; a process which took no regard of human life unless compelled to do so; a process that devastated whole tracts of countryside. The Orcadian longed to be rid of this madness.

Muir's writing may have affected me, but he cannot be blamed for

Glasgow's image – his work was not sufficiently widely read. There is, however, one book and two men who are responsible for doing Glasgow down. The book is *No Mean City* and the authors, A. McArthur and H. Kingsley Long, are now widely resented. Their book is a portrait of the Gorbals in the 1930s, of poverty and unemployment and crowded living conditions and the effects that all three have on human beings, unleashing violence in men and passivity in women. Energy was channelled not into fighting the bosses for better conditions, but in fighting each other with razors. The Razor Kings ruled their patch and when things got too much they went out and slashed the faces and beat the hell out of other men whose fight for survival was just as grim. The only difference was that one gang comprised Catholics and the other Protestants; and then not even this imagined difference was there all the time. The women, submerged by slave mentality, revered those brutal Razor Kings, longed to have them as lovers, and took their beating along with the rest and justified their devotion by arguing that the fights and the Kings were the Gorbals way of making the rest remember that they existed.

The portrait is horrific: the writers knew what they were doing and, just in case anyone was tempted to dismiss the book as 'fiction', they included at the end a collection of newspaper references:

> It is not uncommon for eight, ten or twelve persons to be herded together in a single room. There are [in Glasgow] 175,000 'houses' without baths and 105,000 'houses' without internal sanitation.
>
> *News of the World*, 29 April 1934
>
> John R——, 22, leader of the Billy Boys Gang, and known as the Razor King, was sent to prison for eighteen months at the High Court in Glasgow yesterday for having assaulted William R——, and seriously injured him.
>
> *Glasgow Daily Record*, 17 December 1930

No Mean City put a shiny gloss on the statistics that had coated Glasgow's reputation for a hundred years. The book was published in the 1950s and many a writer since then has clung happily to its ragged trousers. *The Dear Green Place* by Archie Hind, which cut out much of the violence but kept the poverty, was published in the mid-sixties and won three awards. *Growing up in the Gorbals* by Ralph Glasser once again dwelling on rickets and resentment followed in the mid-eighties. Publishers, it seems, could not resist this one brand of paint, this single gloss. We must not forget Jimmy Boyle, 'the most violent man in Scotland'. Even those who do not read books know about

Jimmy Boyle; the man who drank and fought and stole his way from the Gorbals to Borstal and from Borstal to jail, accused of murder. The man whom many a television documentary has portrayed as a 'searing indictment of society . . . an outstanding testament to one man's ability to survive'. To survive and become a legend who writes and paints and sculpts and gets an Open University degree. Boyle's story is a nice little case history for prison reformers, but it made me pause to think of the unlauded bloke who improves his lot without notoriety and public adulation and a prison 'special unit' costing more per year than the fees at Eton. Thirty years of this sort of writing has scarred the face of Glasgow; no wonder outsiders wince.

Cliff Hanley wrote about Glasgow too and he wrote about poverty. His *Dancing in the Streets* was published soon after *No Mean City*. It does not glorify violence. It glorifies a sense of humour. Cliff Hanley shows what so many other Glasgow books fail to see – the wit and the warmth that helps most people get through the worst of times without the help of razor fights. I wanted to meet Cliff Hanley; I wanted to see his Glasgow.

He came to pick me up; a tiny man in his sixties, a sprightly man with a small red car and two accents: the one he used in conversation with me and another he used in conversation with his Glaswegian friends. He is as warm and witty as his writing. He began by showing me tourist Glasgow, by driving down Great Western Road into the centre, all the while keeping up a stream of comment that demonstrated an immense love for a place that remains a Victorian statement of supreme confidence; a monument to a time when wealth and industrial leadership stepped out of line and headed north.

'Look at all this space and grace. Look at these Victorian houses, very handsome, aren't they? And look at the parks! There's a lot of American influence, you must look out for it because it took me a long time to become aware of it. It seems so obvious now. We even had a Wurlitzer in our house because my father had been there. There's been this empathy ever since we started trading in tobacco, and even now there are a number of American businesses here. As we come into the city I want you to look closely at the buildings. We've had an extensive clean-up. The faces of the buildings are clean, but the sides are still grimy. I like to say that they have forgotten to clean behind their ears! The architects say it is better this way. That we mustn't clean the entire building, it wouldn't look good: we'd lose the contrasts.' The difference was obvious and amusing; two shades, squeaky clean and grimy, forming a mosaic.

'Here's the cathedral, St Mungo's. It's 850 years old this year, and today we've had the Queen to a celebration service.' The awnings and endless ropes were proof, but we managed to park the car and wander in. Inside we parted within minutes. There were still a host of people in fancy dress, hats and floating dresses. The Queen had left some time before and these were the remaining guests, reluctant to leave the party. One of them stopped Cliff and asked, looking at his unfancy dress, whether he had been at the celebrations. He said no, and it wasn't clear to me whether or not he'd been invited or whether he just hadn't wanted to go. I wandered around while he chatted, not realizing that the pattern was set for much of the afternoon. Cliff Hanley knows the people of Glasgow and they know him. He turned what I considered to be a large city into a village of 'Hallo Cliff's' and 'Hallo Tommy's'. It turned our attempts at conversation into snippets.

'Would you show me where you were born?' I asked, being a poor tourist and wanting to be shown sides of Glasgow that I wouldn't otherwise see.

'Yes, yes, I'd like to show you that.' We got into the car. 'Now I don't want you to think that all tenements were bad. Some were bad; tiny one- and two-room holes with tiny beds like a cupboard – cavity beds we call them – and a toilet on the landing. Others were quite spacious and well built and the community spirit was great. And here we are at 628 Gallowgate.'

There was nothing there; green grass, trees and railings.

'It's been pulled down. It had to be, it was too far gone. I don't mind. It wasn't an act of vandalism. Some sandstone villas were pulled down to make way for a three-lane highway. Labour did that to show the bourgeoisie who was boss. They destroyed things out of envy because other people had it too good for too long. That kind of thing drove me out of politics. I get angry when I talk about the left, so I'd better stop. In my youth there was a cinema on every corner and you couldn't count the number of dance halls. How we danced! I used to be good.' And he twirled in the street before we climbed back in the car. We drove past the Saracen's Head, where Dr Johnson once stayed, and I insisted on going inside. The pub was seedy and the barman was huge; his name was Angus.

'You're here to learn about Glasgow, Cliff tells me. Well, you take note of the tobacco. It started everything, but it was ruined by the Civil War. That's the trouble with Glasgow, we always put our eggs in one basket: tobacco, cotton, ships.'

At the mention of ships, an Irishman weaved his way across to us. 'Cliff, I want to buy you a drink for all you've done for Glasgow. A large whisky, Cliff, will that be it? Now, all we want is a new ship, Cliff, a new ship on the Clyde. Can you get that for us, Cliff?'

The Irishman also wanted to buy me a drink, but I hadn't taken more than a sip of the first one and was about to decline. Cliff stepped in to save me from a social gaffe.

'She'd love another, wouldn't you, Linda? Writing a book is thirsty work.' To have refused a drink would have been an insult, he whispered hastily. The Irishman, having bought the drinks, stayed to chat and behave like a stage Irishman with his stories of adventures around the world. He gave me a rundown on his wanderings and then concluded: 'I've been in seventeen countries and this is the best place in the world. Now, you promise to say nice things about Glasgow. We're sick of the bad things. Everyone rubbishes Glasgow and don't you do it.'

It was mid-afternoon and the pub was by no means full; there were six or seven groups of men dotted around, small men, all of them, with bad teeth. And there was one table of women drinking together. One had very bad skin, yellow and covered with pimples, and her hair was long and grey and held back from her face with an Alice band. She'd had more than enough to drink and got up and left with her white mac flying as she plodded down the street, clinging on to the arm of an unsteady man. Cliff watched me watching them.

'You'll see a lot of that around here. We drink in Glasgow, but most of it is pretty controlled. You don't see many uncontrolled drunks. The controlled drunks are easy to spot: they seem OK, but their ears are shut off. You talk to them, but they can't hear.'

He decided it was time to show me the Gorbals. He'd had at least three doubles and in London I wouldn't have got into the car, but here it didn't seem to frighten me and the little red car sped off as though it knew its way through the streets. I wasn't prepared for the Gorbals. It wasn't there. In its place were high-rise blocks, soulless barracks looking both weary and tatty; yet they were only twenty-five years old.

'Sir Basil Spence is responsible for this lot – or some of them, anyway. He often said that people should live in the buildings they design, but he never lived in one of these. They design these places and they go off and live in a converted mill in the country.' I counted the storeys to twenty-four.

'Nonsense, isn't it? These places are totally dehumanizing. People meet horizontally, not vertically . . .' He paused for me to appreciate this joke. 'In the old days people walked past each other in the street and stopped for a chat, in these they shoot past each other in the lift. This lot were doomed from the moment they went up. The local authority didn't want to act as landlords for pubs, so they didn't build any, and in the beginning getting a drink meant a bus ride and once you've made that effort, you're going to have more than one drink – you're going to stay until you're drunk.'

Bleak is the word for the Gorbals. To the planners of the fifties and the builders of the sixties they must have seemed a dream. A chance to move people from overcrowded, insanitary cupboards into homes with separate rooms for eating and sleeping; homes with their own bathrooms and lavatories. But who on earth thought that twenty-four storeys was the answer? This is a bad example of American influence. This was the first time on this journey that I had stood staring at post-war housing development; it was by no means to be the last. Renovation of existing buildings was not seen as an option. The fashion then was to tear down and build anew, mostly on the outskirts of cities. This both blighted inner cities and blighted the lives of those who were lured by the luxury of lavatories from the hub to the fringe. What progress! From eighteenth-century rural famine to nineteenth-century urban squalor to twentieth-century bleakness. And with each massive shift, vast numbers improved their lot. Post-war tower blocks, ugly and inadequate, are much derided. They were a mistake. A lesson has been learned. What more is there to say? Designs for new council houses around the country are delightful. And attempts are being made to improve the lot of those who remain on bleak estates. In the late seventies Glasgow realized that the way to humanize such places was to give tenants a greater say in housing matters. Tenant cooperatives were set up to encourage residents to improve their homes and manage their estates. Some estates were sold to the Cooperatives. Glasgow didn't need Mrs Thatcher to show the way. Indeed it could be argued the other way: Mrs Thatcher saw a good idea in Glasgow and bought it. Her plans for municipal housing are far-reaching and little-understood mainly because people have focused on the way in which they undermine local authorities and undermine the Labour party by allowing tenants to buy their houses at favourable prices. The policy of selling council houses was a stroke of genius; a great social leveller. Two thirds of us now own the houses in which we live. That is pretty much saturation point. But what of those who couldn't or wouldn't buy? Mrs Thatcher doesn't wish local authorities to be the sole provider of low-rent housing. To this end she has cut their cash for housing and raised rents on existing houses by limiting rent subsidies. The result has been an increase in the number of homeless people (particularly in London) who live at huge cost to the taxpayer in squalid bed-and-breakfast accommodation. In place of a local authority monopoly the government would like to see more cooperatives; it would like to see housing associations grow as alternative providers; it would like building societies to enter the field. It wants low-rent tenants to have a choice, because choice involves competition and competition brings improvements and higher standards. To this end rent control on new lettings has been lifted in the hope that new landlords will come forward. To this end the government has offered tenants the ultimate weapon, a vote to determine whether they should remain council controlled or whether they'd prefer to be taken over by another landlord, one more keen to please and just as socially responsible. In theory this sounds fine; in practice tenants see it as an open invitation for the wicked private landlords to move in and make their lives a bigger misery: they fear the arrival of profiteers would seek out the best estates, buy them and then ease the poor tenants out in favour of yuppies. And of course no one would want the worst estates and the local authorities would be left with miserable blocks full of anti-social misfits. (In fact, the government's answer to that is to take over the worst areas itself via Housing Actions Trusts and, having put them on their feet, hand them over to the most deserving creature, whether private or public.) It's the government's fault that it has received more brickbats than bouquets for this radical reform. Their case was sound: why should local authorities be monopoly providers? It might well be better to have a choice. But whenever it tried to 'sell' its proposals, the media settled on the complex reforms' one daft mistake – messing about with the voting procedures for such takeovers. Legislation said that those who didn't bother to vote would be counted among those who favoured change. Every piece of electoral research shows that the opposite is the case; those who don't bother to vote generally favour the status quo. I have much sympathy with the view that stick-in-the-muds should not be allowed to halt progress, but I think it would have been much better to have made the vote compulsory. With something so fundamentally important as who owns and runs your home, you'd have thought people would have been only too keen to vote, but if they feel like ducking the issue, the way to make them into active and responsible citizens is to say that they must vote. There would have been cries of anguish from civil libertarians, who would argue that compulsory voting is un-British, but it's fairer than letting the complacent carry forward radical changes by default. Some councils, and not all of them Conservative controlled, have jumped at this opportunity of ridding themselves of all or part of a financially draining commitment and a never-ending round of rent arrears and complaints about maintenance. The whole affair is a classic example of what is good about the reforms being smothered by what is bad, so that the general public is left with the impression that low-rent housing isn't safe in Tory hands. Only time will tell and, cheered by Saracen's scotch, Cliff and I agreed that there was just a chance that out of the jumble good would come. After all, it couldn't be worse than the ghastly blocks before our eyes. And in need of something visually pleasing, we went to look at the Clyde.

The Clyde is muddy coloured; they say it is clean; they say salmon have been sighted. When Defoe passed by it was flush with herring. It is often said that the Clyde made Glasgow and Glasgow made the Clyde. A huge crane catches the eye. It doesn't move. It is a monument, a listed building, a symbol of the past. Glasgow's future does not belong to the Clyde. Like tobacco and cotton, ship-building has had its day; it can no longer support Glasgow. But that dead crane is no longer a sign of despair. Glasgow has seen the worst and decided to tell it to shove off. It hit rock bottom in the mid-seventies, and had plenty of time to get sick of the sight of boarded-up shops, general decay, meanness of spirit and the pathetic attitude of sitting around waiting for something to happen. Glasgow decided to fight back; to stop being a victim and become a victor. Such a change of attitude is impossible to pin to a specific date, but I believe that it can be traced to an Act of God. In 1968 a bad storm, with winds up to 140 miles an hour, caused much damage and since there was no possibility of pulling the buildings down, experts decided they would start a refurbishment programme provided they could get thirty years of life out of a building. Years later, as honey-coloured sandstone began to emerge where once there had been grime, the city fathers began to realize that they had a beautiful city; they liked what they saw and refurbishment and cleaning buildings became, if not a fetish, a symbol that Glasgow was going to pick itself up and brush itself down and start all over again. Glasgow embarked on one of the most ambitious programmes of urban renewal undertaken by a British city since the war. It changed the look of the city and the attitude of its citizens. And once it looked good, it started shedding that old mean image: it had to in order to attract new investment, new industry, new jobs.

It was to be a slow slog. Cleaning up the city was easy; cleaning up the image was hard. Michael Kelly accepted the challenge. He realized that every time a London-based newspaper wanted to write about poverty, crime, street violence, it headed to Glasgow. His answer was to steal an idea from New York. That city had similar problems and it fought back with the highly successful 'I Love New York' campaign. Michael Kelly's answer was a campaign called 'Glasgow's Miles Better'. It was only a slogan, an empty PR slogan, but it took root and grew into a statement of fact. He was expressing what every Glaswegian felt in his heart and wanted to believe. On the bus to meet Kelly, the driver-conductor said: 'You don't come from round here with an accent like that. Where are you from?' I told him I was from London.

'Glasgow's a grand place now. Have a good look round, won't you? It's a great city.'

Michael Kelly had been an economist at Strathclyde University and a member of the city council for fourteen years. By the end of his four-year term as Lord Provost, he had travelled widely, tirelessly promoting Glasgow at home and abroad; persuading people to visit, to use the city as a conference venue, to contemplate investment, and bring their businesses to Glasgow. It worked and he loved it. After this spell in the limelight, he couldn't think of returning to academic life, and now has his own PR company. Of course Kelly did not achieve all this on his own. He was backed by the council. I was told many times that Glasgow was lucky. It had a good council, a sensible council, a council that knew how to get various sectors in the city working together. That council is Labour controlled, forever Labour, stable and solid.

At one point, as long ago as 1979, Michael Kelly thought of twinning Glasgow with Liverpool since they both had a similar history and similar problems and could pool ideas and share expertise. One of Liverpool's Liberal councillors said that he considered the idea a suicide pact. 'They saw their problems as insoluble and we didn't. We said we are going to make things happen.'

Michael Kelly missed no opportunity to invite southern journalists to Glasgow in an attempt to balance those dogeared, out-of-date images contained in newspaper files. In 1983 came the opening of the Burrell Collection, a perfect chance for writers to concentrate on pearl boxes rather than pearl-handled razors. Sir William Burrell and his family made money out of shipping and spent that money on many an *objet d'art*, from pearl boxes, furniture, brass, medieval tapestries, ivories, sculpture, stained glass, bronzes, silver, rugs, to paintings, paintings and paintings. Burrell, as well as being an amazing business-man, was an amazing shopper.

His business secret was to sell his fleet in boom times, invest his money and wait until 'things were absolutely in the gutter', then order a dozen steamers in a week and get them built at rock-bottom prices. By the time they were ready, the economy had invariably picked up and, because he had built his ships so cheaply, he could afford to carry goods for less than anyone else. As I understand it, that sort of thinking marks a good businessman. The shopping secret was to haggle over prices. Burrell left the proceeds of his shopping expeditions to Glasgow, plus £500,000 (and that was in 1940) to build a roof over their heads. He died in 1958 aged ninety-six, without seeing the results of his generous gesture. A gesture which means that Glasgow can boast the best art collection outside London. The Burrell Collection is now a top tourist attraction. Glasgow also is home to the Scottish National Opera, the Scottish National Ballet and the Scottish National Orchestra. In 1990 Glasgow will flaunt the title 'European City of Culture'. That should kill *No Mean City*. Hard luck, Edinburgh. That city, forty-five minutes away, at one time had everything Glasgow coveted. It had the title 'capital' of Scotland; it had a constant stream of visitors who went away sighing over its natural beauty; a comfortable middle-class ambience (the professions congregate there); and an annual Festival of the Arts which provided an international profile. In other words, it had a good image. But it was complacent. It has let its advantages slip away as Glasgow noisily said: 'Look at me!' and set about attracting one of the highest levels of investment outside London. Glasgow now employs more workers in the financial-services sector than Edinburgh. At one time Michael Kelly considered offering his skills to Edinburgh.

By the time I'd talked to Michael Kelly, the head of the tourist office, the leader of the council and the Scottish Development Agency, I felt bloated by the city's aspirations. I floated on middle-class success stories, and had been taken thoroughly by surprise at the image and mood of Glasgow. The city glowed with confidence and energy and swank: its zest was deliciously American – but then America has a dark underside. Over dinner in the sumptuous surroundings of a new and exclusive hotel which resembles a country house in mid-town and is known simply as One Devonshire Gardens, I confessed to a former colleague from the *Guardian* who now works for the *Glasgow Herald* that I felt my glimpse of Glasgow might be unbalanced. Glasgow was clearly on the move and it hadn't needed Mrs Margaret Thatcher to show the way. Labour Glasgow had tackled many problems, but it had not erased them all, so where were the less fortunate? I'd glimpsed them in the Saracen's Head, but where could I meet those who had yet to benefit from this city's self-generated success?

'Leave that to me,' Ray replied. 'I'll find you someone who knows the other side. I've got an idea that could work brilliantly, but then again it could be a disaster. Whichever it turns out to be, you'll have an unusual evening.'

The unusual evening began at the Hilton Hotel, where I was to meet Bill. That is not his name, but I agreed that he could remain anonymous. Bill, I was told, avoids the limelight. He was easy to recognize: he was fat and small, a mere five feet two inches.

'May I offer you a drink?' I asked as we shook hands.

'No, you may not. You are *my* guest in *my* city,' and with that he

71

signalled the waitress and ordered drinks. She came with the drinks and the bill.

'Put it on the tab,' he said, and she stood looking at him, waiting for a name.

'Everyone around here knows me. Put it on the bill.' This show of immodesty did not square with his desire for anonymity, but I let that pass.

'Ray says you are interested in Glasgow. Let me give you some background,' and in a jovial, totally uninhibited way he launched into his story. His father was a sailor and not married to his mother when she became pregnant. She, having to work, 'put him out' to another family where, it seems, they had so many children that one more made no difference. They were poor too; they lived in one room and were ill-fed, which he says accounts for his lack of height. The decent bits of china were seen only when the priest came to call. They were Catholics. Bill is a Catholic. His father and mother married when he was five and took him into their home which marginally improved his lot. His Aunt Maggie had the only 'palace' in the family and the only decent food. He used to love visiting her, and he thought that later in the evening I might like to visit her. She was in her eighties and living in a council flat in Govan. He went on without a pause through another drink, talking about poverty and how he'd once lived and worked in one room, dealing in electrical goods, determined to make something of his life and not be like his contemporaries. All they thought about was having another child so they could collect more benefit.

'You ready? I've arranged for you to meet a few people who work for me.' Ah good, I thought, time for visiting a few rough pubs, which is all I expected from the evening.

We drove off in his car, which had gold spokes and a telephone, and pulled up outside The Bell, in one of those bleak areas where much had been pulled down to make way for concrete slabs that would not look out of place in Eastern Europe. A group of children came towards us and started to talk to Bill. Their accents were thick, but from what I could understand they were raising money for sports facilities at their school by asking people to pay 50 pence and choose a number. Some numbers on the board offered a small prize; others did not. Bill gave them a £10 note. They looked from the note to him, and from him to the note.

'Who . . . are . . . you?' The words struggled for release through a mouthful of amazement.

'I was brought up around here, so I know what it is like not to have money,' Bill replied. The eyes of the boys continued to go backwards and forwards from note to giver, from giver to note. I felt uncomfortable. The gesture seemed flashy and I was glad when a man in his mid-fifties interrupted. It was Joe, Bill's chauffeur/gardener.

'The lounge is closed and the public bar is hardly fit for her,' he told Bill.

'Of course it is,' I said, with a laugh that hinted irritation, and marched into the public bar. Inside Joe's wife Jean was waiting, dressed in a pretty blue frock, her hair newly washed. It was rare to have a night out with 'the boss', she later confided, so she'd dressed up for the occasion. Bill plonked a wad of notes on the table and sent Joe off for drinks. Jean also worked for Bill. She had started as his housekeeper and now ran his office, a twenty-four-hour commitment, she assured me. She then talked about life in Pollockshields, one of the developments that replaced the slums. She talked well of the improved housing, of the space, but lamented the destruction of the community that existed in the slums.

'There's plenty of unemployment in Pollockshields, but it doesn't bother many people, I promise you. They all seem to make extra money easily enough. They know they are being snooped on, but they also know that the Security have to catch them in the act and that's not easy. Most do all right. They can make £20 in an afternoon just walking around the golf course looking for balls and then selling them in the city. There's quite a trade in that.' The message was clear enough. The poverty of her youth, of Bill's youth, had gone; you only had to be a bit sharp to get by. And of course if you were lucky you could get rich like Bill and fly down to London for lunch at Le Gavroche. Bill made his money in the 1970s out of local government contracts to do with drains. That's all I managed to discover.

'I could wake up of a Monday morning and know that by Friday night I could make £10,000. There was a lot of money sloshing around in local government in the seventies.' No wonder Mrs Thatcher was keen to get control of local government spending! Jean opened her handbag and took out a battered red linen-covered schoolbook. 'I found this at home and thought you might like it. It must be years old.' I was moved by her thoughtfulness. The little book, *Glasgow and the Tobacco Lords*, last belonged to 'Norman – 1968'.

After a while Bill asked Joe to get his telephone from the car so that he could ring Aunt Maggie and tell her we were on our way with a 'load of carry-out'. Joe was then dispatched to the bar for bottles of whisky and beer and a paper cup or two full of ice.

'She won't mind us turning up. I always give her £100 when I see her.' Aunt Maggie seemed bemused. She had two friends with her, a mother and her daughter. The daughter was retarded and wore a headscarf. Aunt Maggie's room was too tiny to hold us all in comfort, but we squeezed into every available space and I found myself hedged into a corner next to a glass-fronted cabinet containing ornaments and gifts from many a seaside resort. Everyone was concerned about Jim. Jim should have met us at The Bell but had gone to the wrong pub. He lived off sick-pay laced with whisky. He turned up eventually and Bill asked him to sing for us. Jim liked singing; he stood up and delivered *Begin the Beguine* like a Fifties crooner, with a sob in his voice and violent arm movements.

Aunt Maggie said very little. 'What's all this about?' she kept muttering. No one answered, so I said, 'Bill wanted me to meet his family.' She looked even more bemused. At 10 o'clock Bill declared he was hungry, so abandoning Aunt Maggie and friends, Jim the crooner, and Joe and Jean (who I'm sure expected to be invited), we went off to the Peking Inn. It was crowded and we had not reserved a table, but that sort of thing doesn't bother Bill. They'd find him a table while we had a drink at the bar. Bill spotted, seated at a table across the restaurant, an Italian family whose wedding he had attended the day before. He sent them over a bottle of Bollinger. Such a gesture could not go unanswered. The Italians sent him a bottle of Bollinger in return. Bill told me about his mother. As soon as he had started to make money, he put her on the payroll and each week would send her 'a wage' in a brown envelope. When she died, it fell to him to clear the house. In a wardrobe he found a pile of unopened brown envelopes, containing thousands of pounds. 'She thought my luck would not last and that one day I'd be on my uppers and then she'd be able to give it back to me.'

Ray had said it would be an unusual evening. It turned out to be a bizarre and unforgettable evening. It showed how some of those who start life with a foot not even near the bottom rung of the ladder succeed in a struggle to the top – if wealth enough to lunch at Le Gavroche can be seen as a measure of success. It showed how those who have scraped out of poverty view those who have been left behind. It showed that the nature of poverty has changed from growth-denying lack of food and a bed in a cupboard, to life in a block of flats and afternoons searching for lost golf balls or other flirtations with the black economy. In all it showed how we make progress slowly, gaining much and losing something with every step. I treasure the little schoolbook on the tobacco trade: a symbol of the spirit of Glasgow, warm and thoughtful, proud and eager to display its best profile. This southerner was delighted to discover a Glasgow miles better than I ever expected.

Chapter 5

Northern Ireland:
Bugger Strongbow!

I made a pig's ear of getting to Northern Ireland. The obvious route was to take the bus down the coast to Ayr where I could change buses for Stranraer and hop on the ferry to Larne. But I'd heard talk of Ulster yachtsmen sailing over to Arran and to Campbeltown for the weekend and from this I'd hatched the idea of hitching a ride back with one of them. There was some logic behind this whim. In my mind this was how the first settlers arrived in Ireland – from Scotland by boat some 8,000 years ago. If you glance at the map, there's a leg of Scotland at the Mull of Kintyre which is stretched out towards an arm of Ireland at Fair Head in County Antrim; the distance between the two is a mere thirteen miles. I wanted to travel to Ireland by the oldest, shortest route. My efforts to achieve this were considerable; I enlisted the help of several friends and acquaintances and one even broadcast an appeal on Radio Clyde. All to no avail. Finally, I got on the bus to Ayr, changed for Stranraer and got on the ferry with an ungracious sigh of resignation and the smug thought that the weather was poor and the forecast so bad that few if any yachtsmen would be tempted across the North Channel for some days.

My hands warmed by a polystyrene cup of coffee, I got out my diary. It was empty. I knew no one in Northern Ireland. I had no plans and only one appointment – with the Tourist Board for a lesson in religious geography. This may seem a cavalier way to approach a place where a murderous little war had been going on since 1968, but it was deliberate. In the coming weeks I was simply going to let things happen. I wanted Northern Ireland to reveal itself in the way it chose. Millions of words have been written by those who arrived with preconceived notions and laden address books. What could I add to the struggle whose seeds had been sown some 800 years before, when an adventurous Norman baron called Strongbow had sailed across from Wales and alerted the attention of the English to the possibility of plastering the mark of ownership upon Ireland?

Strongbow, who arrived in 1169, was not one of King Henry's men, and the king was not best pleased to see this upstart showing such initiative. He sent his men hotfoot to Ireland; it was the first time the English had concerned themselves with Irish affairs. Henry's men began to take the land and turn the Irish into tenants, and what he started other kings and queens continued. The north showed the greatest resistance. One of the last of the great Irish Gaelic chieftains to kick up a fuss about being colonized was Hugh O'Neill and his neighbour Hugh O'Donnell. They lost their fight and fled, forfeiting their lands. The English rubbed their hands in glee and began planting Ulster with English and Scottish settlers in order to stabilize English rule. Such plantations had been tried before and failed, but this time the attempt was on a much firmer financial footing. The Irish were shoved into less fertile land to fester with resentment until they were ready to fight. And fight they did, with violence and atrocities that live in the minds of Protestants today. Some argue that 12,000 incomers were killed. Eight years later, in 1649, Oliver Cromwell arrived to avenge the atrocities of 1641, which he did with notable success. A pattern was thus set for the Oppression of Ireland, a pattern of violence and counter-violence that continues to this day.

The average Brit turns away from the mess; doesn't want to know; wishes the little island would float away. But the Irish question lingers on, a running sore, draining politicians and political parties. Perhaps it is true that Lloyd George had no option but to partition Ireland in 1921. Looking back from this distance it seems such a daft idea, but at the time the compromise must have pleased more people than it offended. It was certainly a sop to the Protestants, whom the British dared not abandon but clearly did not want, otherwise they would have been happy to govern Northern Ireland from Westminster. But they would not; responsibility was devolved to Stormont and British political parties refused to accept members from Northern Ireland or to contest elections there. And a blind eye was turned when Stormont abolished proportional representation for local elections and set about gerrymandering to keep Protestants in total control. And a blind eye was turned when the Protestants started discriminating against Catholics.

When the Troubles (as we call them) broke out again in 1968, they centred on civil rights. The Catholics demanded their share of housing, of jobs, of everything. With Stormont disbanded in 1972, much has been achieved in the area of civil rights. The price has been high.

There are British soldiers crawling everywhere. It is now a bloody fight with fear and loathing in the hearts of those who hurl bombs and fire guns; loathing of British rule; fear of Catholic domination from a united Ireland. A solution seems as far away as ever. The latest idea, the Anglo-Irish Agreement, gives Dublin a say in the affairs of the North. The Protestant majority is not pleased; they reckon it shows that violence pays; that the IRA and INLA campaign has resulted in an agreement which brings a united Ireland that much closer. Daily through the newspapers and nightly via television screens another painful episode in the appalling history of this island and of this province seeps into homes across the nation – into humble homes and haughty homes. What's the difference? All eyes are blank with compassion fatigue and ears are blocked by incomprehension. If they knew a little history they might mutter, 'Bugger Strongbow,' and feel better.

Are these seats free? May we sit here? Two youthful English voices slid into the plastic-covered benches, one in front of me and the other beside me. Richard and Alison come from Hull and were heading for Belfast in the hope of a job and a new life. Richard had worked there before, for ten months as a volunteer with a Presbyterian church doing good works with young and old. He'd then gone to Newcastle University to read history and economics and ended up working for General Accident. Insurance in Hull sounded dull. Teaching in Hull sounded worse. Alison, having read French and German at Newcastle and completed a diploma in education, decided within months of reaching the classroom that she hated teaching. The Presbyterian Church in Belfast had been given money by the Manpower Services Commission to set up a centre for the unemployed youth. Richard was hoping for a job there.

'Would the centre be solely for Protestant youth?' I asked.

'Yes, it would. We'd be happy for it to be for both, but that isn't how it works. It has to be for one or the other.'

'But there's more unemployment among the Catholics than Protestants, isn't there?'

'Yes, the figures are higher, but not in a dramatic way. That's propaganda. And anyway what do you expect ... Roman Catholics have much larger families, and that's got to be part of the explanation.'

To Alison and Richard, the challenge of Belfast was preferable to the sterility of Hull. Christian goodwill was needed, so they thought, in Belfast, and yes, there might be violence, but the fabric of life was still intact. Muggings and theft and burglary were not daily occurrences, and people knew each other and cared for each other. I didn't know what to make of this conversation. Had I met do-gooders deserting pagan England in favour of a tortured Belfast where their Christian beliefs still meant something and where they could drink deeply of a strong, pious brew that had caused so much anguish? Or had I simply been given a tiny warning that Belfast had hidden attractions that it might be willing to reveal if I were prepared to listen?

Alison and Richard offered me a lift from Larne to Belfast which I gratefully accepted, only to realize I had forgotten where I was staying. This caused much embarrassment; anywhere else it might be cause for amusement, but in Belfast I felt it was tantamount to suspicious behaviour. Perhaps they thought I didn't want them to know where I was staying. I asked them to drop me at the railway station, where one phone call would revive my memory.

On the ferry I had silently wondered how long I would be in Belfast before becoming aware of the Troubles; a couple of hours, a couple of days? A couple of minutes was the answer. As soon as I set foot in the station a security guard pounced on my luggage and prodded it with a metal detector.

'I only want to use the phone,' I volunteered.

'Sure, hop over the barrier and I'll look after your luggage.'

Seconds later I had the information I needed and went back to claim my luggage.

'Where can I get a taxi?'

'If you hang on for five minutes, they'll be pouring in here to meet the train from Dublin. I'll catch the first driver for you. Would you like a cigarette while you wait?' And above him on a closed-circuit television you could see the taxis turn into the station forecourt, park, and drivers walk up the steps to the single doors into the station. This was Belfast and there would be no avoiding the Troubles.

Within ten minutes I was in Beaumont Lodge, Stranmillis Road, being greeted by the owner, Mrs Valerie Kidd. It turned out to be the best b. & b. of my whole trip. Instead of being, as I'd imagined it, facing the street, upright and dreary, this b. & b. was at the end of a long winding drive; a modern house, some twenty years old, open-plan and with the bedrooms arranged along a gallery at one end. There was only a handful of rooms; there was always a log fire burning in the grate in the evening and, alongside, a trolley to make tea. It was like being in a home (which is just as b. & b. should be) with a fascinating array of other guests.

I watched the news that night with two of them, a couple from Canada, elderly, making a final pilgrimage to the places of their birth. He was an unattractive man, a lorry driver who had never owned a car.

He was born in the south of England; she was born in Belfast. She was silent; he moaned the whole time.

'No one ever asks what we think. They talk to us, but they never ask us any questions. In Canada, there would be a conversation all the time.

'In Canada, if you want a phone number you just pick up the phone.'

'You can do the same here,' I suggested. 'Try it.'

'She,' he said, referring to his wife, 'can't remember the name of the people.'

'I rather doubt if a telephone company in Canada could help you there.'

I laughed. He didn't.

We watched the news. The IRA had floated death threats at all those servicing security forces in Northern Ireland. In return, the Ulster Freedom Fighters had issued, via a video cassette delivered to broadcasting organizations, a counter-threat to all Catholics working in Protestant areas, warning them to stay away until the IRA lifted its threat. Tom King, the Secretary of State for Northern Ireland, had something to say about this. He said that the Loyalists were responding foolishly to IRA provocation. Other Protestants said that the UFF were blood brothers to the IRA and were trying to push the community into all-out war. The UFF message was delivered by a hooded man in a paramilitary dress, flanked by three masked men displaying arms. A portion of the video was shown on the news bulletin. Northern Ireland commandeered twelve minutes of the news. This was no doubt because the marching season was in full swing, the marching season being the time of year when those who turn away for most of the time tune in for a bit of lusty sectarianism. I'd missed 12 July, when Protestants march throughout the province to commemorate their deliverance from Popery. The biggest and noisiest march takes place in Belfast, ever grateful to Protestant King William for usurping Catholic King James. Marching is a sport; the game is for the Protestants to try and march through Catholic areas to show who is boss, and for the police (and the army) to do their damnedest to keep them out. In return, the Catholics will also march to commemorate the introduction of internment, but it isn't quite the same. It's a protest rather than a celebration, and there are no hard hats and white gloves. The next big march would be in Londonderry on 12 August to celebrate the anniversary of the relief of that city from siege, and I was determined to see it. Between the two dates, the political temperature always rises and Protestant blood was higher than usual because of the Anglo-Irish Agreement.

After the news came a repeat of the series *The Thorn Birds*, a mightily popular tall story in which a Roman Catholic priest is seduced. When it was first shown, the episode in which the seduction took place broke all ratings records. If I remember correctly it happened on or near a beach in Australia. The priest was played by Richard Chamberlain and Rachel Ward was the temptress. The nation was immobilized and when the episode ended the Electricity Board could hardly cope with the sudden rush of demand as kettles were switched on, and the Water Board reported a similar surge as lavatories were flushed in unison across the land.

The next morning I went to the Tourist Board for my lesson in religious geography and for advice on how to get where I wanted to go – around the north coast to Londonderry and then south in a sweep back to Belfast. And that was religious geography lesson one: London got added to Derry at the time of the Plantation of Ulster and the mainly Catholic city does not like to hear itself referred to as Londonderry. Yes, but how was I to know whether I was talking to a Protestant or a Catholic?

'Call it Derry all the time; you'll be more often right than wrong. Besides, the Protestants are not nearly so offended to hear it called Derry as the Catholics are to hear it called Londonderry.'

It was here that I met Sharon McAllister, who offered to drive me to Derry. It isn't that far, a couple of hours by the direct route, but she was offering the slow route and the chance to stop wherever I wished, untroubled by bus timetables. My hesitation was fleeting; the thought of having the company of a vivacious twenty-three-year-old was irresistible.

But first I wanted a glimpse of Belfast, just the city centre, the rest could wait until my return. I thought half an hour of desolation, of security checks, of barricades and barbed wire would be quite enough. I saw it as the sort of place to which people came grudgingly to shop and left with all speed. That may have been the picture ten years ago, but the 1980s have seen millions of pounds pumped into Belfast. The barricades are there, cordoning off the main streets. They went up in the 1970s to stop the car bomb attacks. Now no cars are allowed: the area has been 'pedestrianized' and prettied, with hanging baskets and with benches where shoppers can linger and chat. The centre of Belfast on that day was alive and attractive, bustling; no one rushed in and out grudgingly; they strolled and gossiped and sat and ate ice-creams. The shop windows were enticing; the shops were full and several times when I held out my handbag to security staff they smiled and waved me through. They are there to make people feel better. The citizens of

Belfast are so used to them they'd feel exposed without them. I stopped and stared at the barricades and watched as people manoeuvred past them without even a glance. They might have been lamp posts for all the impact they had on those who saw them daily.

My eye caught Micky Marley's horsedrawn roundabout outside Burton's – he's been there for years and is now a listed sight. Then I strolled on to Arthur Square which had a bandstand in the middle being used at that moment not for music making, but as a punks' meeting place; a couple fought each playfully while others jeered between mouthfuls of crisps. I sat on a bench and watched the neon strip advise me to buy vodka, 7-Up, Coke and Budweiser in between telling me the time. A man in a plum-coloured velvet jacket sat down next to me and started to hum. I began to draw a little sketch of the bandstand.

'You on holiday,' said the man in the plum jacket.

'Yes.'

'This used to be called the Cornmarket, used to sell cattle here, they did. Interesting, isn't it? It's history. Where are you going?'

I told him I was heading for the north coast.

'Oh, you must go south. You must go to the Mourne Mountains, it's a beautiful spot. Newcastle is my favourite.'

I told him I'd try to get there.

'You look smart, you know that.'

'Thank you.'

'No, I mean up here,' he said tapping his head with a finger.

I thanked him again.

'You been to college? Yes, I thought so. I've watched you writing in a notebook.'

'And what do you do?'

'I'm unemployed. I used to work in a car park, but I've been unemployed for eighteen months. There isn't much work for a man of fifty-seven. It's OK on a nice day. I can come here for a walk. I live at the top of the Falls Road. Otherwise it's the telly. There's no hope for them,' he said, jerking his head toward the bandstand where the youths had now stopped fighting and were eating apples. 'They'll end in jail.

'It'll rain before tonight,' he said, looking at the sky and then around the square where he spotted a friend called Harry carrying a huge stick of French bread. They wandered off together and I turned back to my notebook.

'You writing a love letter?' asked another passer-by, and I began to think my notebook attracted too much attention. A huge van pulled up. I was surprised to see a van at all, let alone one so big. The driver caught my eye and winked.

'They'll end in jail,' he'd said. Northern Ireland has the highest unemployment rate in the UK, around 22 per cent. It also has the highest infant-mortality rate and the highest housing-unfitness rate. It also has a low-wage economy with some 23 per cent living on incomes under £50 a week, compared to 11 per cent in the UK, and yet the essentials of life – food, fuel and clothing – cost more, particularly fuel. You don't hear much about this side of Northern Ireland; the media is consumed by the violence; they haven't time for the poverty. Besides, you don't *see* it in the streets; you aren't shocked by it. Poverty in the 1980s is hidden. There are no bare feet, no begging, no match-girls. Poverty hides in high-rise blocks, with dark, ill-lit stairways and a television flickering in the main room. Poverty in Northern Ireland means having electric storage heaters you cannot afford to use. You'll have a fridge because food must be stored and you'll have a washing-machine and a dryer because you won't have a garden. And you'll have a television because you can't afford to go out. You stay at home falling into debt over the fuel bills and the hire-purchase on the washing-machine.

The people of Northern Ireland have been much studied, but it is rarely the effects of deprivation that catch the researcher's eye. It is the violence. It is the 'Lost Generation': the young people who have grown up knowing nothing other than violence. How has it affected them? You'd expect the answer to be obvious: badly and deeply. But the research from Queen's University, Belfast does not show this. For a start it shows that most people in Northern Ireland have escaped direct exposure to the violence; that twice as many die in road accidents each year as at the hand of bullets and bombs. And that those who have been directly exposed tend to come from the most deprived areas; areas of poverty, of over-crowding and of unemployment. The researchers conclude that the psychological impact of poverty is far greater than the psychological impact of living in a conflict-ridden community. A survey of maladjusted children showed that 13 per cent had problems caused by the Troubles and 81 per cent had problems caused by parents divorcing or separating. An analysis of suicide cases showed that failure in personal relationships was way ahead of any other trigger.

An outsider can be forgiven for finding this surprising. There have, after all, been some irresponsible bits of journalism. *Newsweek* for example proclaimed one week that the use of tranquillizers in the 1970s had tripled in Northern Ireland. Of course it had, doctors everywhere during that period were prescribing them as if they were Smarties, and there were many countries like Holland and Iceland, trouble-free countries, where they swallowed many more. Also, anti-depressants and sleeping pills were used less often in Northern Ireland than elsewhere in the UK – what's to be made of that? There was also some early research that suggested that when the conflict came to an end there would have to be a massive effort to rehabilitate Northern Ireland's young people. 'Without that the children of Northern Ireland, those who survive physically, those who do not emigrate, will be militaristic automatons incapable of participating in their own destiny.' This piece of research by someone called Field has been much questioned. It is of course true that people in Northern Ireland, both young and old, have become used to violence, they accept it as the norm – Saracens on the streets and soldiers with sub-machine guns, teenagers with petrol bombs and tiny tots throwing stones. They've come close to thinking that violence is an acceptable way of achieving one's aim. For the moment, however, there is obvious comfort to be derived from a body of research that shows that the psychological health of the population, both adults and children, has not been adversely influenced because they happen to live in war-torn Northern Ireland. Outsiders may equate Northern Ireland with violence, but residents see that economic deprivation is far more significant. It is not a message that reaches the outside world.

If Sharon MacAllister is anything to go by, the research is correct. She talked with ease about her life and, like all good talkers, she has the kind of confidence that enables her to add details without ever feeling that she must race through the outline for fear of boring the listener. She remembers little about the Troubles. She recalls her journeys to school when she hid behind a hedge if she felt threatened, in much the same way as other kids must recount playground bullying: an unpleasant but inevitable part of life. She was considered to live in a 'deprived area' and therefore taken on holiday to Scotland and Wales, but she does not see herself as deprived, merely as coming from an area where the Troubles were bad. When she first talked about her disrupted childhood I felt suspicious. I thought maybe she was playing down something too painful to acknowledge openly, or that she simply might be lying. The Irish have a way with lies; they don't call them lies, they simply like to tell people what they think they want to hear. However, in the end I came to accept her acceptance of the extraordinary as the ordinary. Scarred she did not seem to be, even though religious differences had touched both her personal and her professional life.

An early boyfriend had turned out to be a Catholic but, she told me, no ordinary Catholic – a member of the INLA, who phoned one day announcing that he was abandoning the relationship because, as she was a Protestant, it could lead nowhere. Furthermore, her attempts to become a journalist had been thwarted when, having been offered a job, she was subsequently told that the Fair Employment rules dictated that the job ought to go to a Catholic. So it was given to a Catholic whom she believed to be less well qualified. Such positive discrimination is the only way in which Catholics are going to catch up after years of being cold-shouldered. The Fair Employment rules have much improved the lot of middle-class Catholics, particularly in government and government-related jobs, but working-class Catholics have not benefited to the same extent; unemployment among Catholics is still high and there are still major firms and some entire industries employing only Protestants. To improve the progress of redressing the imbalance the rules have been tightened. Sharon accepted her failure to get the newspaper job with good grace. She wasn't totally committed to a career in journalism and thought she might go to America for a while just to see what it is like.

The road north out of Belfast, along the Antrim coast, is beautiful. The shore is rocky, the cliffs are white, the beaches empty even though the sea was smooth and calm after days of heaving waves and sickening clouds. I began to collect wayside slogans: 'Ulster says No' (referring to the Anglo-Irish Agreement) and 'Belfast Still Needs Jesus' adorned the wayside. We stopped for coffee at Carnlough, where the tiny white limestone harbour was full of pretty boats and where Frank O'Neill keeps a glorious hotel called the Londonderry Arms, which, since it is only forty-five minutes' drive from the centre of Belfast, provided a popular weekend escape for city dwellers. O'Neill seemed a little downcast. Business was right down since the Anglo-Irish Agreement.

'People are thinking they dare not leave their homes for too long. They are more influenced by what they see on TV than reality. There are moments of isolated violence, but on television it seems like a blanket danger. People say to themselves, "Am I right, or is the media right?" and not knowing the answer they stay at home. Foreign tourists stay away too, but then you can't expect them to realize that life goes on in Northern Ireland. It's the hesitation of the locals that bothers me.'

We drove to Cushendun, a village preserved totally by the National Trust for its Cornish-style cottages and because it is the home of the smallest pub in Northern Ireland. It was closed. Randall McBride has a habit of opening when he feels like it and, obviously, this Saturday lunchtime he wasn't feeling like it. Or else he sensed that everyone in the village would be busy with The Wedding. And so they were. The service was over and the guests were heading for the reception. A group of them, dressed in all manner of Sunday-best finery, had stopped at the local store and were sitting on the wall eating ice-creams. Costly white weddings are much in fashion; you need to name the day a year in advance if you want to hold the reception at the place of your choice. John Masefield found a wife in Cushendun. Outside the village, we came across our first road-block. At least, I thought it was a road-block from the number of RUC officers carrying long guns. 'SMGs,' said Sharon. 'Sub-machine-guns. A common sight.' As we crawled forward in the line of traffic Sharon decided it was a road accident. It turned out to be a diversion. The Ulster Rally was taking place and certain roads had been cleared. To close roads for such an innocent reason using armed policemen was not something my eyes could take for granted.

As we headed towards Ballycastle, I saw a sign saying Corrymeela and suggested a detour. The Corrymeela community, idyllically sited on a headland overlooking the Atlantic and surrounded by farmland, has had its share of publicity. Here since 1965, a group of Christians, both Protestant and Roman Catholic, have been working to create a meeting place for those who need to retreat from the divided society; a place where they could rest or talk or both. Ray Davey, who was a Presbyterian chaplain at Queen's University, was the leader of the movement and many students joined the early venture. It is still one of the few places where Protestant and Catholic children can spend some time together, in contrast to their daily lives where their schools are segregated and their homes too.

We drove up and walked in. There was no one around, but within minutes a girl appeared and asked who we were. I said that we were passers-by on the road to Derry and simply wanted to look around. 'Good,' said the girl. 'I'll find someone to guide you,' and out bounced Anne. 'You're my friend for life,' she said. 'You've got me off the washing-up. Where shall we start? Right here, I think. This notice-board . . .' The games-mistress from Reading kept up the games-mistress approach to life for some time as we wandered around the half-deserted place. It was Saturday, change-over day; one group had already left and another was awaited. Two thoughts remain with me from that visit; one was the way in which we were accepted without question. The fact that we had shown enough interest to stop was enough. No further questions were asked or needed. And secondly, when I discovered that Anne had been giving up part of her holiday each summer for ten years, I asked what good she thought it did. The children had fun together and what happened when they got home?

The games-mistress replied: '*I* don't know. *We* don't know how much good it does. We don't make claims. All I can tell you is that it has an influence on the volunteers, people like me who keep coming back year after year, hoping that little by little we can change people's attitudes towards one another.'

Our final stop on the slow road to Derry was at the Giant's Causeway. It is of course a huge tourist attraction and thus the sort of place I'm usually more than happy to miss, but there are some tourist attractions with the power to make me feel guilty for being such a poor tourist, and this was one of them. Anyhow, I fancied a long walk, a brisk trot along the cliffs. It didn't happen that way; the weather was not good. Indeed, it was so chilly that as we motored along I noticed smoke belching out of chimneys, proving that those inside were huddled around the fire to keep warm. So I settled for a short walk and a long gawp at thousands of strangely symmetrical basalt columns which jut out of the sea, looking at first glance like stylishly squared off organ pipes, or a daring display of long, thin cigarette packets. The books tell you that the Causeway was the result of volcanic activity, but I prefer the legend that it was built by an Irish giant called Finn MacCool so that he could travel dry-footed across the sea to Scotland.

In Derry I expected to find a march to commemorate the introduction of internment. There had been one in Belfast and I'd been told there was to be one that Sunday in Derry. So, as we drove into town where Sharon was to leave me later that night, we decided to ask the way to my hotel and find out about the march. It was excessively quiet; there were no people walking in the streets and few cars on the road. We spotted an unmarked police car and decided to follow it until it stopped, which it did outside a police station, a sandbagged, barricaded, wired-over block of concrete and brick. The policemen knew nothing about 'a march', but they guided us to the Everglades, an hotel on the Waterside, the Protestant side of the River Foyle. As we approached the hotel we saw a lone army vehicle parked in a lay-by and pulled in. Sharon got out of the car and, as she did so, the soldier closed the door of his vehicle and wound up the window, finally speaking to her from the narrowest of slits. He knew nothing of a march. Clearly our information was incorrect, but having nothing better to do, we decided to go to the Bogside, the Catholic side, and check. Sharon did not wish to take her car and so we hired a taxi. Dessie the driver knew nothing about a march.

'Youse reporters?' he asked. 'Yes,' I replied. From that he seemed to know the ropes and the road, through which he sped at enormous speed, squealing around corners. In the Bogside we found a funeral, but no march. In Creggan we found neither, but on driving towards an army patrol I unthinkingly suggested he pull up so that I could ask.

'You'll do no such thing. I have to work around here.' When the British Army first arrived in Northern Ireland they were welcomed by the Catholics; it was the severity of the Protestant RUC towards the Catholics that had contributed to the breakdown of law and order in 1969. The army then were seen as 'neutral' and welcomed. Now the IRA had made it quite clear that they did not wish the Catholic community to have anything to do with the security forces, and that included talking to them.

Sharon suggested we give up the hunt and call on some friends of hers. Dessie asked for the phone number of the house and said if he heard anything about a march, he'd call us.

Only two members of the five-strong King family were at home. Dougie, a former boyfriend of Sharon's, was in Liverpool. His mother and one of his sisters were on holiday together in England. Deirdre, another sister, was at home with father King who suffered from emphysema, and was never far away from a little machine that helped him breathe. He was watching the racing on television. An enormous fire filled the grate. Deirdre, a graduate of business studies who worked as a civil servant, had just returned from Greece, golden brown, full of her travels and delighted and excited to welcome unexpected visitors. After tea and gossip, Deirdre suggested that she show me the Bogside and Creggan area which she knew well, and she called up a girlfriend, Grainne, in order that we should have a car.

I was much pleased; my dash through these areas by taxi had revealed little except empty streets and a general greyness, which tends to be the tone of all too many council-housing estates. The streets were still empty, eerily so. Occasionally a group of children played together in the gutter, on the join between the pavement and the road, which holds an inexplicable fascination for a certain age-group. Occasionally there were soldiers to be seen on foot, walking down the centre of streets. They were boy soldiers indeed; they looked so young. Only a few years before they'd have been hogging the gutter too. They wore camouflage. What on earth is the point of camouflage against grey stone houses and blocks of flats?

'It's always like this on a Sunday. Dead. You come back tomorrow and it will all look quite different,' said Grainne as we slid into Creggan, an area she declared had once been recognized as the cream of council estates. But not any more. I filled my notebook with more slogans: 'Lizzy Take Your Pigs Home'; 'RUC keep out'; 'Smash H Block'. But though my eyes and my pen were busy, my emotions did not become engaged until we reached the Bogside and the obelisk announcing, 'You are Now entering Free Derry.' Everyone knows this sign; we've seen it often enough on television. There is a grass bank to one side, a pub to another and all around dreary housing bearing the scars of war. The flats seemed the worst, neglected, vandalized, sloshed with paint: 'Brits Out: Up the Republic'. The lamp posts were painted green, white and orange. I sank into the back seat of the car and blinked and was silent. The dereliction in the film *1984* haunted me for days; the Bogside may stay with me forever. The memorial to Bloody Sunday had a small pile of smouldering ashes in front of it. It was here on 30 January 1972 that thousands defied a ban on a civil-rights march. It was here on that day that thirteen civilians were killed when the army decided to break up the gathering.

We can never be certain what happened that day. Eye-witnesses say that the paratroopers jumped from armed cars and shot straight into the crowd; the army and the report on the incident by Lord Widgery claim that the army were *returning* sniper fire and did not start the riot, although Widgery did condemn a number of soldiers for firing without justification. The point according to the British press was that the march should not have taken place. When the ban was ignored there was bound to be trouble. To the Catholics of the Bogside, thirteen of their number had been murdered by British paratroopers. The small pile of smouldering ashes, like a homemade eternal flame, filled me with gloom at the thought that mankind can be so stupid.

Grainne announced that she was heading for the Fountain, a Protestant enclave within the Catholic belt. I registered nothing for a moment, my mind still among the ashes, but within five minutes I'd noticed that she had changed. Her resolve lasted six minutes.

'Look, have a quick glimpse, will you, I don't feel comfortable.' I looked out at houses bearing crimson-coloured flags, crimson bunting across the streets; and at one house on which a replica of the crown perched over the porch, shielding the front door.

'What's the matter?' I asked in all innocence.

'I just feel uncomfortable. This is a Protestant area and as we are the only car around they are bound to look at us.'

'Fair enough, but what are we doing that's wrong? How could they possibly tell that a Catholic is driving this car?'

'Maybe they can't, but I don't feel right. They don't know us, and that's enough to make us look suspicious.'

We went and cheered ourselves up with ice-creams. It was Italian ice-cream and delicious. I think it was the only shop open in Derry that day and it was about to close.

That evening we met again at my hotel for a drink. The Everglades seemed to be the favoured Sunday spot. The bar spilled over into the lobby and it was impossible to move through the crowd to get a drink. Derry had obviously decided to celebrate the ending of a gloomy Sunday. The atmosphere was excellent, conversation nearly impossible and after awhile, as it got close to closing time, Grainne suggested a trip over the border. I was much enjoying Derry at play and eagerly agreed to the three mile ride to the Point Inn, a huge disco that opened three nights a week. It didn't need to open more. One glance at the crowds revealed that the owner could make more than enough money from three days.

'No one will ask you to dance, Linda. Here the men – and they are all mostly from Derry – will eye you for a year before asking you to dance!'

'What if I ask one of them?'

'Joking? You wouldn't dare! No one does that. It would be considered . . .'

'Yes?'

'. . . loose.'

No one did ask me to dance. Two people asked Sharon, but she said no and I guessed that might have been to keep me company or because she was dispirited at the thought of the drive ahead of her back to Belfast. I was introduced to a friend of hers, whose name I did not catch but who looked like a young Arthur Miller and who had made considerable sums from slot machines of one kind or another. After a while he wandered back to his group and by and by, boredom drove me to stroll over and ask him if he'd like to dance.

'No,' he said. 'I rarely dance, and if I do it is slow ones and right now I just don't feel like it.'

For hundreds of years men have been asking women to dance and risking rejection. I found the experience amusing.

We were stopped at the border on our return. A cheeky policeman said: 'Youse haven't had much luck tonight, have youse,' as he peered into the car. I was about to say that there were three men in the boot, but I thought better of it.

The following day was my chance to see Derry on foot. The sun was shining; from my hotel I could look across the Foyle to Catholic Derry, to buildings rising in tiers of homes and offices until they reached the spire of St Columb's Cathedral. I set out to walk along the leafy road to Waterside edge of Craigavon Bridge, named after the first prime minister, Sir James Craig, Lord Craigavon. However, before I had gone a few yards a car pulled up beside me. Two well dressed, well coiffed, middle-aged ladies wound down the window and said, 'Would you like a lift into town?' I said yes because to have said no would have been churlish, like refusing the drink in the Glasgow pub. The journey took a couple of minutes. There was no conversation. The two merely explained their kindness to a total stranger by saying: 'We always look as we turn out of our road to see if there is anyone around who might be heading for town.' They left me to walk around the Waterside where there are a few shops, pubs and cafés. Half an hour was enough to confirm what I already knew. The Protestants for whom these facilities were designed were just as hard-up as the Catholics on the other side.

I crossed the bridge. I had one call to make. The following day was the Derry march. Grainne and Deirdre had been stern in telling me to take care of myself, so as a precaution against God knows what, I rang the local Catholic paper and asked the editor if I might attend the march in the company of his reporter. I was, I explained, ignorant of the geography of the town and would welcome the help. He told me to stop by the office and he'd be only too happy to introduce me to the reporter. His name was Martin, he was in his mid-twenties and did not appear to relish his assignment. There was tension in the city. It might have been ghostly quiet on Sunday, but around 1 a.m. on Saturday morning there had been a gun battle between IRA gunmen and the army at Rossville Street flats, by the Bloody Sunday memorial, after which there had been a search of the area and of the flats, which had caused one woman to claim that plastic bullets had narrowly missed her young twins. As a result police and army reinforcements were being hauled in for the march. Martin and I made a rendezvous for the following day and I continued my stroll around the city.

Derry looked different; it had recovered from gloomy Sunday but still lacked the bustle of Belfast. There were people in the streets but they did not sit around gossiping or eating ice-creams, they went about their shopping and got on with this and that. I found a bookshop called Bookworm and spent two hours leafing through endless books on Northern Ireland and on Derry and finally got chatting to the owners as I asked them to parcel up my purchases and send them home to London. I knew it was a Catholic bookshop, but none the less I asked whether they had a book on the Apprentice-boys march and the background to the siege.

They said *no*, which did not surprise me, but added: 'You are so close to the Apprentice-boys Hall, why don't you go over and ask them? There's bound to be plenty of people about because they are pouring in from all over the place for the march tomorrow.' He walked, as he talked, to the door of the shop to point the way, and as he did so he spotted Tony Crowe.

'Tony, have you got time to tell this lady something about the march?'

'Sure,' said Tony after I'd explained why I was interested. For the next hour he unlocked doors to any number of musty rooms and inner sanctums, told me numerous stories, and confused me with many Masonic-sounding descriptions of chains and badges and other bits of anti-Popery armoury, claiming all the while that few people got to see what I was being shown. He was an engaging character, attractive, well informed and happy to talk. He quickly sorted out my tangled history.

In 1688 England was in the process of replacing Catholic King James with Protestant William of Orange. This, needless to say, displeased Catholic Ireland and made them afraid, so once again they were up in arms killing Protestants. Then in December 1688 Derry heard that a new garrison of King James's men was on its way to the city and the news filled the place with apprehension. James was still king, however, and it was decided that the garrison should be allowed in. But thirteen apprentice-boys – and here I stood looking at their names upon a board – disliking this decision, took things into their own hands and slammed the city gates. The siege did not begin in earnest until April, and by then starvation and disease started to weaken resolve. Fortunately, the troops of William of Orange came up the Foyle in late July – to the relief of Derry.

Tony Crowe was thirty-eight and had been a member of the Orange Order since he was a boy, but he had been inactive until recent years. Then, having seen several friends killed, he decided to take a lead in the community.

'We've got nothing to lose now. We Protestants are seen as lepers the world over. We are almost as hated and misunderstood as the Afrikaners. We've been here 350 years; this is our home and we have given much. We've created work and wealth. You've only got to look at southern Ireland to appreciate this – without the work-ethic the standard of living is that much lower; the Industrial Revolution passed them by. Besides, they are far more class-ridden in the south. No wonder we don't want to be a part of them, but then there's little point in talking about a united Ireland; *a good number of them don't want us!* Let's not pretend. I despise the British for the way they have tried to wash their hands of us, but the south are not sure they want us either. There has been little love lost between north and south from way, way back in history. The northern clans have looked more to Scotland than they did to the south. It isn't just religion. Now, independence is the only way.'

In his case it is not just religion. His mother became what he described as an intellectual Catholic after having lived in France, and at one time he went to a Roman Catholic school, but he remained staunchly Protestant. We began to discuss what was meant by such over-worked phrases, such clichés as 'Protestant work-ethic' and 'the maintenance of a way of life', as he locked up the hall and we took a walk along the deserted city walls. He didn't get too far before our discussion was interrupted, but far enough to encourage me to think further about the division between Catholic and Protestant, to see how their belief systems affect their attitudes and thus their lifestyles. In other words, to find a reason for Catholic attitudes towards work.

To dismiss Catholics as 'lazy' is sloppy thinking. As far as I can make out Catholicism from the beginning saw work as a penalty for original sin; they saw it as an expiation for Adam's fall; a curse. They saw it as something to be done in order to get enough to live on. The urge that drives man to acquisition beyond the needs of simple sustenance was anathema. In this of course they were aligned to the ancient Greeks, who also saw work as a burden, something to be avoided wherever possible, particularly if it was monotonous. 'What is dearest to man's heart is leisure,' said Euripides.

It was the religions of the Reformation that sanctified work. The reformers caused a revolution in thinking of work as salvation. Martin Luther gave work a previously unknown dignity. Work for him was a way of serving God, and to establish the Kingdom of God on earth all men must work, all idleness must cease. To please God this work must be unflagging, disciplined and regular. 'God sent you not unto this world as unto a playhouse, but a workhouse.' John Calvin went one step further. He considered work as an antidote for anxiety over salvation; a way of driving out fears of damnation. Intense activity alone, he considered, makes religious doubts evaporate. To the early Catholics, however, being busy led men to sin; inactivity and contemplation were ways of avoiding sin. No wonder then that Protestants make good capitalists and Roman Catholics prefer cooperation to competition. No wonder there are profound differences in attitudes and lifestyles.

My discussion of these matters with Tony Crowe had been interrupted by the appearance along the city walls of a tall, athletic young man taking pictures, carrying a bag marked *Los Angeles Herald*. He was in Derry to cover the march. 'So is Linda,' said the affable Crowe, which meant that we all ended up in a nearby pub. The man who looked like a tennis player declared that his name was Michael Collins.

'Yes, it's not a sensible name to have up here, is it?' he said nervously as he caught the look that passed between Tony and me.

Michael Collins holds a hero's place in Irish history. Some describe him as an Irish Lenin. Born in West Cork in 1890, he emigrated to England in search of work and returned some ten years later in time for the uprising of 1916, after which he stayed to create 'disorder' throughout Ireland via the Irish Republican Brotherhood, with the aim of establishing an independent Ireland. In the end, Collins signed the treaty agreeing to partition, believing it was but a short step to a united free Ireland. Partition, he felt, was sure to fail and was therefore a mere hiccup. For this judgement half of those who once claimed that they were willing to die for him deserted him, and he was killed by a bullet in 1922. No one knows who fired the shot.

Michael Collins, twenty-nine and an Irish-American, had a biased view of history, and a one-sided view of contemporary events. He regaled us with his account of the previous Friday night in Belfast, where he claimed to have seen plastic bullets fired at children; where he claimed that one plastic bullet missed him by inches, even though he had the word *Press* plastered on his forehead. He had the bullet in his luggage, he said.

'They hate the press, of course, and particularly the American-Irish press, and would do anything to stop us getting at the truth of what is going on here.' I resented this kind of talk. He'd been in Northern Ireland for forty-eight hours. A meddling American with a closed mind was a more apt description than 'a journalist'. I said nothing. Tony Crowe was more than a match for him and this he came to appreciate. They squabbled over history until Collins said: 'I wish all Protestants were as reasonable and as pleasant to argue with.' Alas, the minute Tony's back was turned he added: 'All Protestants are scum, like the British. We had to fight a war to get rid of them. They never go until they are pushed.' I told him that I was only prepared to listen to such talk from those who *lived* in Ireland and I didn't much care for the views of someone who had chosen to make his life elsewhere. 'But we were forced out, my ancestors were forced out!'

'And you've chosen to stay out . . . so why not stay out completely.' He then offered to buy me a drink which I refused, but I did offer to walk over the bridge with him and point him in the direction of a number of b. & bs. I could have walked away, but to the writer unpleasant meetings are as much grist to the mill as pleasant ones.

It was 7.30. Tony had disappeared homewards, carrying his wreath for tomorrow's ceremony, and as we started to walk I spotted smoke swirling into the sky and suggested we go and find the source, thinking that his athletic presence might come in useful if we walked into trouble.

The smoke came from bonfires being prepared in the Fountain. We walked through streets watching men in crimson jumpers erecting crimson bunting across the streets, until we came to three huge bonfires with the tricolour on top and one smaller bonfire surrounded by dirty-faced kids. The smaller bonfire was alight.

'What are you doing?' I asked.

'Having a bonfire. The big ones will be lit at 11.30 and we felt like having one now.'

'What's the bonfire for?'

'To burn the flag.'

'. . . the flag?'

'The Catholic flag.'

There was no trouble. At the other side of the bridge two armoured vehicles were parked and soldiers with guns were roaming the streets. Michael Collins was uneasy. 'I sure dislike walking the streets looking for a place to stay.' Amazed by his inability to handle himself I took him into the pub and while he put his bags down I asked the landlord if he could recommend a place to stay. He called his wife, who picked up her cordless phone, dialled a number and called to me: '£6 per night all right?' 'Fine,' I said. 'What name shall I say it is?' 'Michael. It's not for me, it's for my friend Michael.' Michael Collins looked impressed. It was the last I saw of him.

Chapter 6

Northern Ireland:
Beauty and the Beast of Intolerance

The march was to begin at 1.15. Before that there was to be a wreath-laying at the war memorial in the Diamond, and a church service at St Columb's Cathedral. For most people 1.15 was the moment. Until then, shops were open, some taxis were operating, but after that the centre of Derry would be left to the marchers – the rest of Derry would scurry away indoors.

I left my hotel at 10 a.m. to walk through the cool, cloudy morning, across the bridge once more to watch the wreath-laying and to attend the service. Seconds outside my hotel I spotted my first slit-eyed, steel-grey armoured car, gliding down the street: along this stretch of road coaches would park, bringing marchers from neighbouring towns and villages. Once over the bridge the numbers of both police and army vehicles increased. I felt conspicuous and thought that at any moment I'd be stopped and asked my business. Be that as it may, I was not going to wear a notice saying *Press* on my forehead!

Outside the Apprentice-boys Hall there were as many camera crews as there were groups of people assembling behind banners. A woman smiled at me. She was staying at the same hotel and was from Canada, part of a crew making a documentary about democracy. Towards 11 o'clock I moved to the Diamond, the war memorial, stopping to chat to a group of policemen lounging at a street corner: 'Lot of scrambled egg around here today; each more useless than the next,' they said. The wreath-laying ceremony was brief and rather unmoving. I spotted Tony easily. He was the only one with any idea how to march. The rest shuffled along, their shoulders hunched. There was a flute band; a pipe and drums, some pretty fancy uniforms, including those with kilts and plumed helmets, but also many young people in trousers and sweaters. A few shopgirls stood in doorways and there was a group of tourists seated on the pavement in folding chairs, but on the whole the crowd was small.

As I walked to St Columb's Cathedral, no distance from the Diamond, I passed a pub called the Talk of the Town, where drinkers
were spilling on to the pavement. In the church yard a bent old man
with a stick said: 'You haven't seen the half of it yet.' His breath smelt
of drink. A group of what I took to be members of the press sat on the
low walls smoking, reluctant to go inside but anxious to get a few
notes on the sermon.

It was certainly worth hearing. It was the most political I have ever
heard. Hugh Ross, a Presbyterian minister from Tyrone, gave what was
in essence a history lesson, to the effect that it was God's hand that in
the seventeenth century had guided Protestants to this north-eastern
corner; it was God's hand that had enabled the Protestants to prosper;
and it was God's hand that had guided Protestants through every spot
of bother since then. And of course it was God's hand that had guided
the thirteen apprentice-boys and enabled them to slam the gates of the
city in the faces of Roman Catholics. The boys, he said, would no doubt
have been seen as the yobbos of their day – the hotheads – but they had
saved Derry. Much of Europe had not been saved; much of Europe was
in the hands of Popery. 'The power of the enemy is great; the wealth of
the Vatican is great,' and he listed the real estate to prove the point.

The British, he went on, did not want to settle Irish terrorism for
fear of Catholic opinion in Europe. 'The Protestants in Northern
Ireland have never been so betrayed as by the Anglo-Irish Agreement.
The English scorn us; no one understands us. And yet we were there
to fight alongside the British at the Somme; we were there to fight
against the Roman Catholic Mussolini.' He ended by appealing to the
prime minister to give Ulster the security it deserved against Roman
Catholic terrorism. Hugh Ross was no orator and I can't imagine that
the congregation felt inspired on this day. Outside the press swapped
notes. I went to see Martin. The sun had come out and the crowd
outside the Talk of the Town was increasing by the minute. There was
no need to go inside for a drink; there were stalls outside selling Harp
Lager at 55 pence. It felt like a street party.

Martin and I decided to position ourselves within the Diamond,
which is in fact a square from which four roads lead. Two of the roads
were cordoned off; one with a huge canvas wall and the other by a line
of armoured vehicles. That left one road through which the march
entered the Diamond and one road through which it left. The word
was that there were 10,000 marchers and that could well have been the
number for the parade lasted one and a half hours, a constant stream,
lowering their banners as they passed the place where wreaths had

been laid. Just as the march was beginning, an army officer in camouflage gear and with the kind of cut-glass accent provided by a spell at
Sandhurst wandered up to a film crew alongside me and said: 'Are you
here to report or to manufacture the news?'

No one answered.

'For the last three nights I have watched the news on television and
seen manufactured stuff that put my soldiers at risk.'

The film crew remained silent.

The arrogant, antagonistic young man continued: 'Can you put your
hand on your heart and say you have never manufactured stuff?'

'We're news,' said an American accent. 'We're news and we film
what is in front of us. If it's not there, we cannot film it.'

A drunk came up to me. 'Do you know what the memorial com-
memmorates? 30,000 dead. I fought in Burma. I fought for the Queen. I
fought. They don't know what they are doing. Dipping their fucking
flags. It's a mockery.' He said much the same thing three times over
before realizing that I was not going to engage him in conversation
and he weaved on past, muttering.

At one point a group of young marchers broke ranks and began
jumping up in the air as they came abreast of one of the closed roads,
making V-signs and shouting, 'Shoot, Shoot, Shoot to Kill'. The
message was aimed at a crowd of Catholics that had assembled down
the street, divided from the shouters by three rows of armoured
vehicles. The Catholic crowds began to respond, but I could neither
hear nor see clearly. A policeman touched my arm and invited me to
stand on the wired guard of one of the vehicles. I hesitated. There was
nothing to stop another officer coming along and ordering me down.
He repeated the offer and I decided to take the risk because I needed
the height; the extra two feet enabled me to see what was happening
halfway down the street. The first line of vehicles was edging forward
slowly, and like a snow plough was shovelling the Catholic crowd
back into the Bogside, out of harm's way. The incident was over in
minutes and we settled back to wait for the Reverend Ian Paisley,
leader of the DUP, whom we knew would bring up the rear of the
column of marchers. I knew when he was approaching because I could
hear cheering and because the camera crews began to jostle for better
positions. When Paisley appeared in view, he raised his bowler hat to
the crowd. He was wearing white gloves and looked for all the world
like a 'white minstrel'. It was an amusing image and I stepped forward
to capture the moment with my camera. Arms swung out at me,
reining me back. I don't know whose arms they were; plainclothes
policemen, other marchers, other picture-takers.

'Oh, let the lady get her picture,' shouted the Reverend Ian Paisley. And he halted the march, and leaned on his check furled umbrella and smiled directly at me. I was so taken aback that my photograph is out of focus. I smiled in return. They say that Ian Paisley has great charm.

The march itself was over just before 3 p.m., and Martin and I decided to take a walk through the Bogside. It was warm now, sunless and sultry, and hundreds of people were hanging around, sitting around, strolling around. Waiting. I could feel the waiting. Martin was a little less influenced by the mood and wanted a drink, so we went to a pub and drank cider for half an hour. By the time we got back, the waiting crowd had doubled and a British Telecom van was upturned in the street, close to the sign saying 'You are now entering Free Derry'. Youths, hundreds of them, sat on the pavement with their arms around their knees. Waiting.

'They've just jumped that van and told the driver to bugger off.'

'Why didn't he put his foot down and speed away?'

'His life is worth more than a van. Telecom have told all their men that if ambushed they should abandon the vehicle and run. Happens all the time.' Hooded figures openly poured petrol, slowly, carefully and deliberately all over the upturned vehicle. There was masses of time for the police to come and stop them but that is just what the police didn't do, because that is just what the hooded figures wanted them to do. It was an act of provocation. Suddenly the whole thing went ablaze and thick black smoke swirled into the air. The crowd watched. No one attempted to move.

For ten minutes or so I watched the crowd watching the blaze. There was no chatter; the mood was menacingly quiet and still. Then, as one, the crowd started to move, without speed, but with purpose, towards the Bloody Sunday memorial.

'This is it,' said Martin.

'This is what?' I asked.

'Trouble. Now look, at the first sign, run. When I run, you run. And if you lose me, hop over the nearest wall into someone's garden and crouch down.'

I listened without understanding. 'I don't think we ought to *run*. Surely that looks suspicious? Let's place ourselves close to a wall now.'

Martin agreed. He was becoming agitated. A listless, dull afternoon which he had written off as a 'broken docket' – an Irish phrase meaning 'useless', like a spent betting-slip – was turning into something known to journalists as 'copy', a potential story.

We found a 'wall', a lowish garden wall to a house at the end of a terrace. A youth in jeans, with a pink knitted helmet hiding his face, passed within a foot of me. In each hand he carried a petrol bomb. The sight mesmerized me. I persuaded Martin to follow him and we walked behind the youth until he decided to march down the centre of the road. We stood on a street corner and watched him disappear from view. Within view were half a dozen armoured police vehicles parked on a corner of waste land. On the opposite corner, a similar number of television crews had their cameras trained on the vehicles. There we waited. We waited among a thin crowd strung out along the pavement. A crack shattered the eerie silence.

'A plastic bullet,' said Martin.

'How do you know?' I asked.

'We've heard enough of them to recognize the sound.'

We waited. There was no joking, no quipping, just silence from people who are used to hanging around. After eighteen years of scenes like this it baffled me that the bystanders did not scurry away indoors and put the kettle on. Perhaps petrol bombs *v.* plastic bullets is the modern equivalent of gladiatorial contests or public executions. There were very few women – petrol bombs *v.* plastic bullets is a male sport, like football. An ambulance went past and as it did so the first of the armoured vehicles began to move, gradually gathering speed. You could see guns peeping through the slits. In front of us a handful of youths began to run. A vehicle drew up alongside them and two policemen leapt out. One of the youths tripped. He was wearing black leather and his hair was blond and swept upwards to form spikes. The police were upon him; each grabbed an arm and yanked him up from the pavement and dragged him into their van. As they did so they walloped him with their truncheons. I thought the beating was unnecessary, but then I had not seen petrol bombs being thrown at the police, which is how the incident was portrayed on television that evening. It was all over within minutes, and the police vehicles disappeared from view. Martin said they wouldn't stick around with so many television cameras present. I'd seen enough of the Bogside and suggested we went over the bridge to see what was happening on the Waterside. 'No,' he replied firmly. He was a Catholic and could not be seen on the other side. It would be too dangerous. He walked with me to the bridge, which was sealed off with white tape, and we said goodbye.

I walked across listening to the helicopters humming overhead and to the steady drone of the pipes and drums. What I found on the other side was sickening. It was drunkenness. Wherever I looked there were men drunk, or men drinking. There was vomit on the pavement outside the pub where I had gone the night before to find accommodation for Michael. The building next to it was burnt out. I had seen no drinking or drunkenness in the Bogside. I had seen Protestant drinking since soon after 10 o'clock. It was now 5 p.m. It was impossible to feel threatened by this mob, they seemed incapable. The publican was standing at the doorway of his pub. 'It'll be all right when the trains leave at 6. This lot will be gone.' The implication was that the visitors to Derry were responsible for the mess, the vomit, the drunkenness and the wrecking of the phone box. I wandered to the island in the middle of the road where several columns of police in riot helmets and shields stood in lines in front of their vehicles. From time to time a stone would be hurled in their direction; a stone or an empty lager can. The target turned to look in the direction of the missile, but appeared to accept the stones and the cans as though they were nothing more than irritating flies. In the middle of this a young couple stood, arms entwined, kissing. He wore jeans and had a camera slung over his neck; she wore white trousers and yellow shoes. It seemed to sum up the seriousness of the scene in front of me. The Derry march had turned into a drunken brawl. I turned away and walked back to my hotel.

That night at dinner two men at the next table talked loudly about the price of food; they discussed how much they were prepared to pay for lobster – £14 for a whole seemed acceptable to them. In London, they said, they were prepared to spend £80 on lunch for two people. One of them had a black eye. I asked at the desk who they were and got the answer I expected: representatives of the so-called 'popular press'. I was told that thirty-five journalists were staying in the hotel. Nothing compared to the height of the Troubles, said the man behind the desk. In those days, he said, the bar was always full of intrepid reporters who would look out across the Foyle to the Bogside and when they saw smoke rising they'd make a phone call to the RUC and then write a story.

The man with the black eye had started his food-obsessed meal with a toast: 'To the end of the annual orgy of naked triumphalism.' Is that really how he saw it? I saw it as a sad day; a day without a trace of triumph; a day tinged with hollow ritual that somehow showed all too clearly the position of Protestants in Northern Ireland. Slamming the gates on King James's men had given them a tenuous supremacy which they had clung to at all costs; it had not made them confident; it had made them fearful in the knowledge that at any time they could be toppled. Confident men do not end the day drunk; that is the behaviour of men who are insecure, threatened and defiant.

Next morning I awoke feeling weary. The adrenalin had ceased to flow and I needed a fallow day in which to recover. Two men were

outside my window noisily mending the guttering; all the newspapers
had been gobbled up by the early risers. It was raining. I decided that
my fallow day would be spent travelling a few hours down the road
into County Fermanagh. Border country where one in ten is employed
on the land, fighting against milk quotas and beef mountains. Fermanagh, I'd been told, was beautiful and could be prosperous, could
become the centre of tourism once there was peace. I'd heard about a
country house that had been turned into a small, cosy hotel for those
who wanted to fish and shoot and ride. It was some six miles from the
town of Enniskillen, which sits on an island between upper and lower
Lough Erne. It sounded the perfect antidote to watching marchers. I
checked the bus timetable and then rang the hotel. Arthur Stuart
readily offered to meet me from the bus.

The single-decker 98 took the journey slowly, picking up and
dropping any number of damp shoppers laden with plastic bags. On
these local buses there is said to be ventilation and one cannot open the
windows, and this made it increasingly unpleasant inside. So did the
fact that people insisted on smoking in the non-smoking seats. At one
time three of them were puffing away, but I decided it was too much
effort to ask them to stop. It takes energy to make oneself unpopular:
this was a local bus and folk would probably not take kindly to a
visitor's bossiness. In any event it wasn't the only rule being broken.

There was a sign saying that passengers must not speak to the driver
or distract his attention without good cause. Two pert young girls
were doing just that. One perched on a thin ledge facing him and the
other draped herself alongside him, her arm on his chair. They giggled
and played with his left ear. I averted my gaze and, since I could no
longer see through the rain-splattered windows, took to reading the
advertisements: 'Have you ever been raped or sexually assaulted?
Phone Derry 260 566.'

The towns of Strabane and Omagh looked bedraggled: huddled up
against the weather, or the goings-on at the border, or rape or incest.
Or poverty. This area has the highest unemployment rate. In Strabane
it is said to be around 33 per cent, but hidden by a struggling black
economy. The rate for the county is 27 per cent, as against Northern
Ireland's 19 per cent. The passengers on the bus attested to this, but
then passengers on buses are never a good guide. They tend to be used
by the youthful poor and the elderly poor. The rest have cars.

Arthur Stuart was waiting at the bus station at Enniskillen. His
house is called Jamestown and it dates from 1760, with bits added in
1820. It is in a village called Ballinamallard, which struck me as being
attractive, until Arthur pointed out the boarded up RUC building

that had been bombed several months before. Arthur Stuart had been a beef farmer but he had become disenchanted with working so hard to provide another creature for a beef mountain, and had sold up and bought Jamestown with his father, who had a business selling tools and building equipment. Arthur and his young wife, Helen, wanted to create a country-house atmosphere at Jamestown, but not in a pretentious manner. While she ran the kitchen, he would take his meals with the guests who ate together at one table, and plan with them the next day's fishing.

The other two guests that first night had been married for twenty-four hours. Joanna was a student at Queen's University Belfast, reading biology, and Richard worked for Esso. 'We consider ourselves upper middle class,' she told me as we sat beside a log fire over drinks that had been laid out on a table from which we helped ourselves. Sherry in her hand, she continued. 'People always think of the Irish as poor, but this is not the case. I resent going down to London and noticing the surprise in people's faces when I talk about my skiing holidays or whatever. In fact we have a higher standard of living than you English. House prices are so low here, you see. Someone earning £15,000 a year is on a pig's back.'

Arthur Stuart's father took me on Lough Erne the next day. He owns an admiral's barge, the only one in Northern Ireland. The mahogany and brass showed that it was used to glamorous duties – taking admirals to inspect the fleet off Malta and Hong Kong. Arthur's father is a lay-preacher and it showed in his turn of phrase. 'I'll show you heaven. God is in this boat. He is in this lake, in this morning. He doesn't cause all this trouble. Man brings it on himself. It's the animal in him. We'll be destroyed in the end by star wars, or nuclear war, but God will make sure that there are two birds left and it will all start over again.'

The lake was exquisite. Erne is huge, fifty miles long, dotted with rush-surrounded islands. We went to Devenish Island to look at a twelfth-century round tower. In four hours we saw but one pleasure cruiser, which leaves Enniskillen each morning, and six cruisers with Germans behind the wheel. Arthur's father was born in the south but his mother told him to go north to be among his own people. He loves the north and all things English. 'It's all to do with the standards. You can see the difference once you get over the border; the farms look haphazard, the shops don't bother to open until 10.30. Here we work hard and everything is neat.'

'Is that why you are so against union?'

'It is. We don't want to be dragged down. It's got little to do with religion. Look, they are so similiar; we even share the same Creed.' He used to be a B Special, a member of what amounted to the armed branch of the Orange Order disbanded by the British government. 'You may think the present troubles started in the late sixties, but here on the border we have always had problems with the I R A. For fifty years we have had problems in this area. We're finely balanced in numbers, you know, Protestants and Roman Catholics.' I asked him if he felt that the Protestants had done anything to bring the present situation upon themselves. 'No,' he answered without hesitation.

'When you had your business did you employ Catholics?'

'I never asked. It's no matter to me what a man is.'

I was the only guest that night and agreed to have a simple meal at 7 o'clock so that Helen could go and see *West Side Story*. I would have gone too, but there were no tickets, so I glanced at a review in the local paper instead. It ended with the words: 'This is the type of show the idealism of which could teach Northern Ireland or any trouble-spot a lesson. Even though there is death there were plenty of opportunities for either side to back down. In the end they only agree to fight which led to the inevitable tragedy.'

Enniskillen has a huge leisure centre and an over-sized telephone exchange. Both have been funded in part by the E E C's development programme for poor areas. Fermanagh has done well out of membership. It has had millions towards farming, for draining the land and improving the soil. It now would like millions towards the expansion of tourism; for a craft centre for pottery, lace-making, leather and glass wear, for Romany caravans around the lake, for pony trekking and an equestrian park. Local goverment in this area is headed by a Catholic, a go-ahead, ambitious man who knows his way around the grant system. And, as I sat in the bus station waiting for the bus to Belfast, I hoped he might spend a few pounds on the arrival and departure point. The waiting room was so scruffy, so furnitureless and so smoke filled, I chose to wait outside, battered by the wind and the rain. I shared my bench with an eighteen-year-old who had just completed his A-levels and had spent a summer on a farm in Gloucestershire, where they had worn him out with work and given him not one day off. He condemned the motorway cafés and the bus stations in England. He said he couldn't imagine what foreigners made of them. He was so happy to be home.

In Belfast they were about to celebrate the tenth anniversary of the founding of the Peace People. Everyone, at one time, knew the Peace People, a movement which erupted like a volcano one day in August 1976 when three young children died and their mother was wounded. British troops had fired on a car, killing the driver, I R A volunteer Danny

Lennon. The car swerved on to the pavement wounding Mrs Anne Maguire and killing her three children. Betty Williams was driving along behind; she knew the Maguire family; she saw the whole thing and together with the children's aunt, Mairaed Corrigan, appealed through the women of Northern Ireland for peace; for an end to the IRA campaign. She told the gunmen to get out. At their first rally 10,000 women turned up. The media, ever eager to find new ways of covering a story which had smouldered for eight years, found Williams and Corrigan irresistible. Two Catholic women telling the gunmen to get out. They became heroines; they travelled the world. On television in America Betty Williams begged the viewers to stop sending money for bombs and bullets; in Norway she danced with the crown prince. In 1977 the two women shared the Nobel Peace Prize. But it was all too much: the movement seemed to shatter in a wealth of gossip and bitchiness. What then were they celebrating in 1986? I was intrigued to find out.

I was intrigued because I had met Betty Williams. A publisher in 1981 thought it was time for her to tell the story of the rise and fall of the Peace People, and the story of Betty Williams. She had refused to cooperate with any of the writers who covered Northern Ireland but had consented to fly down to London to meet me. It was a weird occasion. She arrived at my house one afternoon dressed in cream from head to toe and covered in jewellery, and talked for hours at great speed, with great passion. She talked of the place where she was born to a Protestant father, a butcher, and a Catholic mother, a waitress; of a childhood filled with happiness; of marriage to an English merchant-seaman which had meant that she lived for a while in Bermuda before homesickness brought her back to Belfast in the mid-sixties. After that the happiness turned to horror. She talked of young children getting their heads blown off, caught in the cross-fire between the army and the IRA; of this dreary place called Belfast, where people went shopping with great reluctance because it took hours, through searches and blockades, to do a simple task; of a place controlled by racketeers who made a mint demanding protection money. What was I to make of this? I asked her what on earth she did when it all got too much for her. It was twilight, but I had not wanted to disturb her thoughts by putting on the lights. She turned to me: 'I go and have a damn good fuck.' I could not see her face at all clearly, and did not know how I was meant to take the remark. I laughed. We both laughed. And as I got up to put the lights on she said: 'Well, when shall we start on the book?'

We made plans to spend a month together in Northern Ireland, but out of Belfast. She left telling me she intended to find a cottage for us to rent. I never saw her again. Letters from the publishing company went unanswered. It was 1981 and the hunger-strike, in which ten Republican prisoners died, was beginning. This attracted the world's attention in much the same way as had the Peace People. When Bobby Sands died, having just been elected to Westminster, reports state that 400 reporters and 300 photographers from around the globe turned up to cover his funeral. Betty Williams had warned me that the hunger-strike would take up all of her time. It did. And then somewhere in all that her personal life splintered and then was pieced together in a very Betty Williams way. She won a trip to America in a raffle and on her first day in Disneyland met an American engineer whom she subsequently married. She settled in Florida.

Mairaed Corrigan was the quiet one. When things got too much for her she went to church and prayed. At the Peace Weekend I met her. The peace movement had not died, she said, it had merely moved away from the television cameras, out of the limelight, to try slowly and quietly to change people's attitudes. The circus has gone but the work goes on.

'We work now on a one-to-one basis; we have a farm in Coleraine where Catholics and Protestants work together; we attempt to educate children together; we run Lifeline to support people who have lost relatives in the struggle. We have made progress – none of this could have happened ten years ago. It's a lifetime's work.' She spoke softly, her eyes looking directly into mine.

'Our common humanity should bind us. One day it will. We have made gods out of both unionist and nationalist. I reject both. I'll bow to no flag; flags have destroyed too many lives. Change will come through children being educated together. It's hard not to grow up a bigot in Northern Ireland, when you live in sections which care about nothing else except looking after their own. And yet our concerns are common; there's 27 per cent unemployment; a people living in poverty and yet thousands are being spent on security. Social issues have become secondary. We as a small movement cannot tackle social issues, but we challenge others to do so. Rallies don't solve anything, so I'm not sorry all that is over. Those who have remained in the movement are happy to work quietly at practical peacemaking. We are not depressed and we have not given up hope. We'll just carry on. I expect I will be here answering the same questions when I am ninety.'

The Peace People see themselves as part of a world movement of men and women trying to live in a more intelligent way. That's what they say. And certainly there was an international flavour to the weekend. Peace House was a jumble of accents, American, French, German, Dutch and Norwegian. Mid-morning we were invited to form small groups to discuss 'peacemaking'. The group I joined contained a French priest who had met Mairaed Corrigan in Paris ten years before and who said very little; an American called Sally who came from Seattle: 'A place a little larger than Belfast where they make aeroplanes and war machines'; another American called Jim who had come to Belfast in 1984 to see what all the fuss was about and was now back, during law school vacation, helping various projects; and Klaus, a German who said he was a Marxist and talked of workers' unity. What became apparent very quickly was that there was a gulf between the so-called intellectual peacemakers and folk like Kathy who said: 'I'm no good at talking. I sell the *Peace* newspaper door to door and talk to people and I help paint over any graffiti that we think are offensive.' And Betty, who talked of how difficult it was for some Catholic women to become members and of how she got snubbed and spat at and how her windows were broken. And then there was Isobel Bennett: 'I have no difficulty in talking and you'll just have to shut me up. I'm involved in so many projects I don't know where to begin.'

Isobel Bennett's family came to Belfast from Aberdeen in 1920. Her father sought work in the shipyard and couldn't understand why he had to state his religion on the application form. Isobel was born in 1926 and can remember a childhood of poverty with her mother having to buy rotting vegetables. Isobel caught polio and spent many of her young years in bed rather than in school. 'So, God love you, I'm not educated. I'm really not intellectual enough for the Peace People. I often feel my ideas are not good enough. The trouble is that a lot of people come to paddle and are made to swim.'

For all that, Mrs Bennett gives the impression of being a strong swimmer and, as she had said, once she started talking about her projects, such was her enthusiasm she found it hard to stop. Her latest project was concerned with battered wives and she has had a long involvement with Lifeline. She introduced me to a family whose son had been shot by the IRA. The son, who worked in a petrol station, had been a member of the UDR (the Ulster Defence Regiment – a regiment of the British Army recruited in Northern Ireland). He'd only been a member for a couple of months and the family are convinced that the shooting was a case of mistaken identity. The killing does not make sense to them otherwise. Their graphic description of the event and the effect it had on their lives I found harrowing. 'We brought him home to his own bedroom and among the people who came to pay their respects, there were as many Catholics as there were Protestants.' They shielded their other children from the details of the murder only to have their daughter ask them one night exactly what happened. The family sat up until 4.30 in the morning going through it all in the hope that they could help her come to terms with the anguish. They found Lifeline an invaluable support, particularly the holidays that were arranged for similiar victims, both Catholic and Protestant. It helped to be among people who understand; who understand that there were times to laugh and times to cry.

They showed me photographs of such a holiday and as they led me through the pictures they said: 'This woman's husband died of a heart attack when he heard that their son had committed suicide because he could no longer cope with being a policeman.' 'This little girl's granddaddy died when they came over the border one night and fired into a church. When she was on holiday she had nightmares all the while.' 'We found these two sitting together one day. One said, "Protestants killed my Daddy", and the other said, "Catholics killed my Daddy."' By the time we got through the album I was swallowing hard to choke back the tears. For a fleeting second I wished the television cameras were there so millions could see the album, the photographs of these families, of these children, and share my emotion. In the next fleeting second I scorned the thought. What good would that do? The screen would act as a barrier; the viewer would be unlikely to be as affected as I was and if somehow, something got through to some of them, and they too found themselves choking back the tears . . . what then? Unlike pictures of starving children in Africa, you couldn't just reach for your chequebook and feel better. You couldn't organize a pop concert or issue a record or take part in a fun run. It was a great wave of emotion that started the Peace People in the first place and here we were ten years later sitting around contemplating whether or not to attend a strawberry tea to celebrate that ten years had passed!

A member who farmed in Ballymena was putting on the tea and I had decided not to go, but somehow I got swept along as everyone else was piling into cars. I jumped into the back seat of a car driven by an elderly woman who needed to concentrate on the road rather than talk; her husband wasn't the talking kind. Sharing the back seat with me was Kevin Lynch, a student at Queen's who was helping to provide the entertainment during the tea – a sketch about South Africa. Kevin was portraying the UK government's point of view on economic sanctions: 'They'd only hurt those we wanted to help'; another Peace Person portrayed the Afrikaner: 'We made this land profitable; we made this country rich.' A girl portrayed the blacks by reworking the words of Psalm 23: 'He maketh me to lie down in poverty and oppression,' and so on. The crude parallels were there for those who wanted to pick them up. The sketch was followed by peace songs.

Kevin and I got a lift back to Belfast much earlier than we expected and as we arrived he offered to walk with me through the Falls Road. 'You musn't wander around there on your own. You'd be better off in the company of a local Catholic, even though I don't live in the area.' We'd formed a bond earlier in the afternoon when he asked me where I was born. I'd answered west London and he'd fired back, 'Hayes?' 'That's exactly the spot. How did you guess?' 'It's the only place I know. Lots of Catholics from Belfast used to go there to work in the factories.' He'd promised me an hour of his time; one way and another it turned out to be a lot longer than that.

We walked the entire length of the Falls Road, beginning at the Divis Flats, concrete filing-cabinets, some empty, some inhabited. On the ground between them were broken bottles, litter, general mess. Young children played on bicycles and young girls tottered around in spiky-heeled shoes and tight trousers. 'Some of these flats are so damp that they cause health problems as bad as anything you'd find in the Third World.' He'd never been to the Third World but it seemed pointless to tell him that there was nothing in Northern Ireland to compare with the poverty and the problems of the Third World.

Around the corner from the Divis Flats there were new houses, neat town houses, arranged around a courtyard, each with its own front patio. There was no mess, no litter. This estate had won prizes; this is the council housing of the future.

'They're all right aren't they? We're doing quite well despite Mrs Thatcher's cuts in public expenditure. I don't suppose she dares cut back on money to Northern Ireland.'

They did look all right. They didn't look any different from a modern private development. The top end of the Falls Road where it joins Springfield Road did not look any different from thousands of pre-war housing developments. Dreary, boxy, sound. Off the main street, where side roads met at right angles, I could see the peace lines; slatted wood screens rising fifteen feet into the air. It was just possible to see through to the other side by peering through the slats. A scruffy child of four or five was throwing stones at the wall. The pubs were covered in barbed wire. I suggested we stop for a drink, but Kevin said no.

'These are community pubs and they would be very suspicious; they'd stop talking the minute we walked in and we'd both feel very uncomfortable.' I argued that I'd still like to go inside for ten minutes, but he was adamant. Grey police armoured vehicles passed us; green army armoured cars passed us at regular intervals. Kevin had long given up noticing them.

We walked slowly for nearly two hours with Kevin giving me his views on the Peace People and the various conflicting personalities. He had, he said, almost come to the end of his time with the movement. He joined when young because the social life had been good and he'd done his bit helping here and there, but he didn't think that he had much more to offer. 'I'm so materialistic compared to some of them and it bothers me at times. If I couldn't get a job I wanted I'd prefer to join the police rather than be jobless, and that's not going to go down very well is it? I'm even prepared to work for Short's making missiles . . . think what they'd make of that!'

I liked his honesty.

'Do you find the atmosphere tense?' he asked me.

'No, I find it rather relaxed,' which it was, walking along on a summer evening talking as the light faded.

'The other evening I was heading home and a car came around the corner fast, its wheels squealing and I thought, this is it! I could be killed! Any car coming around the corner fast makes me think like that, particularly after dark. We must be out of here by the time light goes.'

We paused for a while to sit on a bench in a square of green which passed for a park and watched children scooting around on BMX bicycles. Then we headed back the way we had come. The streets were deserted, so that anyone walking along caught one's attention and held it. I spotted a pretty girl dressed for a Saturday night and remarked upon her looks to Kevin.

'Yes, she is pretty. Have you read Orwell? He talks about proletarian beauty; beauty that fades very quickly. That girl will be ugly in a few years time. They are all the same; at seventeen they say they'll never get married and be like their mums, and then by nineteen they are married and a few years later they'll be left looking after a couple of kids while their husbands are in the pubs.'

We watched the pretty girl disappear into a bar selling milkshakes and burgers. Since Kevin wouldn't allow me into a pub, I suggested a milkshake. When I came to pay I found my purse missing. For a moment I thought I had had my pocket picked , because I had stopped outside to quip with a couple of boys who wanted to know if I was American. I'd said yes because it was clearly what they wanted to hear, and this particular Irish habit is contagious. It was an unworthy thought and I knew that the only place it could have slipped from my pocket was when we had sat for a while on the park bench. That was forty-five minutes past, and I felt sure it would no longer be there. None the less I felt compelled to go back and check. This we did, hiring a taxi from a video-hire shop.

'I bet this lot is unauthorized and uninsured,' commented Kevin, but I couldn't have cared less so long as we got back to the bench. We both jumped from the car, leaving the driver looking a touch surprised, and ran to the spot. I shut my eyes and then slowly opened them. The purse was there, black and bulky, sitting on the park bench. I hugged Kevin with relief. 'Come on,' he said. 'Let's go home and I'll introduce you to my parents.' We told the taxi driver the story when we got back into the car. He said: 'No need to be amazed at the honesty. The kids probably thought there was a bomb in it – that's why they didn't touch it.' I felt as though he had stuck a pin in the balloon of my spirits.

Kevin's mother and father live in a small house behind Queen's University, in a street in which front doors open straight on to the pavement. His parents, sitting either side of a large fire, were watching a John Wayne movie on the television. They seemed delighted to see us, just as Kevin said they would be.

'OK if Linda stays to tea, Mum?'

'Of course it is. I'll have it ready in a minute,' and she walked into the narrow kitchen leading from the sitting room. There was no door, so she could stay in touch with the conversation. Before long we had in front of us huge mugs of tea and cold meat and salad and a jolly conversation about . . . Northern Ireland. Kevin's dad, who drives a digger for a construction company, enjoys talking politics, just as Kevin had said he would.

'It's your man with the pipe that's to blame. He didn't stand firm. If he'd stood firm against that strike, all this would be over. Sinn Fein would have no need to grow and it would all be over.'

There are many who would agree. Ireland had gone well for Edward Heath's government in 1973. With William Whitelaw as Secretary of State many steps had been taken towards the setting up of a power-sharing executive. The main parties at least seemed to agree on the main points (Unionist representing Protestants; the SDLP representing Labour and the cross-communal alliance and Northern Ireland Labour Parties). Then a conference was called at Sunningdale to discuss the setting up of a Council of Ireland and the carefully built-up cards began to tumble. They always do at this point: power-sharing between Protestants and Catholics in Northern Ireland is a big enough step; trying to include the Republic as well is like watching a baby learning to walk . . . a few steps forward, much cooing and then bump.

And Kevin's father was right about Harold Wilson, but 1974 was a messy year in British politics. The Heath government lost the election in February 1974 by a handful of votes, which meant the new government stumbled around until another election was called in October 1974. Ireland once more slipped through British fingers.

'You've only got your man with a pipe to blame. Now, I don't see much change for the next thirty years. What do you think?'

'I came here thinking it was all nice and simple: a united Ireland had to be the right answer and if that was a hard pill for the Protestants then they had only themselves to blame for misruling the province for so many years. If they had given the Catholics a fair go from the beginning none of this would have happened.'

I paused and he waited.

'Now I see it as infinitely more complicated. I appreciate how the Protestants feel about their place in the north and how they feel towards the south which has made very little effort to become an attractive marriage partner. I'd still love to see a happily united Ireland with both Protestants and Catholics showing toleration and understanding towards each other.'

I told them of my meeting with Tony Crowe and how he'd made me realize the isolation the Protestants now felt; how the south didn't want them and how they no longer felt 'loyal' to the union with Great Britain. And how perhaps the only answer, long term, was a measure of independence for Northern Ireland – not devolution and Stormont as before, but independence within the EEC, which would offer much-needed money provided the Protestants did not go back to their bad old ways. An independent Northern Ireland with good links to southern Ireland, that would be an alternative to a united Ireland, but how to get that position! At that point we all began to toss in thoughts and half thoughts, all of which have been aired endlessly over the years. If only the British government (Labour) had not sent in the troops; if only, once they had committed themselves to such a policy they had backed it with toughness instead of insisting on a softly-softly approach; if only the border were more secure – it would help curb the IRA; if only the protection rackets could be stamped out – it would starve the IRA of funds; if only there could be an end to segregated schooling – it would enable children to grow up less bigoted; if only there were more jobs for both Protestants and Catholics, but in particular for Catholics. If only this and if only that. For the moment, the only *practical* path is to press for greater tolerance and understanding between Catholics and Protestants. We must keep trying to find a way to silence the extremists and let the moderates hold sway.

'All we want is to be left to live our lives,' said Kevin's father. 'It's not too bad around here; we feel safe enough. We say to ourselves we might get killed, but if we do it will be worse for the chap that is left.'

It was 10 p.m. Kevin's father raked the fire. Kevin walked me to the bus stop anxious to be away to his party.

*

The ferry for Stranraer left at 8 a.m. I stood on the deck watching the coastline disappear and marvelling at the patterns made by chimneys belching smoke into the sky. I felt loath to leave. I'd arrived with an empty diary and I was leaving with a wealth of memories, not the sort you have to dredge from the depths of your mind, but the sort that float lightly beneath the surface and return instantly at odd and surprising moments. I would no longer close my ears and eyes to reports of violence in newspapers and on television. I might feel irritated by the squabbling, but the irritation would be eased by a small nugget of understanding and a vast feeling of warmth towards the place and the people. And I might think twice before muttering that religion makes fools of men. It can and it does. But there's Strongbow at the back of it all; one nation trying to swallow another nation is inclined to make men mad. But a murderous little war is no answer; 2,500 people have died since 1968.

'Hallo, we met at the Peace Weekend. I'm a friend of Kevin's. I know all about your purse!'

He was an art student who one day hoped to teach. He'd been in the Peace Movement since he was thirteen and stayed, he said, because he thought about things more than most people of his age and had found no alternative outlet for his energy and his desire to do something to help. On that morning, at that early hour, he was downcast. He needed to get away for a while and was heading for Portsmouth where his brother now lived and owned a shop. He had no intention of leaving for good; he just knew he had to get away for a bit. The Anglo-Irish Agreement had escalated the Troubles and this had prompted the downcast mood.

He had a friend who worked on a building site; the company often did work for the security forces. 'We have always known that the IRA pick off people who work with the security forces, but now it is stated policy and people have become frightened. My friend went to the boss and said he thought he'd better leave and was told that the company were paying "protection money" and therefore would be left alone. Paying protection money does not mean that you are going to be safe, but not paying it certainly means you are not going to be safe.'

We talked of art. He told me stories of five-year-olds drawing flowers and then colouring them green, white and orange. I assume he was a Catholic. They say you can tell by simply looking at someone. But that seems absurd to me and anyway I never learnt the trick. And I certainly was not going to ask. Only once during my visit did I feel the need to ask a man whether he was a Catholic or Protestant. I had to struggle with the words and felt deeply embarrassed.

Chapter 7

Newcastle's Backstreet Butterflies

I broke my train journey from Stranraer at Penrith. I had planned a visit to the Lake District before going to Northern Ireland, feeling certain that I would need a quiet couple of days to rearrange my thoughts. But in the end I didn't flee from Belfast, I left with reluctance and somehow the contrast with the north of England's – or even England's – most picturesque patch was unsettling. I suppose you could call it culture shock. I found that the aloof tranquillity of the hills and mountains and vales and the aching placidity of the still lakes and woods made my thoughts turn time and again to the warmth, vitality and immediacy of those I'd met in Northern Ireland. The permanency of nature; its perfect seasonal rhythms grated against the transiency of human life, the friction of ideas and the rough and tumble of untidy lives.

I am not immune to the wonders of nature, but I am moved more when they take me by surprise. Driving to Kinlochbervie I was surprised; boating on Loch Erne I was surprised. But how could I be surprised in the Lake District, when writers have been evoking the area, often in stylized exaggeration, for more than 200 years? For a couple of days I became a tourist; the kind of tourist that potters around villages, has lunch on the lawns of pubs, and spends hours on boats chugging up and down Ullswater and Windermere. It was a visual feast and, sated with scenic beauty, I resumed my train journey to Newcastle; travelling from a place renowned for its loveliness to a place renowned as a 'waste land'.

The metro yielded my first impression of Newcastle; it's an impressive, extensive and integrated transport system that whizzes Geordies across their city with clean, swift precision. The stations are light and brightly painted and they have clever machines which, once you've told them where you want to go, tell you the cost of your journey and give you change. The metro raised my first question: how come a 'waste land' could afford such a lavish system? The answer began to crack open the myth that Newcastle is a depressing city in terminal decline, resigned to a never-ending retirement reminiscing about past prosperity and past eminence.

The metro was built in the early 1970s. It cost £200 million. Edward Heath's Conservative government was looking for a home for a new, experimental, fully integrated system where with one ticket passengers could hop on buses, trains and ferries and crisscross the city. Newcastle lobbied to be chosen: it was an area of low car ownership, the railway lines were already in existence, running each side of the Tyne to the coast; and the city acted as a regional centre with people travelling some distance to both work and shop. They won the prize and with it a clutch of grants to help pay the cost. If you mention Newcastle to transport planners around the world, they say, 'integrated public transport system', they don't say 'waste land'. That label is for home consumption, awarded by people in the south who never travel north.

What a pity the metro was not on the political agenda in the early 1960s. If it had been, if the politicians then had the sense to see that good public transport was the answer to traffic congestion in towns, then decision-makers might have resisted the temptation to give priority to the motor car and plaster our cities with concrete motorways. If they'd had the wisdom to ignore car lovers and car builders, I might not have got lost.

Stepping out of the metro at Jesmond, I stood and gawped. The road was bisected by a huge concrete arch and I could not see how to cross to the other side. I started to walk and stopped to ask a passer-by if I was going in the right direction. No, he said, you should have turned the other way outside the station. I retraced my steps and walked in the opposite direction, stopping once again to seek reassurance that I was on the right track. No, said the woman, you should have turned the other way outside the station! I cursed the kind of people who can never admit that they don't know the answer to a question and instead, with all the confidence in the world, give the wrong instructions. I also cursed the car and all those in love with gear levers; it was *their* motorway that had impeded my path.

When I finally arrived outside the boarding house that I'd telephoned from the railway station, I was shown up to a tiny room at the top of the house. From the window all I could see was the concrete arch and all I could hear was the hum of traffic. I heard myself saying, 'No, thank you,' to the room. 'It's too close to the motorway.' The owner didn't try to change my mind. Instead she suggested I call further down the street where a friend had a similar house. I did. The Riley family were most welcoming. The room was again at the top of the house, but the motorway was out of sight.

'We have some lovely boarders,' said Mrs Riley. 'The Royal Shakespeare company always stay here on their tour to Newcastle. Lovely, they are, good little drinkers. They always come back after the show and have a few. You'll love the breakfast. We do a "full house" – eggs, bacon, sausage and tomatoes. We always get fresh eggs from the country and we always pay a few pence more for the best bacon. The evening meal is at 6.30.'

The room was tiny and the double-bed practically filled the space. There was a cracked basin, a red chair covered in cat hairs, a gold-and-green carpet and pink-and-brown curtains. Everything looked weary: the colours had clashed for so long they were drained by the fight. A shower cubicle was sited on the landing outside my door and when it was in use my basin belched with indigestion. The towels were tiny; there was an electric bar on the wall to provide warmth and the only plug (which I needed for my hair-dryer) was hidden, cringing above the skirting-board, suffocated by the bed. And when I pulled the bed out to reach it, a layer of dust met my eyes. It was a regulation English boarding house. I'd been told that Tourist Boards around the country were doing their best to improve standards of such places; perhaps they hadn't reached Jesmond Road or perhaps they had and had decided, as I did, that the friendliness of the Rileys more than compensated.

I settled speedily into my room, eager to walk the streets of the city centre and discover whether the metro was a mirage, or a monument to misspent money – a fine example of regional aid as temporary balm rather than a pathway to a permanent cure for the disease of economic decline. Such a cure is not easy. As with Glasgow, the Industrial Revolution made Newcastle wealthy. It has always been strategically important. The Romans gave it a fort; William the Conqueror's son gave it a castle, a new castle, from which it took its name; and coal gave it wealth, aided of course by its position at the head of the Tyne River. Coal, iron, steel, glass were all exported in bulk from this city; ships in huge quantity were built along its banks. All that began to crumble between the wars; it was briefly revived during the last war, but since then decline has continued. When the party began thousands flocked to Newcastle for work; when the party was over thousands left again, either reluctantly or gladly, but many could not and would not move.

I turned left outside the front door, and left again, past the Playhouse Theatre, past the Civic Centre. When I came to a bookshop called Thorne's I went inside. It was huge, a reminder that this is a university town. I browsed and thought of J. B. Priestley. He'd included Newcastle in his *English Journey*, 'a rambling but truthful account of what one man saw and heard and felt and thought during a journey through England during the autumn of 1933'. It was raining when he arrived and he had a cold and was full of self-pity (even though for the most part he was chauffeur-driven and stayed in decent hotels). In this mood, he cursed his publisher in London who, he speculated, had just finished another good lunch and was about to arrange for some other poor author to leave home for months on end. Having wallowed awhile, he set out to find the one person in the city whose name he knew. He was a bookseller specializing in rare books and first editions. This chap (who was never given a name) took Priestley under his wing. The two were inseparable for a couple of days. He took Priestley to a boxing match; to a pub where they were rehearsing a Greek tragedy in the rooms upstairs; and he introduced him to Bob, who worked long hours for £2 a week and who had risen above the beer and betting mindlessness of his mates to spend his spare time helping at the People's Theatre and the centre for the unemployed. Bob saw the 'workers' as incapable of selfishness, indolence or corruption and employers as cunning tyrants; he saw the world in black and white, which gave Priestley a fine opportunity to try and paint in some shades of grey.

I continued my walk. A group of Chinese children were playing on the pavement, outside a Chinese takeaway. Two were using an empty Coke can as a football, and two were using an empty Coke can as a tennis ball, which they batted to and fro between miniature tennis rackets. Teenagers hung around in groups eating McDonald's products – chips in paper cups, minced beef and cheese encased by a bread bun laid to rest in a polystyrene cradle. Their hairstyles were intriguing. Some were just well cut, but others were grossly exaggerated, sticking up into the air cockerel-like and often multi-coloured. The sight of them caused me to remember that Geordies have a reputation for being trend-setters. Marketing men love the city, they say it is a good place to test new products because the kids loved trying stylish new things. They discovered this by coming up from London to tramp the streets with clipboards, stopping to ask teenagers all manner of questions. Rumour has it that 40 per cent of those stopped told the clipboard bearers that they thought designer clothes were worth the extra money *and* that they loved to try new things. The clipboard bearers went back south to London and wrote: 'In Newcastle there is intense awareness of cult fashions among the young.' And as a result Newcastle was the first to get hair-styling mousse and gel.

I took Grey's monument as the centre of Newcastle. Lord Grey, as prime minister, fought with much difficulty to get the 1832 Reform Bill passed, and this monument was erected in memory of him and of that occasion. He looks down upon an array of wide Georgian streets, beautiful streets; streets of great dignity; streets that hark back to a time of great confidence. Like Glasgow, many of these once-grimy buildings have been sandblasted clean. Cynics suggest that Newcastle waited to do this until there was no industry left to make them dirty again. But this was a coal-mining area, and the miners took home free coal to heat their houses and therefore no local decision-maker dared to adopt the Clean Air Act which forbade the use of anything other than smokeless fuel. In the early 1980s there were few miners to enjoy free coal, the Act was implemented and the sandblasters moved in.

The shops in this area surprised me. I expected them to be forlorn and empty and they turned out to be numerous and glossy and bustling. There's a story that one branch of Rumbelows, a store selling electrical goods, had sales which topped those throughout the rest of the country and won the staff a free trip on Concorde. And that's not all. As well as the Georgian streets with their shops, there's a modern intruder called Eldon Square. It's an undercover shopping centre. If you want to go shopping when it is raining, I suppose it has some merit. A thing of beauty it is not.

For many years, with or without Eldon Square, Newcastle was seen as *the* shopping centre for the north-east region, which is why the centre is so much bigger and more bustling than I'd expected. It services a very large area. Now, believe it or not, there's a rival on the other side of the Tyne, in Gateshead. It's called the Metro Centre and it has a vast parking lot, an indoor fun-fair, a cinema, American trees and shops, shops and shops. It was built by John Hall, a former coal-board surveyor turned property developer. Mr Hall courts publicity and the media is happy to oblige. Poor-boy-makes-good has always been an attractive tale; even more so in the 1980s. Some of this publicity has suggested that Hall is one of Mrs Thatcher's favourite entrepreneurs; *he* is what *she* is all about.

Hall's father was a miner and a life-long Labour party supporter. Hall, who left grammar school at sixteen, believes that the Labour party has failed to keep up with people like him: 'Labour is backward

with that damn philosophy which makes people believe they're op-
pressed and that they can do nothing for themselves.' I intended to go
over the water to see the Metro Centre site, but I never got there.
(Since then I have seen it several times on television.) I dislike shopping
malls and I hate shopping. It is a necessary evil and not a hobby. I
realize that for many people it is pure pleasure, a jolly day out. If such
people had an entry in *Who's Who* it would under 'Recreation' read:
'going around the shops'.

Defoe would be speechless. In London, in the early eighteenth
century he spotted a brightly decorated pastry-cook's shop with a glass
window in which 'trifles' were displayed. He was displeased. How
could a shop spend precious money on its appearance – it was a
stepping-stone to ruin! And if he thought pastries were 'trifles', what
would he have made of electric toothbrushes and gadgets to squeeze
oranges and all the other daft consumer luxuries? He'd think – quite
rightly – that we'd got our priorities wrong.

The north-east has one of the highest unemployment levels in
England; it's around 20 per cent. I can't be more specific. Who has
confidence in the government's statistics anymore? The basis on which
the unemployment figures are worked out has changed six times since
1979. I've never heard a justification for all these changes that sounded
convincing. The Labour party argues that the changes were made for
one reason alone: to hide the true figures. They no longer include the
sixty-year-old who hasn't got a job and is unlikely to get one before he
reaches sixty-five. They no longer include sixteen- and seventeen-year-
olds because they are on training schemes. Whatever the true figures,
there's no disputing one fact – the north-east has one of the highest
unemployment rates.

Jeremy Beecham, the leader of Newcastle council, has a hard task.
Potential investors down south are reluctant even to make the journey
north, so he makes the journey southwards and talks and talks trying
to convince the City to travel to Tyneside and discover for themselves
that it isn't a waste land, an area beyond hope: that it is dying for the
opportunity to respond to new ideas. Mrs Thatcher decided to help.
After the 1987 election victory she became determined to leave her
mark upon the 'Inner Cities'. The result is the Newcastle Initiative, a
blueprint for inner-city revival. A group of agencies is busy promoting
the virtues of life in the north and backing projects to revive theatres,
tart up tatty bits of the city, cheer up council estates and transform the
banks of the Tyne. All this face-lifting is intended to create a new
northern image and that new image is meant as bait to encourage those
who can create jobs. It is said to be working; something called the

Great North Conference took place, and it was announced that by 1991 the Japanese would have invested £700 million, and that two officials from a Chinese bank were said to be interested in property and manufacturing industries. Oh yes, and British Telecom was considering a project or two. At least the journey from London is considered worthwhile.

But until these overtures reach the finale, who is doing all this shopping; who is breaking all these retail records? The answer is too simple; most of those in work, say, 80 per cent of those in work – those with decent wages – have never had so much money to spend. They're flush. A good number of them have money to spare for the first time in their lives and are relishing their new-found freedom to spend. Who can blame them? But what of the rest? If we say that the unemployment rate in Newcastle is 20 per cent and that 20 per cent of those in work are poorly paid, that leaves 64 per cent who have money to spend. It also leaves a sizeable under-class with no money to spend and, as my long walk ended, I decided that rather than face another 'Bill' with an 'Aunt Maggie' I would find a council estate and a school and see how the pupils were being prepared for a world where work was precious. These youngsters are the unlucky ones, born during the baby boom of the heady sixties to emerge from school in the eighties into a dramatically slimmed workforce. Those born in the seventies were substantially fewer and when they emerge in the 1990s they are likely to be *courted* by employers.

Fifteen years ago Longbenton Estate had a poor reputation. It was like a battleground, with trees torn up, cars abandoned, holes in the road which the council did not mend and graffiti-scarred buildings. There were gangs roaming the streets known as Longbenton Aggro Boys – or LBABs for short. Today the picture is much more pleasing. The council has been slowly renovating the estate, rewiring the dwellings and adding central heating and modern kitchens. Outside porches have been built over front doors to add a little character to faceless houses, and fences have been erected around front gardens.

Longbenton Community High School stands at the end of Hailsham Avenue. I chose to visit it because I had only the haziest idea what the word 'community' meant, and the estate itself was said to have an unemployment rate reaching 40 per cent. John Burn has been headmaster since 1979. He's large, laid-back and extremely likeable, and in true Geordie fashion made me feel most welcome. He claims a working-class background – his father was a clerk – and after grammar school he went to Bristol University to read chemistry. 'I always wanted to become a teacher. I felt it was unjust that I had got to grammar school and most of my friends had not. But the grammar school was not friendly. The top stream kids did well, but no one bothered much about the rest, and I got the firm impression that the teachers did not like the kids. I wanted to change all that.'

Outside his study are two large photographs, one of the first pupil to go to Oxford, in 1983, and one of the first pupil to go to Cambridge, in 1984. That's no mean achievement on an estate where most of the parents left school at the first opportunity for labouring jobs or, at best, apprenticeships. His first task was to break down the resistance to higher education: to make parents see the power and importance of staying on at school beyond the age of sixteen, let alone aiming for Oxbridge. Now 50 per cent of his pupils enter the sixth form, two thirds for A-levels and one third for business studies and other vocational training. 'I tell them that if they leave at sixteen they are unlikely to get a job of any kind, and that if they stay until eighteen they have a better chance. I work hard to persuade as many as possible to go to university or polytechnic. Jobs for those with no qualifications are vanishing by the day. No, I'm not depressed by the unemployment picture. I can see how young people are reacting positively by staying on at school and becoming better qualified and aiming for university. That's good. I watch them growing in confidence. It's as simple as that.'

But it can't be that simple: if youngsters leave at sixteen and take a training course they stand to get paid around £27 a week and they are not paid to stay in the sixth form. But Burn has done his job so thoroughly that most families, both parents and children, are prepared to forgo these early gains; training courses do not invariably lead to jobs, neither does further education, but at least they enable youngsters to cope better with life. Acquiring the status of community school has helped. When Burn arrived the school was a 9 o'clock to 4 o'clock factory, and he was determined to change that by seeking official recognition as a community school, a school that is open from 9 a.m. to 9 p.m., six days a week, one that serves the community and not just a small group of young people. It's a lengthy process and he started by improving the school's sports facilities. With a grant from the Sports Council he improved the options and slowly began enticing non-pupils to use them. Then the school hall was hired out for birthday parties and golden-wedding celebrations and gradually the school itself became a focal part of the community rather than a feared institution. Pupils who rush off to taste the world of work and find it disappointing are encouraged to return and seek qualifications. The middle-aged, whether mums who have brought up families, or dads who need to change course, are to be found in the daytime A-level classes alongside sixteen-year-olds. In the evenings the school bustles with classes from cookery to mathematics. John Burn believes that education should continue throughout life. He does not see it as something to be grabbed at until the age of twenty-one and then abandoned. He is the kind of man who gets invited to Downing Street and to sit on committees. His school costs money, perhaps several hundred thousand pounds a year more than a traditional school because of the need to have extra administrative hands, a recreation officer and a crèche. He reckons that much of that is recouped because the school is never vandalized. When he first arrived the place was broken into every month and videos, typewriters and televisions were stolen. Now, he says, the school belongs to the community and, on the whole, the community does not vandalize something that *belongs* to them.

I listened. I wanted to believe every word he said. He gave the impression that unemployment had a silver lining; it was building a better world, a world in which children valued education. He gave the impression that at his school youngsters, as well as courting qualifications, were encouraged to cultivate interests so that they saw the world in wider terms than 'going around the shops' and stuffing their homes with objects. He gave the impression that the threat of unemployment could finally rid this country of its infamous position as one of the worst educated of the industrialized nations. The figures are a disgrace. In Britain only 31 per cent continue with full-time education to the age of 18 (an increase of three per cent since 1979), and a further 7 per cent continue part time. In America the figure is said to be *84 per cent* and in Japan *94 per cent*. If Longbenton Community High School on a council estate in the north of England can encourage 50 per cent of its pupils to see education as something valuable, valuable in economic terms and valuable in personal terms, then we are on our way! Can it be true? Since time immemorial Britain has underplayed education; for decades those who have been busily analysing the country's decline have argued that lack of education is as much to blame as anything. Could it be that it has taken a hefty dose of unemployment to see the wisdom of these words?

I said yes immediately to Burn's offer to wander through the school and talk to the pupils, or, as they are called, students. Paul, a teacher, took me into his lesson, which went under the grand-sounding title, 'Personal and Social Development', and, explaining my presence, asked the class, at my suggestion, to write down on a piece of paper what their aims are for the future and what they most feared. The response was as heartening as John Burn had led me to expect. All these youngsters came from working-class homes. The girls in particular showed that they had accepted the message that education was to be prized. There was Lyn, who had a modest ambition to become a hairdresser or beautician but who intended to get A-levels in biology and chemistry first. There was Elaine, who had a similarly modest ambition to become a medical secretary but who intended to do maths and English A-levels and, if those results were good, she might just be persuaded to go to university.

The boys predictably were somewhat less mature and tended to let their written answers be jokey. Paul wrote that he wanted to be very, very rich so that he could watch television all day and have a villa in Spain; Christopher said he wanted to win the Tour de France and join the Navy; and Tommy said he wanted to be free of debt, have a nice home and a wife whom he could trust. Under questioning, even those who said that they wanted to leave school at sixteen admitted that if they failed to get a job they would turn right round and come back to Longbenton. What they feared provided a common thread: they feared a world without work.

Paul was pleased. His enthusiasm for widening the horizons of his pupils was as potent and infectious as his headmaster's. 'What we are trying to do is to get the kids to believe in self-empowerment. We want them to believe that they have control over their own lives and that with effort they can do anything. This area has no tradition of further education, but we are overcoming that. It also has no tradition of self-employment, so we try to show them that it is a viable alternative to being an employee.'

In the afternoon I was invited to take over the A-level sociology group. I was nervous. The class lasted two hours and I made a point of asking the teacher to return after an hour to check that all was well. I'm not sure what I feared; I suppose I feared that two hours was too long for me to hold the attention of a dozen seventeen-year-olds. What I didn't realize was that schools these days encourage their pupils to *talk*; encourage them to have views of their own and encourage them to believe that their views are interesting and important. Twenty years ago we sat behind desks and were talked *at*; we were never asked our opinions about anything and if a stranger had come into the room and started asking questions, we'd have been tongue-tied and embarrassed. Maybe it is true that young people leave school nowadays with a poor grasp of syntax and an inability to spell, but they are infinitely more articulate and aware of the world around them.

The two hours sped by. The group contained one mature student, Margaret, a former nurse who, now that her children were grown up, wanted to return to work and found the thought intimidating. She decided that an A-level or two would prove that her mind still worked. She had just received the results of a mid-way A/O exam and had got a grade A. There had been three mature students at the beginning of the course. A man had dropped out and the other woman had made it to the A/O exam and was having second thoughts. The younger students much appreciated being mixed with an older age group; it made them think that there must be something to this 'education' if the middle-aged return for more. And Margaret felt that she benefited from the presence of younger people because she had to fight to keep up.

Longbenton has an 'open' sixth form. That means that anyone who wants to take an A-level can do so even if the teachers think they are quite likely to fail. That may not be so good for published records of exam results, but it is good for the students. This group contained a twenty-one-year-old who had left the school some years before, worked in a supermarket and hated it and now felt in need of further qualifications. Another had done a one-year business-studies course and then decided to embark on a two-year A-level course. A third boy had seen his father go 'south' in search of work and was determined to get his A-levels and try the police force as a career. There was a quiet blonde girl who didn't talk unless I specifically addressed her. She wanted to be a solicitor but had great doubts about her ability. (The school shared her doubts, but there was no way they were going to tell her.) A rather perky blonde told me she worked in a Wimpy Bar two evenings a week and on Saturday. She hated it but needed the money to spend on clothes and to be able to put petrol in her mother's car. A third girl said her boyfriend had told her she placed too much importance on this word called 'work'. He'd been unemployed for two years. And lastly there was an impressive young girl who started the whole afternoon off on the right foot by opening the discussion with a moving account of how her father had died, leaving her mother, a born-again Christian, her sister, a university student, and her brother who hadn't done a day's work in seven years. Attempts to get him to return to school had failed; he was tired of competing with his sisters.

All of them also feared a future without work. Each of them knew full well what that meant; they'd seen it at close quarters either through their parents or their brothers and sisters. Unemployment was, it seemed, a regular topic of conversation among them and with their teachers. They wanted work because they wanted money and a sense of purpose.

Stimulated by what I'd learned, I headed for the failures. This school has them just like any other. But instead of ignoring them they have a club for the unemployed; for those who have left school and failed to get jobs. They use the premises to keep in touch with each other, to gossip, to play snooker and table tennis and to take advantage of the fishing trips that are organized. The club is run by another Paul. He'd left school four years before for a job as a supermarket cashier, which he had hated and abandoned. He'd been unemployed for more than two years before he was asked to run the club. He is paid by the Community Programme, £63 for twenty-one hours a week. He has a council flat: 'I got that through someone I know. That's how we get things around here, jobs too.' He liked nice clothes and he wore seven rings. He was well dressed the day some while back when he went to sign on and was hauled in. 'They asked me straight if I was fiddling because I was so well dressed and my hair was well cut. I told them my girlfriend was a hairdresser. They fielded that one by pointing out that they now knew my face and would be looking out for me. And I answered by saying, "How long do you intend to keep me here? I've got to go windsurfing." "How come?" they said. "It's free at my old school," I said. I remember the look on their faces! To be truthful, I was shocked. One of my mates had been caught and got six months in prison. I thought someone had been ratting on me and I was worried about my flat. That's when I decided I'd better look around for something.'

We all laughed. That day's local paper had a story about fifteen men, all employed by the same security firm, who had been caught working while claiming the dole.

Paul then asked me if he could put his feet up and relax. 'All of us here will be absolutely honest with you, but if you identify any of us we'll simply deny that we said anything and accuse you of making it all up. OK?' OK.

Wayne (1) had left school three years before at the age of fifteen. He has a wife and a three-year-old daughter. At first he'd worked with his father in a fish-and-chip shop, then he became a labourer on a building site, then he'd taken a welding course and since then he has had a two-year spell of unemployment. He takes any work that comes along.

'There's this darkie that gets me jobs. He comes to my house and pays me in the hand and that's all I want to know. I get some kind of work most months. Last time I had to drive down to Peterborough and pick up £10,000 worth of shop fittings, bring them back and work until all the fittings were up. I started at 9 a.m. on a Tuesday and finished on Wednesday at 3 p.m. I got 85 quid for that. We get £53.15 a week for the three of us plus £28 a month for the child. I manage to run a car. The dole will do me. I've been to Scotland for ten days with the fishing club. I play a lot of rugby and the blokes there say they could get me a job for £80 or £90 a week, but I'm not touching anything under £150. Yeah, sure I'd like a steady job, on the railways maybe, but I'm not working for slave wages. I can manage on the dole, but it's not like having a decent wage. Those in work can spend 30 quid on a night out. I can't do that.'

Wayne (2) had left school seven years before. He was twenty-three and had ten jobs at the last count. For nine years, from the age of eleven, he had done a milk round, and had left school to do it full time, but when his friend sold the round the job had ended. All the other jobs – gardening, painting and decorating – had been poorly paid. Now he cleans a few windows when he needs a bit of extra money.

The other four Waynes had much the same story to tell. They had no qualifications and no inclination to get any qualifications. They despised poorly paid jobs and were prepared to live on the dole plus as many cash-in-hand jobs as they could pick up without Social Security officials becoming suspicious. I wondered if they wouldn't soon get sick of this kind of life. They thought they might as they grew older, but it hadn't happened yet. They were resilient, unambitious, street-wise and very entertaining company. They looked fit, through rugby, tennis, football, windsurfing and snooker, and seemed happy enough. They certainly didn't moan. They had each tasted work, low-grade stuff and didn't like it. They were not frightened by the dole. They were not frightened by the future.

J. B. Priestley came across a club for unemployed youth on his travels. The organizer, a man called Bob, was trying to get them interested in rehearsing for a concert party. Bob had little sympathy for the boys because, unlike older men, these youngsters did not 'fret' about lack of work. There was no loss of self-respect, no anxiety in them. They seemed undisciplined and carefree. They were below the level of worry. Priestley commented: 'They were not citizens, though some of them soon would be husbands and fathers. If the time ever came when they had to work hard and to obey orders, it would find them resentful and untrustworthy. Having grown up in one kind of world they would be puzzled and probably annoyed by any other kind of world. They knew nothing about responsibility. They are the new playboys of the western world . . . the dingy butterflies of the back-streets.'

My backstreet butterflies were not dingy.

I walked down Hailsham Avenue in the best of moods. I'd expected to find Newcastle depressing and it was not. I'd expected to find the students at Longbenton Community High School a little resentful of a world that seemed to offer them so many problems at such a young age. Instead they seemed to understand the nature of this current bout of unemployment; when we'd discussed what was causing it they seemed only too glad that the world was ridding itself of back-breaking jobs which needed merely muscle power and which caused ill-health and enslaved men to a funless life of long hours of work and free time in which they were too tired to play. The world of their fathers. The future had to be better than that.

Although the community school movement is several decades old, there are still very few such schools. I hadn't seen a 'typical' school; I'd seen a school that fired my imagination. Why are we so slow to catch on to such a good idea? Presumably because there are too few headteachers and too few teachers with vision and stamina. And that's not surprising, when teachers are treated like detritus while merchant bankers get rich. Why shouldn't teachers be among the most highly regarded and the most highly paid? Headteachers in state schools can aspire to £30,000 a year, but most achieve a modest £20,000, and only in the last year has training for headteachers been available, yet practically every piece of research has shown that a good headteacher is the most essential ingredient. Teaching must become a prized profession with good teachers being well rewarded. The country can easily afford it. It's useless to keep tinkering with the system, with what children learn and how and where they learn, unless there's an adequate supply of top-quality teachers. And we've been tinkering away non-stop since the 1944 Education Act first offered free secondary education to everyone.

In 1944 a system was laid down on certain crude assumptions. And those assumptions were that since we need only 'X' per cent of professionals to keep the country going, then only 'X' would be selected through examination at the age of eleven to go to grammar schools. The rest could go to secondary modern schools where the brightest of that bunch could form a pool of skilled manual workers and the others, unskilled, could be relied upon to do the donkey work. The great charm of this system was its honesty in recognizing that that was the way society worked. The justification for such rigorous selection at such a young age was that the examination was open to everyone and that the poorest could just as easily end up in grammar schools. But then educational researchers got to work and proved that those from poor homes did not in sufficient number reach the grammar schools. The middle classes hogged the places and the working class were consigned to the stigma of failure. The system was divisive and had to be changed.

I well remember the day I heard that I'd failed the 11-plus. There was no mistaking the importance of that examination nor the feeling of failure. I spent two years in a secondary modern school before passing the 13-plus and moving to the local girls' grammar school. At that point one would have thought the problems would have ended. But 13-plus successes were still thought of as 11-plus failures, not least because no languages were taught at secondary modern schools and I was dumped in the bottom stream of the year, where the standards were lower than the top stream in the secondary modern school. Within a year I had caught up two years of missing French and was moved up to the top class. I beat the system, but none the less felt that the introduction of comprehensive schools in the sixties was a step in the right egalitarian direction. Yet other changes were needed.

The hideous, examination-obsessed curriculum had to go. All that rote learning and memory testing had to give way to something more engaging; something that increased rather than curbed one's desire to learn. A new examination has been introduced which is far more practical and which encourages pupils to find things out for themselves instead of sitting behind desks being spoon-fed. Progress is assessed on a continuous basis and the marks gained form a substantial part of the final assessment. This prevents the short-term swots from getting away with it all and is a much more suitable apprenticeship for a working life, where one is expected consistently to give of one's best. Teachers complain, of course. They say the system involves much more work for them. Pupils complain. They say the system involves much more work for them. But almost everyone agrees that it is a fairer system. Before long the same thinking will have to be applied to A-level courses, for there is little point in abolishing the supremacy of memory-testing at sixteen and then reasserting it at eighteen.

So far so good, but the Thatcher government has gone much further. It has introduced a national curriculum designed to offer a broader education for everyone – science and a foreign language even for those who up till now have been considered too stupid to cope with such subjects – and with checks at seven, eleven, fourteen and sixteen to establish what children have learned. The Education Reform Act also aims to break local-authority monopoly of education by introducing a new tier of independent, state-funded technical colleges designed to improve our poor performance in both science and technology, and it gives power to parents to remove a school from the controlling hand of the local authority and be funded directly by central government. This is undoubtedly the most controversial measure; it is designed to enhance the power of parents, which is a good thing, but it is also designed to diminish the power of local authorities (as with housing reforms) and enhance the power of central government, which is not a good thing. No one could deny that local authorities needed a good shake, but to curb their complacent bureaucracy by adding hundreds more civil servants to the payroll of the Department of Education is merely displacing a problem rather than curing it.

This heady brew of change is enough to make anyone punch drunk. The Thatcher government has made much of educational reform. It will be some years before the results can be adequately assessed. Whatever one's political colouring, it is vital that the package improves both the quality and the quantity of education. I dwell on education because it is a subject of great importance: Britain's economic well-being now depends on having a properly educated workforce. It's also important for the country's social and cultural well-being. No country can afford to have an illiterate and socially uncivilized underclass with no communal sense. Folk not frustrated by ignorance enjoy better lives, they don't feel powerless, they demand more of the society in which they live, they strive for better homes and a better health service, and governments of whatever colour have to respond to such demands. No one should begrudge taxes being spent on education: we will all benefit if improved education, from nursery schools through to universities, is made available to more people.

Since the Labour party in the sixties missed the opportunity to abolish private schools, they are now – I think – with us to stay. Newcastle Royal Grammar School and its 1,000 pupils occupy a site within walking distance of my temporary home. Its headmaster is Alastair Cox. For years the school has offered places to boys who pass the entrance examination but whose parents cannot afford the fees of around £2,000. Some sixty boys a year benefit from such a scheme. In recent years however some of these assisted places have been awarded to fee-paying boys already in the school whose parents fall on hard times. Alastair Cox said that in the previous year or so twenty or thirty parents had been made redundant and had been forced to seek the school's help. It isn't only the unskilled who suffer in a world where working practices are changing so rapidly. None the less, the number of those affected is small; small enough for the school to ignore the topic of unemployment. Cox admitted that he did nothing to introduce the pupils to thoughts of a workless world. He had noticed however that the boys were more inclined to aim for careers in secure professions like medicine, the law and accountancy, and avoid such subjects as philosophy and the classics. Some 82 per cent of those leaving Newcastle Royal Grammar School head for a degree course at a polytechnic or a university; 9 per cent head for other kinds of further education; only 9 per cent go straight into the workforce. The figures speak volumes. Cox did not know what a community school was. I think I embarrassed him with my questions.

For me the visit added a vital piece to the jigsaw. I will never again be able to listen to a discussion about the widening gap between the north and the south of England without thinking of Newcastle Royal Grammar School. If Newcastle Royal Grammar School is able to ignore unemployment and two miles down the road Longbenton Community High School is obsessed with it, then we'd be doing the country a favour by talking *less* about the north–south divide and *more* about the real divide: the divide between rich and poor. To keep suggesting that the north has little and the south has much is to do a disservice to both. It paints both an unnecessarily gloomy picture of the north (that seriously deters potential investors) and an undeservedly golden picture of the south. It is a misleading basis for discussion.

On my last day in Newcastle I decided to pay a sentimental visit to Jarrow, to a place made famous by the 1936 March when 200 cloth-capped men walked into history and touched the nation's conscience, to a place which has done more than its share to promote a poor image of the north. The town still has high unemployment, but you don't see the abysmal poverty of the 1930s. There were no bare feet and no ragged children. What you see is an environment ransacked by the town planners. The old centre dominated by terraced houses has gone; instead there is a shopping-centre, a boring, blank-eyed shopping-centre, full of shops that take welfare tokens for clothing. The Co-op has the prime and the biggest site, closely followed by Comet Discount. The Freezer Centre windows covered with garish stickers shout their generous offers of meat-and-potato pies at 95 pence. The bread shop offers chip butties for 30 pence. The Job Centre offers work to a waitress for £1.98 a hour; and work to a chef for £5 a hour; and work to an exhaust-and tyre-fitter for £115 a week. John Ross and Sons, Estate Agents, suggest that an end-of-terrace house within reach of the town centre would suit a first time buyer at £12,500, and there's a semi-detached bungalow in a quiet position going for £35,000. The Venerable Bede's monastic church still stands. Bede is a great name in ancient literature, for he told us all we know about England down to AD 700. How many people associate him with Jarrow? He's over-shadowed by Catherine Cookson. Her sixty-odd books have sold some 80 million copies in seventeen different languages; that's 80 million people who see Jarrow and Tyneside through bug-infested walls, scrag-end of mutton for tea, drink-sodden men, and worn-out women.

At the metro station I paid my 55 pence for the ride back into central Newcastle and then found I could not persuade the ticket machine at the barrier to accept it. I tried another machine but the same 'Not valid' sign appeared. An elderly man was watching me. 'Just walk through that door there,' he said. 'The one that's marked for push-chairs: just shove it open. What are you doing paying for your ticket anyway? I've never bought one. You just walk in one door and then walk out the other. You've got to learn these tricks when you're not working.'

'But what about inspectors? What if you get caught?'

'Oh, you've got to keep an eye out for the inspectors, of course. But that's easy, there are always two of them together and when you see them coming, you get off. Once or twice they've caught up with me on the train and I've said that I was just about to get off and had dropped me ticket on the floor. Then I bend down and start looking for it and one of them'll say, "Hang on to your ticket next time." Best time to travel is the morning before 9 a.m., with the workers; the ticket inspectors don't start until after 9 o'clock anyway. I go everywhere free in the nice weather. I'm going to see my mate now for a cup of tea.'

I asked him how long it was since he'd worked: 'I'm sixty-three now and I was fifty-six when it happened. I was a driver with the electricity board and my left foot went bad. All I could offer was driving and I had no chance of another job with all these youngsters around. I manage. I have to economize. I have to watch the beer – I like a beer. And I shop around for bargains.' He reached into his pocket and pulled out a tiny packet of Virginia Gold tobacco. 'This costs £1.09 in Jarrow, but in a kiosk outside South Shields Station they sell it for 96 pence. That's a saving of 13 pence and remember, I don't pay for the train fare!'

We got on the train and sat together. He wore a cloth cap, a pullover under his jacket and carried a plastic bag. He smiled all the while as he told me his stories. George Orwell, writing of the struggles of the poor in the 1930s, said: 'Instead of raging against their destiny, they have made things tolerable by lowering their standards.'

Chapter 8

The Durham Moors:
Country Matters

The bus to Wolsingham took some time to track down. Repeatedly my request for a timetable met with a blank stare and a shake of the head. At the bus station in Jarrow I was lucky. The man behind the counter showed his dogs at the Wolsingham Show and knew all about the bus. It was a small single-decker that left from outside the Co-op in Newcastle. Its main function that Saturday morning was to bring in women from the dales for a day's shopping; on the return journey there were only a handful of us, including a woman who was going to spend a few days with her sister and who sat behind me and sucked sweets.

Within fifteen minutes the city had given way to the countryside, one of the reasons Tynesiders consider themselves fortunate. Before I could sink into contemplation of things rural, I spotted a road sign to Consett. Consett in 1980 became labelled as the first post-industrial town when British Steel closed its ironworks, putting nearly 4,000 men out of work. Since then the media from Britain, Europe and America have crawled all over the place making depressing documentaries and writing sad articles to sandwich between the glossy advertisements in newspaper colour supplements. I felt the place must be talked-out and resentful at being constantly associated with shops selling day-old pastries; it does nothing for their self-esteem nor for their efforts to attract new employers.

I believe, in time, when the new revolution is complete and new industries have relocated from the south – which is already happening – there will be dancing in the streets. After all, we hated the Industrial Revolution didn't we? Having started and exported the Industrial Revolution, having become the workshop of the world, having pioneered urbanization, we poured scorn on the satanic mills and sweatshops; we turned against industry and disparaged cities. I suppose we were right in the beginning to be suspicious of the massive upheaval that made a few men rich while the rest lived in mean homes and huddled into even meaner factories; the work was loathsome and life was ugly. But what a pity our Victorian ancestors did not curb the excesses of greed, insist on fairer shares and better working conditions, without turning up their snobby noses at the monster they had created.

I was in America in 1970 at a summer school doing a course or two in American studies when my mind first came upon these thoughts. A first-time visitor to America tends to be overwhelmed by the difference in attitude between our two countries and, while not eager to endorse all their attitudes, I was eager to understand the differences, particularly those relating to wealth creation and the acquisition of material goods. When I asked several American academics for their explanation they turned my thoughts to industrialization and how once Americans had discovered that it was the key to future prosperity they had no qualms about embracing its potential. They had no reasons to feel sentimental about their difficult rural past; they had no aristocracy they wished to ape.

On the other hand, we, in England, they argued, never came to terms with the Industrial Revolution, we never whole-heartedly embraced its potential, and our decline, surely, dates from the peak of our success, when we shied away from the future; when we saw enterprise as the enemy of stability and sought refuge in the rural past. For the most part all the Victorian entrepreneur wanted to do with his new-found wealth was to imitate the aristocracy; to buy land and become a 'gentleman' and send his sons to public schools. At such schools the sons of the newly wealthy discovered that industry and commerce were considered vulgar, and since the study of science, if indeed it was even offered, was associated with industry and commerce, they rejected it. Greek and Latin, they were told, was the key to a superior future administering our far-flung empire, or entering the professions of law and medicine.

At first I felt that all this was very much an American's eye view of our past, but since the early seventies several British academics have endorsed the thesis. I was on the road to Wolsingham to see if I could discover the deep attractions of rural life. I was born in a city and have no feeling for country life, and certainly no sentimental yearning to be either yeoman or squire. Green wellies have I none. I don't even listen to *The Archers*.

The bus dropped me right outside the show ground. I met Frank Collingwood in a tent under a sign saying NFU. We had made the arrangement during a series of phone calls and we looked at each other in that special way reserved for those who have talked just long enough on the phone to have formed a mental picture. And now we were checking the accuracy of our thoughts: Frank looked younger than I'd expected. He was busy manning the stand for another hour, which gave me time to explore on my own the first agricultural show I'd attended since I'd been a cub reporter in Wiltshire some twenty years before. Ignoring the sheep, since Frank would be teaching me all I needed to know about sheep in the coming days, I glanced briefly at the cattle and wandered through stalls selling farm tools and country clothing such as waxed coats – which have become fashion items for those walking their dogs on Hampstead Heath. I paused at a stall selling delicious-looking homemade truffles and finally came to rest among the prize-winning fruits, vegetables and flowers. The chrysanthemums were the focus of much discussion. I learned how their petals had to be coaxed downwards by gentle hands painstakingly winding them over cotton buds bought from Boots the Chemist. But that's as nothing compared to the sight of Frank's son Robert attending to the noses of his favourite sheep; dabbing on meths to make them shiny and using tweezers to remove surplus hair from inside.

We were to spend many hours at the show over the next two days. It's one of the highlights of the farming calendar; there were three such shows over three consecutive weekends, at St John's Chapel, Wolsingham and Stanhope. Needless to say there was a healthy rivalry between the three and needless to say village life for three weeks was completely geared to the shows; worries about the weather concerned the curtailment of fun rather than work. Frank's teenage sons, Robert and David, were showing swaledales – hardy sheep with intelligent, alert faces, well used to the exposed hills. The tweezers did it; a second prize was won and Frank's nephew Stephen won the championship in his class and that meant £30 and a cup which he had to fill with whisky or brandy and pass around. To fill the cup took up most of the prize money, but that is part of the fun. Indeed, drinking is an important aspect of show-going, and the members' tent was packed at all times, the noise indescribable, but at least the Geordie accents had softened. I spent a lot of time in that tent with Frank's wife Barbara, straining to catch the Weardale gossip. Frank's sister Dorothy and his sister-in-law Ivy both worked in an old-people's home and both had been told by the matron that they needed qualifications and that she'd arranged for them to spend one day a week in Darlington studying psychology and sociology. Neither was keen, neither could see the point, but felt they might lose their jobs if they resisted. I was introduced to the lady of the manor, who wasn't the lady of any manor, merely someone considered to be a bit of a toff. Five years ago, they said, she wouldn't have stopped to talk, but then she discovered she had no friends. There are five families like that in Weardale, who think themselves above the rest, I was told. They have no more land than anyone else, but they go out of their way to impress; on occasions like twenty-first birthdays they insist on formal dress. That was considered a joke.

Stewart Shields Meadow, Frank's farm, is a good thirty-minutes' drive from Wolsingham. Stewart Shields Meadow is exquisite. It is high up – 1,300 feet – above sea-level and almost at the top of the heather-clad moors. There are few trees. Once this land belonged to the Bishop of Durham and it was a deer park, but the bishop and the deer have long since gone and so have the trees needed to service wars and the Industrial Revolution. Now there's heather. That's all. The light does the rest; a few dark clouds and the scene is golden-brown and purple and sinister; a blue sky and the heather fades to mauve and the golden-brown gives way to half a dozen shades of green. At the top, at 1,700 feet, on a fine day you can see both coasts, Whitby Bay and Solway Firth. The farm borders Stanhope Common, which is more of the same exquisitely coloured, unadorned moorland. It has a melancholy beauty, not wild and rugged, but rounded and welcoming. Once again I was taken by surprise: I'd heard of the Yorkshire Moors, Heathcliff and Catherine had seen to that, but the Durham Moors were new to me and I was enchanted. The nearest house is six miles away. In the winter with snow on the ground it is easy enough to lose your sense of direction: there are no landmarks. You can find it again, if the snow isn't too deep, by brushing it aside and looking at the heather. It always leans to the east.

Stewart Shield Meadows covers 145 acres. Frank's great-grandfather came from Tyneside a hundred years ago as a tenant farmer. Frank's grandfather was not much interested in sheep farming; he worked all over the place, including Consett, and the property skipped a generation and passed to Frank's father, who was devoted to sheep. In 1930 he had the opportunity to buy the land and took the gamble. It cost £1,100, and in 1930 that was a huge sum; after all, it is a very isolated farm, which had no proper road then, no motor vehicles and no electricity. Frank's father bought two other farms of around 200 acres each before he handed over the reins to his two sons, Frank and Tom. As well as the land he owns, Frank has access to 8,500 acres of common land; thirty-four people have the right to use the land, and it is very important. The land he owns could not alone support his flock. Some 1,200 ewes graze on the common all year, being fattened, until they are ready to be sold to farmers in the south of England. And since

Frank's grandfather's day they have rarely used hired labour, only the family. Hired labour is something no one wants. When his own boys were still at school, Frank accepted a few boys on the government's training scheme. The government pays the wages and the boys come to learn a few things. It didn't seem to work too well. The boys on the whole were lacklustre and the government was so worried about their being misused that the contracts were restrictive. The boys, if they were so minded, were perfectly entitled to say: 'You can *show* me what to do, but you can't make me do it.' His daughter Marian used to help, but once the boys were available, she decided to work away from home at a trekking centre. She's of a mind to come home again now. The Collingwoods want to build an extension and take in bed-and-breakfast visitors for a few years and that would provide work for Marian. And in years to come the extension would provide a home for Barbara and Frank, when they were ready to hand over.

'I'll do that when I'm sixty. The boys will then be twenty-eight and thirty, and that's quite old enough. Some families go into partnership earlier, but there's no need for that here. I give the boys plenty of responsibility. I let them choose stock. We have 1,200 swaledales and ten blue-faced Leicester rams. Everything depends on the choice of rams. I'm an expert on rams and Robert is coming along.

'There's no doubt about it, both boys could earn a lot more than they do now by being in a factory. The same applied to me at their age. I was paid 50 shillings by my father, and my friends were earning £7 a week, but now I can say that I'm much better off than they are. The same goes for the boys. It's a slow start but a secure one. We pay them £80 pounds a week, but £30 of that comes back for their keep. And they have to work. This is *not* an eight hour a day, five day a week job. It can't be. Forty hours a week wouldn't put dinner on the table. During lambing, shearing and haymaking I work from 6 a.m. to 9.30 p.m. seven days a week. In between it's less, of course, but then you are on call twenty-four hours a day. Those who achieve the best results from farming don't have time to spend their money!'

Frank Collingwood didn't have much education. He didn't start school until he was seven because he was the only boy of that age up on the moors and they wouldn't provide transport for him. And while he was at school he missed a lot because in winter the weather made the road impassable. He left school at fifteen. In recent years, however, he's taught himself a great deal. He's had to, since he became a leading light in the NFU. It all happened by accident.

'I went to a meeting to hear the chairman of the Countryside Commission talk about a report on the Uplands. This area is well-drained. It was first done by Irish gangs during the last century when the land was needed for food during the Napoleonic wars, and it's been kept up since then. We get grants for it. The Countryside Commission don't like all this drainage. They say it's bad for the wildlife, that snipe and other creatures need "wet land". The chairman came to persuade us that draining is wrong. I told him that it had improved everything for us and he said that he had every sympathy with my point of view, but ... Well, I just got back on my feet and said: "My grandfather couldn't live on sympathy and neither can I." A great cheer went up and ever since then I've been put on various committees. I've had to do a lot of reading up. I've had to learn about milk quotas and common land becoming more available to the public, but it's been worth it.'

Farming is in a state of flux; some would not mince words and admit that it's in a state of crisis. It all began after the war. Before the war, in 1939, two thirds of our foodstuffs were imported, mainly from the empire. During the war, with help from the Land Army and rationing, we just about got through without fear of starvation. But after the war it was decided that we must never allow ourselves to come so close to the bone again. We had to become self-sufficient at least in the sort of foodstuffs that grow or can be produced in a temperate climate: wheat, barley, potatoes, beef, pig meat, poultry, eggs, cheese. And so we embarked upon a series of subsidies to encourage farmers to modernize and to grow more and more food. Over in Europe they had the same idea. During the war shortages were far, far worse and so in 1958, six countries signed the Treaty of Rome. One of its prime intentions was to ensure that they didn't stare starvation in the face again, plus the added desire to see that farmers, who formed 25 per cent of the workforce in the six countries, were able to enjoy the same standard of living as industrial workers. It was the beginning of the Common Market, the European Economic Community and the Common Agricultural Policy. The basis of the policy was price intervention, a system that guarantees that when the market price of foodstuffs falls below an agreed price, the EEC will buy up the produce offered to it at that price.

The CAP to which we became a party when we joined the EEC in the early 1970s is now a laughing-stock – a dangerous laughing-stock. The policy was so successful, the farmers grew so much, that there is now a food surplus; there are now mountains of butter and beef and cereals. Some of it is sold off cheaply to other countries, thus messing up their agricultural policies, and some of it finds its way to famine areas, but mountains remain in store. That wretched pendulum once again has swung too far. Who would have guessed that the combination of chemical fertilizers and clever scientists producing high-yielding wonder wheat and super cows producing gallons of milk would within forty years leave us with a problem? Well, one person guessed. His name is Sicco Manholt, one of the founding fathers of the EEC. He warned the EEC that it should start paring down the farming community and take marginal land out of use. He was ignored. Instead, in this country alone cereal production doubled between 1975 and 1985.

Only in the eighties, when two thirds of the EEC's budget was being gobbled up by intervention-buying and storage, did it become obvious that the policy of boosting production of unsaleable food surpluses was no longer tenable. And it was Mrs Thatcher who made the loudest noise, insisting that the community stopped ignoring the problem. In 1984 milk quotas were introduced, telling each country just how much milk they could produce and compensating farmers for their loss of income. These quotas have since been tightened further, and beef quotas have been introduced.

The government has cut back on agricultural research, which may or may not be a good thing, but it still leaves the fundamental question: what to do with 45 million acres of agricultural land in Britain. We clearly don't need it all. One answer is to pay farmers to leave land fallow, which has a certain appeal because it at least means that land is effectively 'on hold' in case circumstances change. Other answers would be irreversible, like freeing acres for development, and this the government, amid loud protests, has agreed to do. A further option is to encourage farmers to use some of their land for other purposes, like planting trees. In Britain woods and forest occupy only 10 per cent of our total land; in France it is 27 per cent and in West Germany 30 per cent. We still import some 90 per cent of our timber and timber products, adding millions to our imbalance of payments. The trouble with planting trees is that it takes years to yield a financial return – sixty years for conifer and perhaps 150 years for hardwoods. Farmers would need grants and tax concessions and the rest, but then the tax-payer would be happier paying for these than supporting the production of useless food. There's also tourism and recreation; encouraging farmers to provide picnic areas and bed-and-breakfast accommodation and horse riding – again, it's better than allowing them to churn out too much milk.

In the seventies when we joined the Common Market our farmers much benefited. Farming seemed so profitable that land prices rose; they went on rising until the early eighties, when all these food mountains made folk realize that something was wrong; land prices dropped by some 20 per cent. Those who'd borrowed heavily – and in the seventies money was thrown at farmers – found themselves facing bankruptcy. Some farmers tried to sue their banks for lending them so much. This makes Frank Collingwood laugh.

'They don't stand a cat's chance. They didn't do their sums properly. I'm a cautious man. It's like those yellow boxes on the road – I don't enter until the exit is clear. People are being silly if they mortgage their home. I've borrowed money for land, but not so's it would affect the house in which I live. I own this. And I'd never borrow money for buildings. A lot of that borrowing was for buildings. The grants seemed so good that people just went ahead and thought they could find the rest. But buildings make life easier, they don't help you to make money. My buildings are dilapidated and I'd love to have new ones, but I wouldn't borrow money for that.'

Frank's income after he's paid all expenses is around £20,000 a year. Since the farm is situated in what is known as a less-favoured area, he qualifies for support from both the EEC and the UK government and reckons that without this support his farm would not be viable. Some 20 per cent of his gross income is from subsidies. 'I'm approaching fifty; I own my house, I have a guaranteed income, I have freedom to work as I please and I can offer my sons a future. What more do I want?'

Frank feels no envy for the cereal barons who made fortunes during the 1970s. 'Our fortunes are linked to theirs; they are the main purchasers of our lambs, a lot go down south to be fattened up. Anyway, horn and corn tend to go in cycles; when corn is high, horn is low and vice versa. The beef men had a bonanza after the war because of shortages; then it was the turn of the cereal men, but that's all over too. The press like to concentrate on the big boys, the so-called barons, but most of the cereal men are small and it's a high-risk business. You only need one hurricane to flatten everything, and that can't happen to us.' Barbara feels the same. Their life is solid and sensible; they do not crave material goods or bright lights, their fun outside the three weeks of shows centres around the Grey Bull, where they will happily drink and talk the night away among people they know and who know them. Their sense of continuity and of family unity, of fathers providing livelihoods for their children, generation upon generation, is profound, and strikes an outsider forcibly. Barbara's dad was a fine example. He sat in a corner, watching television or reading cowboy books and eating sweets. He'd done more than his share of work – seven days a week as a tenant dairy farmer until he had a heart attack at sixty-three. Now his family cared for him; no one fussed and he made no demands. Such family closeness might raise questions in my mind, but at Stewart Shield Meadows it is unquestioned; it is the way of things. And I felt privileged to be a part of it for a short while. It was a welcome antidote to all those gloomy stories of the demise of family life in general and the fate of elderly people in particular. Some 15 per cent of the population is over sixty-five, and that percentage is rising each year; by the turn of the century there will be more than 1 million people over the age of eighty-five. Television's obsession with the problems of the elderly gives the impression that most of them are senile, stuffed into homes and sedated, when in fact more than 90 per cent live at home, cared for by friends and family. There will always be some families who cannot or will not cope with the elderly. The annual costs to the taxpayer of keeping such elderly people in private residential and nursing homes is £900 million. A massive increase compared with eight years ago, when the bill was £18 million. This sort of care, apart from being costly, is not ideal. Old people – unless they need twenty-four-hour care – are better off in their own homes with adequate back-up help. But such help is woefully thin on the ground. A report by Sir Roy Griffiths suggested that community care of the elderly should be firmly in the hands of local authorities. And not just care of the elderly, but also of those who were once incarcerated in mental homes and who are now filling faded seaside boarding houses that were emptied as affluent workers headed off on package tours to the sun. The report was cunningly published the day after the Budget in 1988 and was swamped by budget analysis. The government took eighteen months to accept Sir Roy's advice. The next battle is to find adequate funds for community care.

I discovered by accident that grouse shooting took place on the Durham Moors. My ignorance of this rich man's sport is such that I thought it happened only in Scotland. However, during all the drinking that went on in the members' tent at the show, I heard two women discussing their children's attitude to acting as beaters while the show was on. One women said that her son had said no because he'd miss too much and be too tired to enjoy the fair in the evening, and another said her daughter Helen was delighted because it would mean she had more money to spend at the fair. Once I heard that shooting was about to take place, I nagged Frank to get me an invitation. I wanted to go out with the Arab syndicate. They are famous in these parts for their generosity: beaters might get £50 a day from the Arabs rather than £10 from other syndicates. The reason they paid so much was because they came rarely and always at the last minute. Their gamekeeper was usually given only twenty-four hours' notice of their arrival. I settled instead for another syndicate where Frank knew the gamekeeper, Robbie Grey; an invitation proved to be no more than a phone call away.

My excitement that Saturday morning was childlike: I anticipated a long, healthy day outside on the moors seeing something I'd never seen before. We assembled just before 9.30 at Smith's Field. Robbi looked the part, in a greenish tweed suit, the jacket full of pleats and belts, plus-fours and socks peeking over long green wellies. There were others in gamekeeper suits, and they turned out to be from neighbouring estates and were, for the day, to act as loaders, who stand beside each 'gun' (the man doing the shooting), loading each of his identical twin guns in turn. They have to be identical so that they handle in the same way and the shooter is hardly aware of the change. Loaders get paid £20 a day and there were nine of them. There were around a dozen beaters and half a dozen flankers, each of whom gets paid £10 a day. The beaters are mainly teenagers from nearby villages; the flankers are experienced beaters who have moved up a grade. Then there were six older men with dogs, who were on hand to pick up the grouse; they get paid £25 a day. Two of them were characters: a former brigadier who had spaniels and who likes to be called 'sir', but no one takes any notice, and Albert, a former army sergeant, who breeds labradors. Their dogs like to compete. In all, there were 34 extras to service nine guns; I began to see why the sport was expensive.

As my eyes took in the scene, my ears were assailed by two voices, the kind of voices I had not heard for months. One belonged to Colonel May, a member of the syndicate that had rights to shoot on 8,000 acres of moorland so glorious that it had been designated an area of outstanding natural beauty. This was a 'let-day': the syndicate had let out their right to a group of farmers from Sussex and Hampshire who shoot together regularly, all manner of things, but grouse only once a year. Let-days are useful: they provide the syndicate with money to maintain the moorland, spraying the bracken so that it doesn't smother the heather. Colonel May had turned up to wish them well. He didn't stay long, but his son Charles was remaining all day, to keep a watch on things.

Robbie decided that I should begin the day as a flanker. The first two drives were exceptionally long, which meant a lot of walking for the beaters, and he felt that might be a little tiring for a newcomer; instead I could remain with him and I welcomed the chance to gossip. We set off over the moors in a convoy of Land Rovers, twelve in all. Charles May quipped that British Leyland would have been pleased with the sight. Half way, we stopped and doubled up. The convoy slimmed to six and I got in the back with a couple of flankers and a dog called Cindy. That didn't suit Charles May. 'Shove up,' he said to the passenger in the front seat. 'I don't want to sit with smelly dogs.' We stopped within sight of the shooting lodge. It took some time for this military operation to get in place. The guns, with their loaders, headed for the butts, a row of semi-circular waist-high stone walls, and waited while the beaters took up their positions in a line far out of sight but parallel with the butts. Robbie's son-in-law David was in charge of the beaters. They kept in touch through walkie-talkies. We, the flankers, waited too. Our task, once the beaters appeared on the brow of the hill, was to turn the beaters' line into a horseshoe, thus filling the gap between the two.

'Am I about to witness wholesale slaughter?' I asked Robbie. 'Wholesale slaughter? – No. Shooting grouse is not easy, the odds are stacked in the birds' favour. They have every chance to turn and fly away once they hear the first shot, and even if they don't do that they have every chance of getting through. They'll be flying at seventy miles an hour up there. It takes a skilled gun to get a hit at that speed. It has to be done you know; the grouse need culling, otherwise they get all manner of disease – nature's way of keeping the population down is far more cruel than man's.'

They came at last, marching over the brow of the hill like soldiers waving white flags of surrender. I heard a whistle, the signal to the guns that they could shoot; I heard a 'pop', the first shot, and then we started walking at a fair speed through the knee-high bracken. I waved my white flag dutifully to frighten any grouse that fancied a last minute get-away. A few did; they swirled overhead and changed course without any sign of panic. Others flew onwards, dicing with death. It was all over then, all that waiting for the sound of 'pop', 'pop', 'pop'. As we approached the butts, the guns – the farmers – began to saunter off, chatting among themselves. It would be ages before the next drive was in place, and they spent the time back at the Land Rovers drinking sloe gin and champagne. The drinking is all part of the shooting. I wandered off to watch the grouse being picked up. I stopped to talk to a couple of beaters; young boys who were sitting on the top of a butt, holding a grouse. They were squeezing its head between thumb and forefinger and watching blood ooze from its mouth. 'What the hell are you doing?' I said without thinking. 'Squeezing its head to see how young it is. If its skull is still soft then it is a young one.' 'How disgusting,' I said and they smiled without a trace of guilt. 'It's dead,' they answered.

'Here! Here! Here!' shouted a girl's voice. And again, more urgently, 'Here!' She thought she'd found a half-dead grouse and was calling for a gun to finish it off. A loader came running and as it did so the grouse took off, spread its wings and flew away. The sensible bird had been hiding in the heather. It was a cheering sight and helped to wipe away the previous image. Then we found a dead snipe. I held it in my hands; I hadn't seen a snipe at such close quarters. 'Upset you, does it?' 'No, not at all,' I lied. It would take more than a couple of hours for me to feel a kinship with the sport. I moved over to the Land Rovers and decided to sit down for a while; it would be ages before I was needed. A farmer stopped by and held out a packet containing bits of pork crackling. I hate pork crackling, but I accepted a piece. It was a friendly gesture. 'Here, keep the packet,' he said, and walked off.

The second drive was to be even longer than the first, and so once again it was decided that I should stay with the flankers. Charles May had discovered that I was no ordinary flanker and came to join me and chat. 'Got the hang of it?' 'No, not yet,' I answered truthfully. 'I'd better stay with you then.' We moved off to our next position and then sat in the heather to wait. Charles is a stockbroker and he lives just outside Newcastle. We gossiped about the Arabs.

'They've got so much money, they don't bother to have let-days. And that's a pity because it means that there are too many grouse around catching diseases. The Arabs fly up in little planes, bang, bang, bang, and fly away again.'

On the last drive before lunch I became a beater. Helen took me under her wing. She had just left school. She had got eight O-levels and began an A-level course but hated her teachers and quit. Now she was looking for a job as a wages clerk. She walked so fast I could hardly keep up with her, but after a while I got a decent pace going and was enthusiastically waving my flag, glad at last to be on the move and loving the melancholy moors. They had to be more beautiful than their Scottish counterparts, I decided, because they were not haunted by the memory of the Clearances. Amid such thoughts I heard a shot. I couldn't see the butts, because we'd yet to reach the brow of the hill. Once we did, there was trouble. Beverley, who had been marching at my side, had been hit by a pellet. It had whizzed past her, grazing her neck and leaving a red mark. David went to remonstrate with the farmers. It's Robbie's job to blow the whistle that is the signal to the farmers not to fire forward again. This chap had ignored the whistle. The culprit came over and said he was sorry. Beverley was philosophical; she shrugged her shoulders: it had happened before. I was shocked. 'There I was enjoying myself and not aware that my life was in danger!' The culprit reached out and touched my arm: 'Your life wasn't in danger. The pellets only burn the skin.' He moved off, and the other beaters crowded round Beverley and told her she was a fool not to have burst into tears. 'He'd probably have given you a fiver.'

At lunch time, I went down to the shooting lodge with my sandwiches in a plastic bag. The weather was so good that the farmers with their extensive hampers decided to stay with their Land Rovers and not move everything down to the lodge, which was in the hollow below, surrounded by rhododendron bushes and boarded up against vandals. It wasn't ritzy at all. There was one large, whitewashed room with a big table and chairs. There was an open fire which, lit on a cold day, must have been a splendid sight. The loaders and flankers were in the next room, which was scruffy and offered only a table and benches. Outside the male beaters sat on one side and the female beaters sat on the other. The conversation in the lodge was tedious. Most of it was about dogs and how they got lost on the moors and how they managed to stay alive for ten days.

I decided to spend the afternoon with a farmer; that way I would have seen the shoot from all angles. Allen agreed. He was a local farmer, loading for Ronald Langmead, a southern farmer. They'd known each other for ten years. Allen sold his sheep to Ronald. Ronald allowed me to hold his Holland, but that's all he would allow. I wanted to try to shoot, but he said it was unwise and he was probably right. We weren't using butts, we were down in a hollow and Ronald said it was more difficult and thus more sporting.

'Have you had a good day, so far?'

'Oh, I think we'll make seventy.'

'And how many have you shot?'

'A few. You know, we don't count individually. That's too competitive. We just count the total.'

They came; he fired; and fired; and hit something. Jenny, his dog, was ecstatic; she rummaged around until she found her prize and then came back and dropped it at Ronald's feet and looked up at him. He ignored her.

The shoot was over. Since I had got no further than fondling a gun, I had not been able to appreciate the excitement, the rush of adrenalin experienced by the farmers as they made their split-second decisions as to which bird was to receive their shot. I could appreciate their skill, but at the end of the day, I still did not understand the joy of killing. The day had been feudal in structure. The beaters, the flankers, the loaders, the pickers-up and the southern farmers each knew their place and there had been no mixing, unless mixing is offering someone a piece of pork crackling.

I decided to take a taxi to Darlington; the rural bus timetable took no account of someone needing to make connections with buses to Leeds and Bradford. The local taxi driver, Keith, had said it would cost me £10, and that seemed a fair price to pay to be rid of a slow and all too complicated cross-country bus ride. Frank ran me down the hill to Stanhope to meet Keith at the petrol station. As we drove up, I saw them. They were filling up their Land Rovers with petrol. They were dressed in country tweeds, but their headgear gave them away. The Arabs had arrived for a day's shooting.

Keith was thirty-three and unemployed. He'd done all manner of jobs, but mining was his favourite because it paid the most. So he knew about coal and minerals and building tunnels. 'There's no mining jobs in Weardale now. It's all gone. We used to mine for fluorspar, a lead off-shoot used in the steel-making process, but steel's gone, so it's gone. The Third World can provide all the steel now; they've got opencast mines, so they can get at coal and stuff cheaper, and Weardale can whistle. Serves us right, really. I saw what went on down the mines, particularly at the lower management levels. And the workers were as bad, we saw that some of their practices were stupid; robbing the mines they were, taking stuff out the cheapest way, which is OK in the short term, but in the long term it meant the mine wouldn't be usable. We all knew what was happening, but we were all too frightened for our jobs to make a fuss.'

Keith's wife works for the council as a secretary. 'It's OK for the moment. For years I've been earning four times what she earns, but it does cause tensions and rows over housework. I keep myself busy helping friends, like today, driving the taxi. They ring if they need me. Fortunately, I've paid off the mortgage on my house. All that inflation in the seventies helped, you know. Inflation is a real friend to the working man trying to buy a house. A house is the biggest worry in the working man's life, and inflation helps him get through. He keeps pushing up his wages to cover inflation *and* he finds his mortgage getting easier! I'm glad I own the house, but we don't think we can afford to have children, not until I get a job. Once, a few years back, there seemed so many jobs abroad for those who liked working underground, now all I get offered is South Africa and I'm not going there. It's all lifestyle, you know, they don't pay big wages, but they give you a house with a pool and I don't want that. I want big money and forget the pool.'

He asked what I was doing, so I told him about Frank and his family. 'I'm glad you saw it like that. I'm glad those sort of families still exist. But they are becoming rare, you know, even around here.

This generation, yours and mine, is different, you know. We've been spoilt, no wars, no worries, and we've become selfish. Ties are getting looser all the time. First it was the community ties that went; then the street ties and now it's family ties. It's no good.

'Voting doesn't change much. No point in voting Labour up here; Labour doesn't bother with us. They know they've got a rock-solid vote and they just take us for granted. At least the Tories have to try and get our votes. I voted for Mrs T. in 1979, but by 1983 I was out of work and she'd cut the dole! I guess if I'd had a job, I'd have voted for her. Those in jobs are all right, but she cut our dole and that's it from me. The working class are too accepting; we ought to kick up a fuss. But we don't seem to want any of that left-wing nonsense. We get by. The next few quid is only a phone call away. That's what I like to think.'

Chapter 9

Bradford:
The Police – 'If you print that I'll deny that I said it.'

The folk in the queue for the bus from Darlington to Leeds looked drab. Their clothes, designed to be dateless, had been chosen to cover their bodies rather than adorn them, and the colours were dull. I felt conspicuous in bright pink. For the most part the dozen or so passengers stood in silence. They were aged around sixty, the generation that grew up in the war and were taught not to complain – 'Don't you know there's a war on!' They were also taught an undue respect for authority, with the twin result that they avoid contact with authority figures and accept without complaining abysmally low standards of service. At 10.55 a.m., the appointed hour, there was no sign of the bus. The queue seemed unperturbed. At 11.00 I asked if they would keep an eye on my bags while I went in search of an inspector and an explanation. The inspector was easy enough to find, the explanation was not. 'I've heard nothing, so the bus can't be in serious trouble. Nothing has happened to it. It must be stuck in the traffic.'

'Stuck in the traffic!' The daily excuse for millions of latecomers all over the country. Anyone would think we were a nation of car owners, but we are not: there are a mere 320 cars per 1,000 population, compared with 400 in Italy and France, 450 in West Germany and 540 in America. It hardly matters if a gypsy writer is running behind schedule, but I wonder how business efficiency is affected by all this. The Confederation of British Industry once estimated that sitting in traffic jams cost each family £300 a year and that congestion on the M25 (the ring road around London) was costing companies more than £1 billion a year. I was doubly irritated; irritated by my bus being 'stuck in traffic' and by the fact that no one had bothered to tell us anything. The latter – poor service – could be improved overnight and with little or no cost; no one seems to have the answer to packed roads. The Transport ministry boasts that it has an 'enormous road-building programme' for the nineties, but new roads and improved roads only seem to create more traffic, because everyone takes to their cars and shuns shabby public transport where no one can be bothered to tell you that your bus is going to be late.

The bus takes one and a half hours to reach Leeds. I whiled away the time pondering the rural way of life and wondering why I had no desire to be permanently part of it. D. H. Lawrence understood. Having spent a weekend at some grand country house he said, 'One is tempted to give in, and to stay there, to lapse back into its peaceful beauty of bygone things, to live in pure recollection, looking at the accomplished past which is so lovely. But one's soul rebels.' Yes, it does. It rebels at such worship of the past. The past is something to be studied and understood; something from which to learn. I do not see it as something 'golden' or 'glorious'. I see it encrusted with conflict and poverty. Ten minutes recalling images of child labour convinces me that the past is not that admirable. Even the recent past, the 1950s, meant a dreary life for most women. Without fridges and washing-machines days were a cycle of shopping, cooking, cleaning and child-rearing, and year after year was the same and horizons were severely limited. Historians tend to present a very male and very middle class view of history; the working class in general and women in particular have benefited much from progress. It is indeed a pity that progress brings pollution, that the pill encourages promiscuity, that women's liberation loosens family ties. It is indeed a pity that with every step forward we lose something of worth and value; but we should concentrate on retrieving the good things that have been carelessly cast aside. We should not daydream of the past.

The bus station at Leeds was a dump. There was nowhere to leave luggage and the girls in the office refused to let me leave my bags while I wandered into the town. I walked across the bus park to the parcel office, a wooden hut, and asked the man inside if he would be willing to keep an eye on my bags. He readily agreed and also gave me advice on where I could get a haircut. Cheered by his civility I headed off down the hill to the city centre. My eyes refused to register buildings or anything else of interest, they rested instead on one black face after another. I hadn't seen black faces for months. If there were any in Scotland, Northern Ireland and the Lake District and Newcastle, they were so few that they had not made an impact on me. In Leeds there are 20,000 Afro-Caribbeans and 17,000 Asians and in Bradford, ten miles down the road and my destination after a haircut, there are 70,000 Asians and 6,000 Afro-Caribbeans.

I can just recall the arrival of the first influx of immigrants in the mid-fifties. I lived in Hayes, and in neighbouring Southall a factory making rubber tyres was one of the first to encourage black labour. Their arrival was a topic of both interest and concern at school and in street gossip. In my youthful ignorance I remember thinking that they had been needed to swell the labour force because so many men had been killed in the war. Churchill had gone to the Caribbean and specifically invited West Indians to come and help 'rebuild the Motherland'. But when my music teacher left on a £10 ticket to start a new life in Australia, I became confused. If Britain was short of labour why were we encouraging folk to leave the country and travel to the other side of the world by giving them a passage for £10? It didn't make sense; it still doesn't make much sense now, even though I appreciate that Australia, frightened by the Japanese during the war, was desperate to increase its population and Britain no doubt felt obliged to help in some way; and even though I now realize that part of the labour shortage was created by white men being reluctant to do jobs they considered dirty or poorly paid. In Bradford that was the case. The mill owners eager to counter competition from abroad had invested in new machinery and found that they could only make a profit if they kept that machinery going twenty-four hours a day. White Bradfordians did not fancy night work and so the mill owners recruited in Mirpur, Pakistan. They would have preferred West Indians, but London Transport had got there first. The British, when they had an empire, were adept at moving men and muscle around the world and it is a policy which has left festering wounds. The British imported Tamils into Ceylon, considering them to be better workers than the local population; the British imported Tamils and Chinese into Malaya to work the mines and plantations; the British imported Indians into East Africa to build the railways. And look at the problems that have resulted and in some cases have yet to be resolved!

In the 1950s the same game was being played here. In 1955 there were 50,000 immigrants in Britain and Sir Anthony Eden's government was bothered enough to discuss the matter in cabinet. Papers released under the thirty-year-rule reveal that measures were considered to control the influx. There was no immigration policy at that time, and millions were eligible to enter the country. The cabinet considered limiting the number of entrants but ministers were worried about the impact of such an act on relations with the Commonwealth. They considered directing and managing settlement in order to avoid friction in areas where immigrants tended to concentrate. They considered admitting immigrants to work for a period of up to five years. Many immigrants at that time would have been comfortable with such a scheme, since they themselves intended to come only for a short stay in order to earn money and then return home. Often one immigrant would return home and a relative would come over in his place to keep the money flowing. In the end nothing was done. Sir Anthony Eden took no action. He was fascinated by foreign policy but not that interested in domestic matters.

To my mind Bradford was yet another town born of the Industrial Revolution; it is near coal and a supply of soft, lime-free water, and its mills have made it famous. It has until recently been overshadowed by Leeds, which had the railway and the university and was the centre of much while Bradford got on with making money. It seemed pretty good at that. The mill owners had plenty and the workers had a rotten time in some of the grimmest houses built by greedy men who squashed sixty-five homes into an acre; in 1860 they were forced to improve that to forty-two, but still the back-to-back dwellings with one room up and one room down meant that inhabitants had to walk as much as 200 yards to a shared earth-closet. I can only suppose that the builders thought this set-up was an improvement on the smoke-filled, windowless huts from which the inhabitants came. And while they were building these things the mill owners were also erecting splendid public buildings. My first afternoon in Bradford was spent searching for fine buildings. And I was disappointed. In 1972 the city indulged in an orgy of rebuilding and in the process they sacrificed the old and the interesting. And, it seems, Bradford was not so rich in glorious buildings that it could afford such a loss. J. B. Priestley said the place was charmless, if not exactly ugly. And he has the right to say that, since he was born there. Of course, I was not seeing the city that Priestley remembered from his childhood, nor the city he saw on his 1930s journey, but I was seeing a city rebuilt by men who were used to charmless surroundings. Such men must have been inured to ugliness and inclined to rebuild in a similar mould. Priestley felt that no one had bothered with the city's looks in the first place because it had the good fortune to be on the edge of some of the most enchanting country in England. The city was merely a place where people worked and as soon as they were free of their chores they walked through the dales and on the moors. However poor you were in Bradford, he said, you never felt walled in like London folk, the countryside was but a walk away: a countryside made famous by *Wuthering Heights*. Or nowadays, no doubt, people prefer to think of it as a landscape made famous by James Herriot, a vet, who attracts tourists from far and wide.

In 1980 Bradford had few tourists; indeed, the thought would have been the subject of music-hall jokes. But everywhere now has tourists and even the most unlikely places have been dressed up as 'attractions'. Bradford is seen as an ideal centre for touring the dales; visitors tired of walking can then visit the National Museum of Photography and watch a film on a very large screen, or perhaps they take a peep at an area known as Little Germany, which is being restored as a monument to the German Jews who flocked to Bradford and as a reminder that Bradford has always welcomed outsiders and courted a cosmopolitan reputation. I used to think that tourism was toy-town stuff and no answer to unemployment since it provided mainly part-time work for women. But I can see that tourism could enhance a place's standing. So far Bradford has attracted a good few grants to renovate hotels and pretty itself up and this could attract further investment. With this in mind I went into the tourist centre, but stayed only a few moments; it contained little but pictures of small hotels and boarding-houses under the word 'accomodation' (arguably the most misspelled few syllables in the language).

Abandoning my search for pretty squares and eye-catching buildings I went into a bookshop to ask the way to Drummond Middle School. It's an odd destination to include on a late-afternoon walk, but for a while the school's headmaster was almost as famous as James Herriot. The school had 500 pupils aged between nine and thirteen, and 85 per cent of these pupils were Asian. Ray Honeyford had written some highly controversial words on the way in which these youngsters were being educated since the council had abandoned its policy of assimilation in favour of a policy of multi-culturalism. That is to say, instead of expecting immigrants to shed their skins and become part of a bland and homogeneous stew, they had decided to embrace diversity and encourage immigrants to retain their differences and become part of a salad where each of the ingredients retains its individual flavour. In educational terms this means allowing Asian children to learn Urdu, wear ethnic clothes, eat ethnic lunches and absent themselves from anything that conflicts with their religion. Supporters of the policy say that it has raised Asian self-esteem and that this in turn has improved their performance in school. Ray Honeyford felt that multi-culturalism was leading to a lowering of educational standards and that the white minority were suffering. He disliked the policy, believing it to have been trumped up by the ever growing race-relations industry.

In the first instance, Honeyford voiced his views in *The Times Educational Supplement*. They went unnoticed. Then he began writing in a more outspoken fashion in the right-wing *Salisbury Review*. These articles provoked a fine furore. He was, after a lengthy legal battle, forced to retire early.

This incident saddened me. I dislike seeing men or women pilloried for their views. Of course Honeyford put himself in a difficult position by openly opposing the stated policies of his employers; of course he put himself at risk making such remarks in a city which at that time had an Asian mayor and where the number of Asians is likely to reach 30 per cent by the turn of the century; of course he should have been more careful in the way he expressed his opinions. But having said that, the handling of the affair was hardly a good omen for democracy and freedom of speech – words which we English use with great abandon. A man lost his job for daring to voice his fears in public; that encourages hypocrisy; that encourages people to settle for a quiet life. And the saddest thing of all is that the whole episode appears to have achieved nothing. There was no serious debate about multi-culturalism, which is on the whole a popular policy but which none the less could have benefited from rigorous examination.

It was 6 p.m. and the gates to Drummond Middle School were firmly shut. But in the dusty, dull, adjacent streets many youngsters were to be seen with western anoraks covering their flimsy tunics and trousers. In groups they chatted and dawdled, alone they strolled along without speed. I knew something of the lives they led once they had closed the front door to their red-brick houses; I knew something of their attitudes and their state of mind from reading Dervla Murphy's *Tales from Two Cities*. To write this she had lived in Bradford for a while and mixed and mingled and indeed got involved with their lives. Her book is invaluable, especially since her viewpoint is decidedly un-English. As an Irish woman she happily admits that she is 'a non-member of the Master Race and a citizen of a country plagued by England for 800 years!' She liked Ray Honeyford despite a pre-conceived notion that he would be a 'ghastly man'. She thought it unjust to accuse him of being a racist.

Many people do not consider Enoch Powell to be racist either. They consider him to be a man who tried to tell us not to sweep race-relations under the carpet; who tried to warn us that ignoring the growing numbers and hoping that all would be well would lead us into trouble. Once again a man had chosen his words unwisely. All anyone remembers twenty years on is three little words: 'rivers of blood'. Enoch Powell's speech is referred to as 'The rivers-of-blood speech'. Powell is unrepentant. He tells anyone who will listen that as he goes about on public transport in Britain, 'the commonest thing is for a West Indian or an Asian to come up to me and say: "Mr Powell, may I shake your hand? I have always admired you. You are absolutely right."'

Sitting on a low wall outside Drummond Middle School, pretending I was waiting for someone, I wrote notes into a little book, one of which says: 'Who is there to teach us the difference between being mealy-mouthed and being diplomatic?' One martyr, Enoch Powell, was quite enough. What we need is solutions, not martyrs. We attempted to restrict immigration in 1962, but in the first instance this brought a steep increase in the number of Pakistani and Indian families wishing to settle here, in place of temporary male settlers who intended to return. There are 4 million Asian and Afro-Caribbeans in this country now. Many of them were born here. They will form 5 per cent of the population by 1991 and, while they account for less than 1 per cent of people over sixty-five, they will form 7 per cent of those under fifteen. In the sixties we also played around with laws to stop race discrimination. This provided jobs for well-intentioned liberal thinkers, but it has done very little to reform people's attitudes: racism and race discrimination exists and it is stupid to pretend otherwise. Centuries of propaganda against the black races has left its mark.

Our ability to fool ourselves led to riots. One weekend in April 1981, Brixton in south London saw 'disorder and violence, the like of which had not previously been seen in this century in Britain'. Hundreds of black youngsters attacked the police with bricks, iron bars and petrol bombs. The events leading to the riot are confusing. As far as anyone can tell it all began when a young black was stabbed by other blacks; when a policeman tried to help the wounded man, the other blacks either thought that the policeman was responsible for the stabbing or that the policeman was preventing him from getting to hospital. No bricks were thrown at that stage, but the following night police stopped a mini-cab driver when they saw pound notes sticking out of his socks. He said he kept them there for safety; the police suspected the money had come from drug dealing and searched the car. A crowd gathered. When a policeman found a black youth blocking his path the cauldron of discontent bubbled over – the festering boil that was the relationship between the forces of law and order and the black community burst. Let the statistics speak: 279 police officers were injured; 45 members of the public were injured; 61 private vehicles and 56 police vehicles were damaged or destroyed. Lord Scarman was asked to head an inquiry. His report is an indictment of our indifference; thirty years of pretending that we were not a racist nation had finally choked the white man and spewed the truth all over the pavements of Brixton, as West Indians, poorly educated, poorly housed and mostly without work, showed what they thought of the motherland their fathers had been invited to rebuild.

without prompting; it was the only way I was going to discover what he knew and what he thought. Inspector Kear is responsible for race-relations training: he organizes courses for policemen so that they have some understanding of the religious and cultural backgrounds of ethnic groups. They are taught simple things, like the fact that Asians and West Indians tend to get agitated and shout more easily than the British; that they are taught by their leaders to *complain* about the police (which the British are not); and that sometimes they are happy to accuse a police officer of having called them 'a black bastard' when this has not happened. They are shown videos of policemen talking about 'coons' over the car radio; and of policemen in canteens gossiping about 'coonstables' and 'coonductors'.

Inspector Kear mentions Scarman often. If it hadn't been for the Scarman Report he would not have his present job. He had to start from scratch in the early 1980s and build bridges to the Asian community. He considers the Brixton riots to have been a blessing in disguise. The police weren't equipped to cope and had little or no training in crowd control; they were taken by surprise.

'We are ready now, though. We've had plenty of riot training. Oh yes, we're ready now. And of course it meant that we had to do more to get to know the community. That's where I come in. I've many good links now with the community. Scarman said we must have input from the community into police training. So they come and talk to us and help us to understand. And there's much to know! The Asians came in the late fifties, you know. There was a textile boom then and the mill owners sent their representatives to the sub-continent to recruit labour. Then they chartered a troop ship to bring them out of Pakistan. It isn't like that any more, of course. They get to Heathrow and ask the taxi driver for 'Lumb Lane' – that's a £200 ride! Of course textiles went into decline in the sixties, but still they came. Bangladeshis it was then, and they're different. They're not astute like the Pakistanis and the Indians. They have below-average intelligence, and they are unemployable. They're fanatical Muslims; the women don't come out of their houses, which makes it impossible for them to learn English. The Koran more or less says that women should be servile. The men are often to be found in Lumb Lane, the red-light area, between noon and 3 o'clock is their time – it's their dinner time, if they are in work.

'There must be 207 organizations for Asians in Bradford alone. The Asians are very fragmented, culturally and religiously. They seem to split into factions easily and I don't understand why. But that's the reason for all these organizations. The communities need to have their own leaders to turn to for advice. If an Asian is in trouble, he will go and see the leader of one of these organizations, and that leader will come and see me to ask my advice, and then this leader goes back and *sells* that advice to the guy in trouble!

'Their religious leaders carry a lot of weight too. A Muslim boy is expected to recite the Koran by the time he is sixteen, so he comes home from school and has to go to the mosque and not play football with his mates. Some of them decide to skip off and go to the pubs rather than the mosque. When the imam finds out he beats them. We've had calls from headmasters saying, come and have a look at this boy. If it had been a white boy there would have been a prosecution. But you can't prosecute a religious leader. They get let off with a warning. We have managed to arrest two imams for GBH: We got to the court and the judge said: "Holy man, promise you won't do it again." The whole thing melted away.

'We've got second-generation Asians now, Yorkshire-born blacks who do not know their own country and are pulled both ways. There's quite a rebellion against arranged marriages. One day they come home from school and the girls are told they are going to be married because there's someone in Pakistan who wants citizenship. The worst case I know is of a Bradford Pakistani boy who was sent over there to bring back his fiancée. He brought her back and took her to the Register Office and while they were waiting she collapsed. She was only twelve or thirteen, but she had said she was seventeen to get in. The boy had been instructed to get her pregnant and had damaged her internally. The marriage couldn't go through; she was adopted instead.

'The whites' view of Asians is not so bad. They are the ones who own their own homes and whose kids go to school, private schools sometimes, and university. Pakistanis are the best financiers and businessmen, better than us sometimes. The Asians around here are becoming affluent. When the textile industry went into decline, Asians bought out a number of mills and started printing their own cloth – sweat-shops they are, but we're on to that! They go into the market and sell the stuff themselves. And in Dewsbury there are 137 off-licences, and every one is owned by Pakistanis, and all of them can be traced to five families. On the whole we've been lucky with the Asians.

'It is the West Indians that suffer, and they are mostly in Leeds where their drinking parties cause all the trouble. They'd wire the whole house for sound, including the toilet, and then sell booze and drugs. We used to spend a lot of time raiding them. But we've stopped that now; we had to improve our relations with them to stop another 1981. We've gradually got their confidence, and nowadays they cooperate with us. We can go into a house and say we are looking for "X", who has mugged an old lady, and they will turn the guy over. The whites have a poor image of the West Indians; they are seen as muggers, and lazy people who won't work. They have brought it on themselves. They won't work, whereas the Asians will. But then again, I could show you reliable young West Indians who have come through the system well, and made friends with whites and got good qualifications. They try and get jobs and they don't get them because of this reputation, and they get demoralized and are prey to the mob, Rastafarian locks and the lot. But the best West Indians are better than the best Asians. They don't have this religious pull to contend with. They don't have much culture, really.'

To aid my understanding of the local scene, Inspector Kear suggested we take a drive and he would show me Manningham, where the Asian community congregate, and Lumb Lane. He said Lumb Lane sported a prostitute on every corner. We couldn't find one, and they weren't hiding from the police, since we were in an unmarked car and Kear was not in uniform.

'That's a doss house for whites, over there; they're the only whites who live around here. And over there, the building with the red-and-green doors, is Pakistan Centre. That's a Bangladeshi fish-and-chip shop, and all the little corner shops are owned by Asians. And I must show you Drummond Middle School. Have you heard of it?'

I said that it rang a faint bell and asked him to refresh my memory. I wanted to hear his version of the story. His version of the story was very straightforward. He said that Ray Honeyford was merely trying to point out that the white kids were disadvantaged being in a school with so many Asians and that standards were falling.

'He was a bit of a left-winger, you know. At one time I'd say he was a left-wing extremist. I think he quite liked being a martyr. He must have enjoyed it all because he kept on expanding on his original remarks, and that's what caused the trouble. The majority of people, including a policeman like me, think he's right. I go to church, so I wouldn't want them to give up their faith, but I think it is wrong to encourage them to carry on here as they did in Pakistan. It's so damn false. A lot of people are afraid to speak out because they are afraid of the race-relations lobby. I don't think Honeyford is racist. The school's governing body supported him, you know. It was the council who wanted him out.'

We had stopped the car outside the school and were gazing at the sand-coloured building. I asked him what he really felt about the black community now that he had so much contact with them.

'I've no feelings towards the blacks,' he said, giving me a safe answer. I remained silent, knowing that he would go on. 'Except that my upbringing as a miner's son is still there. Miners have no time for blacks. Look, 90 per cent of whites don't like blacks. If they had close ties, as I do, they still would not be converted. Things are better than in the past. When I was a child, parents would scold their kids with: "A black man will come and get you!" I don't suppose they say it now. But there is no genuine tolerance; and there won't be in my lifetime. I'll be honest: I can't say that I *like* them. No way would I like one of my daughters to marry a black.'

I warmed to his honesty. I warmed at times to most of the policemen I met during those few days, but underneath I felt strongly that I wouldn't want to cross any of them. What was warming was their humour and their bluntness, but there was a hardness that was easy to detect. The police force is mainly made up of working-class men, and many have come from poor families and have had to struggle. They tell stories of how, when they first joined the force, they earned £9 a week and by the next pay-day they were 'down to a bag of carrots'. Their attitude is that they have struggled and made it, so what's stopping other people? Their attitude is that there is no poverty these days compared to the past. Today's poor have videos and don't know what it is like to be 'down to a bag of carrots'. What was most chilling was their habit of saying something, and then adding: 'Now if you print that, I'll deny that I said it.' Those words are a nightmare. Are policemen born thinking like this, or does someone teach them; does someone offer up the little sentence as a near impenetrable shield? No wonder journalists have become fond of hidden tape-recorders.

I decided that I would like to take a look at Chapeltown police station in Leeds, an area torn by riots. I based myself in the Community Involvement Unit, a post-Scarman invention. Sergeant Peta Platts was my guide. She was twenty-nine and had joined the police force at the age of twenty-three, having got a geography degree and started training as an accountant. She found a structured office life not to her liking and toyed with joining either the RAF or the police. Her sister is in the army.

'I decided against the RAF because I didn't want to train for something I didn't want to happen – a war. And I chose the police because I wanted to do something useful and I wanted to experience the world beyond my upbringing. My mother is a teacher and my father is a business consultant. I'm glad I did not join the force any younger; there's just too much for an eighteen-year-old to cope with.'

She had been with the unit for just a few months and her job was to make contacts and friends with the ethnic groups. 'I have been surprised at the welcome I have received from the vast majority. It's only a small minority who are anti-police, and they are going to stay that way for some time. *They* are the ones I really need to get to know, but it's a hard nut to crack. For the moment I have to be content to help the ones who are willing to be helped. And there are enough problems there to keep me busy.' She described her job in some detail. 'I might for example get a phone call saying that a girl known to have been beaten by her husband hasn't been seen for weeks. I've got good links with the battered wives groups in Leeds, so I'd then get on to them to try and find out where she was. Or a Pakistani whose wife had left him might come to me and ask if I could find out where she was and if she was O K, or if she had gone off to Pakistan with the kids.'

'You sound like a social worker.'

'I'm not a social worker: I'm a police officer and we've always done a lot of missing persons work. But it's true that in this unit we want the ethnic groups to come to us with their problems. We are here to try and help.'

'In that case, it sounds as though the police are trying to put the clock back twenty-five years. Then we all thought we could go to the police for help.'

'Very good. I hadn't thought of it like that. But you're right. We want to get back on that footing and it's working. We do get families coming to us because they have disputes with other families and they want us to try and calm things down.'

And if I hadn't been there, taking up her time, she would have been out on the estates talking to nineteen- and twenty-year-olds, trying to persuade them to spend a few days at the station, seeing police work at first hand, trying to interest them in a career in the police. Much time and money has been put into recruiting black and brown policemen and women. It has not been successful. A recent open-house for community leaders yielded nothing. Far too many view the police in the worst light and would be seen as traitors if they joined. Part of this, I was told, was because the police forces in Asia and the West Indies are aligned with military and political aims and this cultural difference puts up a barrier. The miners' strike and the concept of 'Maggie's boys in blue' which had resulted had not helped the communities to appreciate that there was a significant difference in this country. The West Indians are more inclined to see the act of joining the police as one of betrayal to the community; but Asians can be persuaded in small numbers. They quite like the snob appeal attached to 'knowing a policeman'; sometimes they get invited to family weddings.

There was an Asian policewoman in Dewsbury and I was anxious to meet her. And *en route* for Dewsbury I stopped at Pontefract and broke my promise to myself to stick firmly with race relations. I'd been listening to canteen gossip about the miners' strike. The official word was that relations between the police and the mining communities were back to normal, but several people had told me that this is what they told the press, but the truth was very different. It would take a generation to put things right.

Pontefract police had been in the thick of the troubles. Inspector Hufton had the task of dealing with the media. 'My father was a miner; he was fifty-two years down the pits, so you can see that I was brought up in that fraternity. It is my honest belief that it will take one or two generations to forgive. Miners are very proud people. The older ones had a great deal of respect for the law.' And he told me the story of a south Kirby boy called Davy Jones who had been killed on the picket line in Nottingham, and how he had to organize the policing of the funeral which was attended by thousands. 'I did it with six men. Six. My uniform had to go to the dry-cleaners after because my back was covered with spit. I've taken a lot of abuse to my face, that's one thing, but spitting is another. Each year there is an anniversary march for Jones and each year you can feel the hostility towards us. Not one person says good morning. We are having to build bridges via the young people – through the schools – and through the old people.'

Dewsbury is the heart-attack capital of Britain. It's not a very pretty title; perhaps in time another piece of research will dump the crown on another town. The community physician blames smoking, diet, lack of exercise and alcohol, in that order. But nobody seems to know why those four factors should be any worse in Dewsbury, with a population of 50,000, than in any other place. Sickness rates aside, it is a modest little town, its skyline dominated by the largest mosque in Yorkshire. The police station is modern. It lies next to the bus station and within a step or two of the main shopping streets. Jagjit Dehele, born in Mombasa, Kenya in 1953, came to England in 1968. Her father, a joiner, had left India long before she was born and had his own business in Mombasa. Then one day he was told he had to become a Kenyan citizen; he chose to stay a British subject and came to Leeds, where his son was at university. Jagjit completed her A-level studies here and very easily made up her mind to become a policewoman.

'There was all this talk of lack of integration and it seemed one way of learning what goes on. Life was pretty restricted here for me. In Kenya we had a good lifestyle and plenty of money; coming here we had to start all over again. When I filled in the form I had no idea that I was the first Asian to apply in Leeds, but I discovered that when the superintendent visited my home. I was frightened. I hadn't told my father, but that night I ran to the bus stop to meet him and tell him. My father was very supportive and has been a community leader, so that if the community disapproved of what I'd done, we didn't hear about it.

'I've been in the police force for fourteen years now, and I'm happy being a police constable; I'm not interested in promotion because I don't want to run anything, that's just not me. I'm happy working with people, particularly with the Asian community. I speak most Asian dialects and this is really useful. After one year in the service an Asian girl was murdered and I was called on to the case. At least the family felt at ease with me, especially as they couldn't speak English.'

We went out on the beat together. It was my idea; I wanted to see how people reacted to her. Jagjit Dehele is exceptionally good-looking, poised and authoritative. Her fingernails are polished and pointed, her hair is scraped back and there are tiny blue painted lines swinging upwards from the outer edges of her eyelids. She would turn heads anywhere. She turned numerous heads on our walk. As we strolled through the town centre I had the curious sensation of being invisible. Those walking towards us would fix their eyes on her, and then when they had walked past, they would turn around and stare. Jagjit was used to it.

We wandered along, chatting about her work, through the main streets which had lamp posts adorned with hanging baskets of flowers, newly watered and dripping spots on to the pavement; past the market with a huge sign saying: 'Don't talk tripe, eat it!' There was a smell of chips, of frying, perhaps a clue to that heart-attack title. A Ford car pulled up at the curbside and asked her the way to Daisy Hall. The town was quiet. The previous day, Wednesday, had been market day and the place had bustled. Thursday, the day before pay-day, is always quiet. We talked of recruiting problems: 'Where we come from the police force is considered a lowly job, so once a person gets O- and A-levels, their parents want them to do something better.' The West Yorkshire police do not parade her as bait for recruitment, which showed more sensitivity than I might have expected. We talked of those who settled in their new country, and those who constantly went backwards and forwards; of girls who run away from home to avoid arranged marriages, which Jagjit said was a class-based problem; the more affluent and better educated Asians don't try to marry off their daughters. We talked of the murder cases she had covered and was covering, which often proved difficult because some Asians use false names to cover up the fact that they are illegal immigrants. Murder cases make interesting work and had taught her the most, because that's where the detailed questions can be asked. She talked of Asian men who drink and 'bird around'. Their wives know nothing until something happens and then they tend to close the net and deny that their husbands could ever do such things. 'Of course, there are married Asian women who have lovers and drink too. It's not just the men.'

We were heading now for the Asian heartland. Neat rows of identical houses, some of them in poor condition, some of them with messy gardens. Children strolled home from school. I saw a little girl in a white shroud come out of one house and dump a cardboard box in the garden of the neighbouring house.

'They are all owner occupied, but often overcrowded, and they will sometimes have a television and a video and no carpet on the floor. They have greater need of the television and the video because it means they don't need to go out; the video is for those Indian films that are so popular. The girls get all sorts of romantic notions watching them. Why are the families so hard up? Well, it's often because they send money home to their relatives, and not just their immediate family. Such ties are strong and they don't question it. Whatever they have here it is a great deal more than their relatives back home.'

Her radio began to crackle; 'To all radios: look out for red Escort car stolen from the car park at 9 a.m. this morning.'

'Well, it won't be anywhere near here now,' she answered in a precise voice.

Minutes later it crackled again: '50/50; 50/50'. That was her number and she was being asked to go to the bus station where kids were drinking cider and lager and causing a nuisance. We turned around and headed back to the bus station. Whoever had been drinking cider and lager and causing a nuisance had disappeared. Dewsbury is an average sort of place, with no special problems, except the high rate of heart disease. Jagjit says she will marry, but not have children, and that she would like to spend thirty years in the force. She doesn't mind being called a 'black bastard' from time to time. White policemen get called names too.

Chapter 10

Liverpool:
City of the Left

I was more than a little excited at the thought of visiting Liverpool. Inspector Kear had said that Bradford was a city without 'oomph' (and he was right); no one could say that of Liverpool. Indeed, every writer associates Liverpool with vitality; to me there is only one city that oozes vitality and that is New York. How could Liverpool compare with such a city? Liverpool was a poor place; the kind of poor place that didn't mind the world knowing that it was reduced to ragged trousers. From the outside it seemed like a rich, over-rouged old lady who had fallen on the worst of times and yet behaved as though she was still important, and bored everyone with tales from the past. There were so many questions I wanted to ask and so much I wanted to see. Liverpool, the city that put Militant on the map; Liverpool, the city of one of my favourite films, *Letter to Brezhnev*; Liverpool, the city of two of my favourite playwrights, Alan Bleasdale and Willy Russell; Liverpool, home of the Beatles.

But first, because my mind was still full of police talk, and the plight of black people, I found myself drawn to Toxteth. I just wanted to *see* it and I wanted to listen; to find some black people willing to talk. Bradford had convinced me that necessity has forced the police to try to change, but my brief chats with a couple of Asian leaders had been unrewarding. They had said little and what they had said had displaced the real problem from the brown community into the black community. Bradford's 'browns' were relative newcomers; Liverpool's blacks had a long, long history; Toxteth has the oldest black community in Britain. They, the blacks, are the key to the transformation of the place from a small fishing port to a wealthy city, the nation's second seaport – by 1700. Liverpool was then the centre for much colonial trade, West Indian trade in particular. Liverpool got rich not just by shipping the products of slave labour – sugar and tobacco – but by shipping the slaves themselves; hauling them from Africa to the West Indies. The blacks were meant to pass through, not stay, but some stayed in the face of Acts of Parliament making sea-captains account for the numbers that arrived in port and the numbers that left. Despite this, Charles Dickens in 1861 found pubs in the slum area full of blacks. There were race riots in 1919: white soldiers returning from war to find a shortage of jobs led to several days of violence against the black community. There were riots again in 1948 for much the same reason.

The scars of more recent riots were still visible in Toxteth; shops and houses were either boarded up or were girded by metal grills. Granby Street used to be lively, with people walking up and down and chatting and gossiping, with shopkeepers displaying their wares on the pavements outside; with opening hours that meant you never had to worry about running out of anything. There was a real sense of community; now there was silence. Too many shops had been abandoned and there was no pavement life, nothing much to catch my eye, except graffiti: 'Kill Maggie'; 'Smash the system'; 'Do your own goddam thing'; 'Police fuck off'; 'Police, enter at your own risk'; 'No pigs'; 'Hail Lion of Judah'. Rasta colours, stripes of red, yellow and green, had been painted over the street signs. A small black girl held out a handful of change and asked me if I had a 50 pence coin. As I delved into my purse I asked her what it was for. 'The leckie,' she answered. She wanted 50 pence for the electricity meter. 'It's right. It's 50 pence,' she said in a Scouse accent, handing me over the sticky contents of her tiny hand and hoping I wouldn't waste time counting it.

I was looking for Linda Patterson and the South Liverpool Personnel, an employment agency for blacks. It was started in the early seventies, partly funded by Liverpool City Council and partly by the Commission for Racial Equality. 'Of course, everyone *says* they believe in equal opportunities for blacks, of course they say so, but racism is ingrained on Merseyside; everyone thinks of blacks as lazy and dirty, but they won't admit to being racist. Blacks get a better deal in London than they get in Liverpool.

'When I go down to London and see black shop assistants, black bank clerks, I say to myself: "What's this?" Here they try to hide us away. Years ago, my mother went for a job in Lewis's store as a kitchen assistant, and they told her the job had gone, but a while later her white friend went in and got the job with no experience of kitchens. Ma ranted and raved all over Lewis's and got thrown out by the police. Things have improved a bit; a black can get past the first post before getting stuck. I know a young black girl who is a buyer's assistant in a big shop. She's done that for eight years and put in a dozen times for promotion, but they just won't promote her. She feels unsafe tackling them on racist grounds: they'll say she has a chip on her shoulder and threaten her job. She could move to London – it's the only place where she really could get on with her career – but she doesn't *want* to move.'

Linda Patterson was born in Liverpool. Her grandparents came over from somewhere in Africa, she isn't sure where, sometime in the last century. They worked in a travelling road-show and finally ended up in Liverpool, where her grandmother started a boarding-house in Toxteth. She is the youngest of nine children. Of the nine, three brothers, one a former docker, one a builder and one a cook, are only intermittently in work, another brother is a community worker; of her sisters, one works in television, one in a hospital, one in a factory in London and another in a factory in America, having married an American soldier. Linda married at seventeen and had two children by the time she was nineteen. Her husband, Jimmy, is white. He was once a sales assistant, selling jewellery. One day one of his colleagues referred to Linda as 'a nigger' and a fight broke out and Jimmy was dismissed. He was unemployed for six years and is now a mature student studying sociology at Liverpool Polytechnic. At twenty, Linda rebelled against motherhood.

'I woke up one day and thought, "Shit, another day of screaming kids." So I went on a course called New Opportunities for Women and found another me. That led to evening classes and I finally got my first job as a teachers' aid at the Charles Wootton Centre, an educational centre for black kids. We call the centre "Charlie"; Wootton was a black guy who died during the 1919 race riots in Liverpool. He was being chased by white people and he got to the Pier Head and had nowhere to run, so he dived into the water and drowned. Oh, you've heard of those riots, have you? Most people haven't; it's a part of Liverpool's history that gets swept under the carpet.'

Linda has been in her present post of job placement officer for three years. She has 2,000 blacks on her books. Perhaps fifty jobs a month come in, many of them from white employers paying lip-service to the notion of equality. She says that those on her books have skills, but they are not given the chance to prove themselves; they are not taken seriously in the job market.

'It was no surprise when the rioting started in 1981. There's only so much you can take. From the day you leave school you're on the scrap heap. Blacks like me have to struggle to get where we are.

'I remember the rioting very well. I was coming home from work –

I had an evening job then as a waitress – and when the bus didn't come along, I decided to walk. Everywhere I walked the roads were blocked off by scores of policemen. One of them stopped me and asked where I was going. I told him I was going home and he said he'd walk along with me. And he did for a bit. Then suddenly I felt a hand on the back of my neck; my arm was broken and my head was thumped – it looked like a mountain. They left me in the street. I got up and ran and finally got home and to hospital. It took me eight weeks to get my arm right and months before I felt mentally all right.' While she recalled these events she stared out of the window. Then suddenly she turned back to me and her voice hardened: 'I've always had a hatred for the police; my brothers were constantly harassed. My brothers are not angels by any means, but one ended up in jail for an offence he had not committed. I've seen this community wrecked by police. They will never be able to justify what they have done.'

'Do you think the riots achieved anything – anything good?'

'I don't know that they *achieved* anything; they were not rioting to achieve anything, they were rioting to prove something – that we've had enough of police brutality, and not being able to lead our own lives. Yes, I've heard talk about race-awareness courses for the police, but I don't know how true it is. I get the feeling that everyone is chasing their tails to improve things. But all the police really learned from those riots was how to prepare themselves for more riots in the future; they now have CS gas and heat-resilient clothes. Oh yes, of course, we got Michael Heseltine, the minister for Merseyside. That was great. He gave us some rose bushes and some trees and called it a garden festival and then told us we have to pay £4 to get in!'

'Well, what about Derek Hatton? What happened when Militant ran Liverpool City Council – did things improve for the black community?'

'Militant, or "Milo" as we call them, did nothing for the blacks! They didn't even have a race-relations policy. Derek Hatton did appoint a race-relations officer, a Militant black from Brent. He understood nothing about race relations and nothing about Liverpool. Most of the black groups refused to work with him. We refused and then when we needed a new deputy manager the post was frozen – it was their way of paying us back. *No one* takes the blacks and their problems seriously. Militant was just another group, just another bloody left-wing group.'

Linda Patterson's views were echoed by a handful of other blacks with whom I talked. It all adds up to a shameful tale. No one has ignored the blacks in Liverpool; for nearly sixty years – since 1930 –

there have been any number of reports analysing the problems – I have beside me a list of thirty-nine such reports – but all these words, all these concerned and learned studies, have done little to eliminate racial prejudice and little to remove the black community from bottom-of-the-pile lives with poor housing, health, education and poor job prospects. It came as no surprise to me when late in 1988 yet another report was commissioned: Lord Gifford was asked to chair an investigation into policing and law enforcement in Toxteth. Setting up a committee and producing a report might allow woolly liberal thinkers to bask in a warm glow, but all too often it is a substitute for action rather than a prelude to action. Lord Gifford, a Labour peer, says that his inquiry could be a catalyst for change. I bet his thirty-nine predecessors said much the same thing. The black community forms 8 per cent of Liverpool's population of 500,000; they have 1 per cent of the jobs with the city council (Liverpool's largest employer) and less than 1 per cent of jobs with other city centre employers. Why the hypocrisy? Why are we so good at pretending to care, pretending to take action and yet all the while hiding behind another report? Look around, where are the prominent black figures in our community? A handful of them are in Parliament; there are a sprinkling of lawyers; they are woefully absent in the media; we have one Black bishop, the Right Reverend Wilfred Wood of Croydon. At least the Church of England has tried to improve black representation with a touch of positive discrimination in the appointment of black members to the General Synod, the Church's parliament. It tried, but was voted down. Why are we so reluctant to embrace positive discrimination for blacks – making employers take a representative percentage of their workforce from ethnic communities? It works well in America. And for those who are allergic to American imports, let me point out that fair employment legislation is having an effect in Northern Ireland, where we have been forced to find a way of overcoming centuries of discrimination against Catholics. No party has had the courage to fight for such a step here; not even Militant.

What is Militant – 'Just another bloody left wing group?' I don't think so. I tried to meet Derek Hatton. It was the tail end of his reign in Liverpool. I phoned his office at 8.45 one morning from a call box in Bradford and asked his secretary for an appointment. I could hear her asking his approval in the background and the appointment was made. When I arrived at city hall a thug-like person with broad shoulders and bad teeth barred my way and asked my business. I said I had an appointment with Derek Hatton. He picked up the phone and said: 'There's a lady here who *says* she has an appointment with Derek.'

The thug seemed surprised to learn that I had. I was shown into a waiting room where several men were arguing with a beleaguered looking woman about housing problems. I waited, whiling away the time reading a beautifully produced official guide to Liverpool. Suddenly my name was called.

'Linda!' I looked up and saw Derek Hatton in the doorway. 'Come this way.' What a promising, friendly start, I thought. Inside his office he told me that he could spare me a mere ten minutes as he was loaded down with problems. 'I did say I wanted an hour, and I heard your secretary asking you if that was OK.'

'Yes, yes, it is OK. But not right now. Will you come back tomorrow?' I agreed. I had no reason to doubt his word, he seemed friendly. Tomorrow never came. My calls to his secretary met with excuse after excuse. Instead, I went to meet Terry Fields, Liverpool's only Militant MP, one of two in the House of Commons. I met him in the city centre, in a building that used to be the police headquarters and was therefore spacious and a touch grand. It is now used by the trade unions to run, among other things, courses for unemployed members, telling them about their welfare rights. Terry Fields was a fireman for twenty-six years before entering Parliament. He takes £150 a week plus expenses and gives the rest to the Militant movement. In the Commons he is said to have an angry speaking style, but in Liverpool on a cool September morning there was no trace of anger. He was relaxed; he talked well of himself and his family, but was evasive on Militant. That he loves Liverpool to the point of being sentimental soon became obvious. 'There's nowhere like it. I remember national service; I remember coming back from Germany and getting out of the train at Lime Street and hearing the girls' accents and knowing I was home. It is the same now when I return from London each week. This is a tremendous place, but badly neglected. I've never known anything but poor housing, poor education and lack of jobs, but for all that the place is vibrant. Nowhere like it.'

I asked him what he meant by the word 'vibrant' and he answered by suggesting somewhat vaguely that despite all the problems the people of Liverpool seemed alive and 'perky' and added that the vibrancy comes from the port and the trade, the fact that it's always been open to outside influences, particularly American. The seamen would go there and come back with the confidence born of travel.

Fields' dad was a docker. 'He died on the docks, in harness as it were. He worked like a horse all his life and died like a horse, in harness. He was about sixty then. He was a big bloke and he gave his all to make us a good home. He gave us a room when I married in

1961; we paid 15 *s.* a week rent and shared the kitchen. Then when my wife's mother died we moved in to look after that family. It took us six years to get a council house in Bootle.'

Terry Fields is an old-fashioned class warrior. He can't be doing with the Labour party because it doesn't fight for fundamental change. When I asked him what Militant wanted, he said it wanted the best for Liverpool. And when I asked him to describe the best, he said better housing, better education, more jobs. Housing and education had been the target of Militant's first efforts. They had made an impressive start on massive problems by setting the demolition squad on high-rise blocks and by cutting off the tops of low-rise blocks, to transform them into the kind of homes that people wanted. They had reorganized secondary education and attempted to create some twenty community schools. When I asked him why Militant hadn't done more for the blacks in Toxteth he said that Militant had done much in the field of housing and education, and had not been able to do more in other areas because it had been constantly under siege both from the Labour party and from the Tory party. In the end he came clean on the blacks: he didn't want positive discrimination. You can't solve the problems of the blacks in isolation, he said; you need a complete policy of socialism.

He wouldn't be drawn any further on Militant, which isn't surprising, because until recently most supporters refused even to admit that it was an organization, they merely said it was a 'newspaper' of the same name. They had to lie because once it was admitted that Militant was a party with principles and policies, then it would be chucked out of the Labour party, whose constitution does not allow for a party within a party. Well, it has now been chucked out, so it no longer has to deny that it exists. To the best of anyone's knowledge Militant came into being in the mid-1960s, centred on a newspaper. Membership is not easy to acquire; those wishing to join often go through six months of meetings and assessment. What they join in the end is a deeply committed group of socialists influenced by the thinking of Marx, Engels, Lenin and Trotsky; what they want is socialism by revolution. Their model is the Russian Revolution, which they see as the most important event in world history. What exactly they want for Britain has never been spelled out, but it seems to include public ownership of some 250 major companies and monopolies, a planned economy, a minimum wage, full employment, a thirty-five-hour week, the abolition of the House of Lords and all MPs to receive the wages of a skilled worker.

For some time communists were happy to work outside the system;

when this did not work they decided on a policy of 'entryism', of infiltrating the Labour party and outwitting members simply by working hard and turning up to meetings and getting their point of view voted in. They took over Liverpool Labour party by this method.

Why on earth should Liverpool be ripe for such a socialist takeover? The answer is simple. Economic conditions are poor and the Labour party is weak. The Labour Party has always been weak in Liverpool because the city has a large Catholic population, and, since the Catholics voted Labour, the Protestant working class voted Tory. This splitting of the working-class vote kept Labour out of city politics until 1955. When it finally got control, it was a Catholic-dominated, right-wing Labour party. This party, then, with true sixties fervour, got busy cleaning out the city centre slums and building high-rise flats. Once the nasty things were occupied, the council maintained them badly and voters retaliated. They deprived the Labour party of its majority. Although the Liberal party had the largest number of seats, it did not have an overall majority; some of the time it could rely on Tory party support by adopting Toryish policies, but for the most part this hung council could agree on nothing and, for ten years – from 1973 – the council was paralysed.

In the 1970s public spending in Liverpool was somewhat lower than in many other cities; the Liberal–Tory coalition kept it that way. When Mrs Thatcher's government came to power one of her first aims was to cut local-authority spending and therefore she instructed councils to trim their budgets from the levels of 1978–9. This was bad news in Liverpool because the budget was hardly flabby, and Labour–Militant was in office dying to go on a spending spree. They refused to accept Mrs Thatcher's dictat; they refused to cut services, they refused to increase the rates by more than a small amount. To fund their spending spree they decided to run up an illegal deficit. If Mrs T. didn't like it she would have to sack them all and put in her own commissioners to sort out the mess. What they hoped was that the Tories would not fancy running Liverpool and that to avoid such a fate they would make out a nice cheque to balance Liverpool's budget. After endless negotiations this is more or less what happened. The government gave Liverpool some money (there is argument about how much) and in return the city council had to put some of its spending plans on ice. Needless to say, Militant made much of this victory and tried to play the same card the following year – refusing to set a rate in the hope that the government would once again come to the rescue. The Thatcher government was stony-hearted; it didn't even want to talk to Liverpool. It threw the rule book at the place instead. Councillors were suspended for acting illegally (by not setting a rate in the allotted time) and fined. End of revolution in Liverpool. At least for the time being.

I say for the time being because I cannot imagine that Militant will pack up and go away. Undiluted socialism is not fashionable at the moment, either in Russia or in China, and diluted socialism in Europe has taken a turn to the right; what is called 'socialism' is tinged with social democratic ideals, but despite this there are still people who believe that capitalism must wither, or be made to wither, and that there is a fairer way of organizing society. The Labour party once believed in this; in the beginning the Labour party believed that a fair society was one in which the means of production did not remain in private hands. They did not want the source of economic power to remain in individual pockets.

The first two spells of Labour rule in the twenties did not produce socialist policies. The excuse was that although they were 'in office', they were not 'in power' and therefore could not do the things they wished. It was a sign of what was to come; a battle between those who were content to tinker and those who wished for fundamental change. The latter have always been overruled. By 1937 it became respectable to argue that the Labour party ought to put less emphasis on public ownership of the 'commanding heights of the economy'. Douglas Jay produced a book in which he argued that such a policy of nationalization might hinder speculative risk-taking and therefore it might be better for Labour to put more emphasis on the use of financial measures, like taxation, to iron out inequalities and redistribute wealth.

When the Labour party came to power under Clement Attlee in 1945, it took impressive steps towards socialism. It nationalized a handful of key industries – coal, steel, electricity and so on – as well as introducing the National Health Service and welfare benefits. Its achievements during six years of both foreseen and unforeseen difficulties make it one of the most significant governments of this century. The sadness for idealist socialists is that it was an end and not a beginning. By 1951 the Attlee government was worn out and uncertain where it was to go next. It could have put forward much-needed plans to *restructure* nationalized industries so that there was an element of workers' control, but it did not. The workforce merely swapped one sort of boss for another, who seemed as them-ish as ever. Nothing was done to enhance the dignity of labour, so why should the workers feel that much had changed? It hadn't, nor was it going to. In 1955 the right wing via Hugh Gaitskell took control of the Labour party. Socialism had lost; Labour from then on was happy to fight for the workers to have a larger slice of the cake rather than aim to bake the cake itself from a different recipe. Is it so surprising that those who still have faith in socialist philosophy should try and start again through Militant?

I wanted to visit Kirby. The two girls in *A Letter to Brezhnev* came from Kirby. They worked in a chicken factory, taking the innards out, putting them into plastic bags and shoving them back in again. Such a fate had not destroyed their zest for life. But my overall impression of Kirby was that most people's zest had withered. The people of Kirby once lived in central Liverpool; they were decanted in the sixties to a site eight miles down the road, boxed into high-rise blocks. There were no facilities to go with new homes, but at least, in the first instance, they had jobs. An industrial estate offered some 24,000; this has now been halved. Kirby was described to me as a transit camp. The people were physically better off than someone stuck in a Palestinian equivalent, but just as displaced in other ways. Unskilled and jobless, they lacked a role in the modern world; they had no sense of their own worth.

My point of contact in Kirby was a school that was now a trades union resource centre; a centre for the unemployed. When I rang the coordinator, Christine Davidson, she was reluctant to come to the phone and rude when she did. 'You can call in if you wish, but I'm not promising to talk to you.'

'What's the problem?'

'There's no problem. You can call in and explain what you are doing here and then I'll see.'

I called in, intrigued by her attitude. Christine Davidson fixed her eyes on me. Everything about her was hostile. It took ten minutes to get to the point. She felt that I was yet another journalist come to see the hotbed of Militant; I had come, she persisted, because Robert Kilroy-Silk, a former Labour MP for the area, and now a television personality, had written a book in which he had described how he was ousted by Militant. And Kilroy-Silk had argued that Militant's campaign had been masterminded from this very building. I laughed at her analysis of my motives.

'I'm not interested in Kilroy-Silk. I'm interested in Kirby.'

'We wish he'd been interested in Kirby! There he is on television talking to prisoners about the awfulness of prison life . . . *This is a prison. Kirby is a prison.*' I stayed for five hours. During that time I talked to a number of welfare rights experts and to a number of women who came to the centre for help and advice. Very few men come for advice. It is women who bear the burden of unemployment; it is they who handle the family budget; it is they who have to juggle with inadequate incomes; it is they who fight to keep the families together; it is they who struggle through the maze of benefits. The government has since simplified allowances, and listening to these people talk made me realize how badly that was needed. There was talk of a heating allowance, which was much needed in these damp flats made of concrete: if you live above the fifth floor in the suburbs or above the ninth floor in the city then you are eligible for more money than if you live below the fifth floor in the suburbs or the ninth floor in the city. Then there was a special laundry allowance for those who had bed-wetting children – £3 each week, which was not enough. It cost £1 to use the machine in the launderette and 20 pence for the spin-dryer, but you'd need at least 50 pence to dry a sheet, and no you couldn't go and buy a washing-machine because it was difficult to get credit in Kirby. The only thing you could do was go to loan-sharks and pay huge interest. There are lots of loan-sharks in Kirby; loan sharks are mostly working-class people themselves, who prey on the poverty of others. The centre wanted to start a credit union, but such a venture takes much organization. A credit union would work well in Kirby; it would mean that each week the women could pay into a fund and then, after a number of weeks of paying in, borrow from that fund; it is seen as a form of self-help; a form of saving, where each member knows that others just like her are saving. Few people default because to do so would be to rat on people you know. The loan-sharks are eliminated. The loan-sharks need to be eliminated, but they thrive on Merseyside.

Listening to the women trying to weave a way through the web of benefits made me think of negative income tax. Whatever happened to the prospect of negative income tax? Once a year I have to write down my earnings against my allowances, have them checked and send them off to the tax man, and he writes back and tells me how much money I must pay to the Exchequer. Why on earth can't everyone do that, and those with no incomes or low incomes then be given money according to their needs? It would mean an end to dreaded means testing and an end to the boring debate about universal benefits *v.* 'targeting'. Computers can take the strain, there could be tax officers to help people with the paperwork – and it would need only a fraction of the ever-growing welfare rights industry. It is not beyond the wit of man to devise such a scheme. It hardly demands an intellectual revolution. In the early seventies the idea was much debated. I remember spending an afternoon at Conservative Central Office having the seeds of such a scheme explained to me. Edward Heath was very keen on tax credits. I suppose that Mrs Thatcher is not very keen on tax credits because she is not very keen on Edward Heath.

That afternoon we talked of many things; we talked of men who leave Liverpool in search of jobs and then don't come back because they can't face their responsibilities; of women who drink – Martini is cheap and popular – and of kids who sniff petrol. The Thatcher government's attempts to streamline benefits and to channel them towards families most in need, and in particular towards families in low-paid work, were much derided. Topping up low-paid jobs merely encourages employers to remain stingy. And low-paid jobs are all that is on offer now; cowboys coming on to the estate setting up workshops demanding long hours in lousy conditions for appalling wages. The clock was going back, they said.

There was June, whose husband had been a docker and who was now unemployed and, she said, unemployable, because he was an alcoholic. She was trying to bring up three children, one of whom wanted to take a two-year secretarial course. 'She is studying Spanish at night school as well, because she wants to work in Spain. She wants to better herself, but it's a struggle for me.' There was Kitty, whose eldest son had gone to Germany for a job as a bricklayer and who had to return because his wife couldn't cope with two young children on her own. There was Dot, who didn't want her son to join a Youth Training Scheme because she saw it as cheap labour. Kitty agreed; the kids on those schemes learned nothing, she said. And then I met Karen, a single mother. She'd got a council flat because her father had told her to leave when she was pregnant; she had received several special payments to help her buy essentials for the flat and the baby. These have now been stopped by the government. They can be had now only as a loan. Karen said she couldn't contemplate a loan because she was already making weekly payments for her cooker and her clothes. She was nineteen. I asked her if she felt she had a right, once she got pregnant, to a flat and income from the state. She said 'yes' without hesitation. She'd worked for three years before getting pregnant and had paid her taxes. Mrs Thatcher doesn't like this attitude. Mrs Thatcher has watched the social security bill rocket, mainly because of the rise in unemployment, but also because of the growth in welfare rights workers, who make sure people get every allowance going and also because young people, like Karen, no longer feel that there is any kind of stigma attached to living on 'the social'. Indeed, for some having a baby has become a passport to a life infinitely preferable to being a shop assistant and living at home. Figures for the mid-eighties suggest that of the 126,000 births outside marriage, 37,000 are to women under the age of twenty. The figure for 1979 was 20,000, almost half. These mothers tend to have low educational achievement and poor employment prospects. A mere thirty years ago, when contraceptives were not freely available, teenage mothers were frowned upon and forced, through a lack of support systems, to hand their babies over for adoption. No one could argue that such a situation was right. On the other hand, no one can argue that the current situation is right either. That wretched pendulum has swung too far again. Mrs Thatcher considers that Karen and others like her have become dependent on welfare as an easy option, and she doesn't like it. She'd be much more interested in June's daughter, struggling to educate herself out of poverty.

The afternoon was depressing. There was a strong whiff of fatalism in the air. 'Isn't it awful,' was a phrase used all too often. The women felt they have no control over their lives. They get moved out of city centres on to vast estates; they get humdrum jobs; those humdrum jobs disappear; progress always leaves them one step behind. And then I met Tony. Tony has a vision. He works for the Transport and General Workers Union. He's involved in a campaign to persuade union members in work to pay something each week to help those out of work. He'd been a shop steward at British Leyland until the factory closed in 1979. 'They said productivity was low. We were making the TR7 – "the bullet", as it was called. We knew it wouldn't sell, but BL spent £50,000 on a marketing expert to tell them what we could have told them for free! Nothing will ever change in this country until the workers have some kind of say in what is going on.' How true that is, and yet democracy in the workplace or worker participation remains little more than a slogan. Neither of us could understand why such an obvious step, such a vital step, had not been embraced long ago. I'm not naïve enough to think that greater employee participation is easy; it demands a degree of toleration and cooperation between unions whose political and social views are different, let alone unions and management. But in the early seventies I looked at the working practices of Saab in Sweden and I was much impressed by the efforts being made to find a pathway. Fifteen years later, British companies are still at the report-commissioning stage. It shouldn't need legislation to make men see that one group of men wielding power over another group of men and giving orders without explanation is a lousy way of existing. There's something rotten in human nature when men delight in denying others scope to develop potential.

We had a long chat about the future. Tony's vision was clear. He did not see full employment returning. 'There could be full employment for a time, because the infrastructure needs building up; new sewers and roads would mop up labour and an area like this needs shops and cinemas. But this would only last a while. We need to teach people to share out work and in the end we are going to have to pay people a social wage not to work.

'What is so magnificent about working like a dog, spending your spare time in the pub and then dying six months after you retire? What is so marvellous about that? My vision is that people won't have to work like that and they will have the opportunity for all sorts of leisure and education. Anyone who wants a degree should be able to study for one, even pensioners. Think of the jobs that could be created, with books and schools and teachers and so on. You know, now that all that grinding work of the past is over, the world could be our oyster!'

I strolled off down the street to the station, thinking of the world as an oyster and delighted that someone else had seen the end of our industrial world as the beginning of something much better; someone else saw education as the key. This fragment of conversation was to stay in the front of my mind; it was like a building brick, it joined a little pile of bricks that I was gathering on my journey and which would by the end form a foundation of understanding.

I was staying at a hotel called Feather's. It is in the centre of town, around the corner from the once-grand Adelphi, which is so un-grand now that it has a banner outside saying, 'Rooms from £12'. If I'd known that I'd probably have stayed there, but by the time I discovered it, I felt too lazy to move. I went to meet Paul Feather. He was yelling at someone on the phone when I walked in. He continued to yell at that person for some time. His parents were first-generation Liverpudlians; his grandparents had come from Russia. His parents had the first Feather's hotel; he now has three in the area and the one in which I was staying was the cheapest, 'definitely for those without an expense account', he said. Paul Feather is the Tory candidate for Liverpool Garston, and very flashy indeed. He plays polo, has long curly hair, a diamond earring in one ear and a very large, multi-coloured watch. 'Liverpool deserves what it has got. The people keep voting Labour and although in the past they have been well intentioned, they have no experience of business, no experience of life in general. All they are used to is poverty. There is no vision. The place has been badly mismanaged. Government after government has put money in Liverpool and the city has behaved like a spoiled child and wasted that money. But that's the past; the future is wide open. Let me tell you a story: two salesmen go to an Arab country to sell shoes. One sees that the people there have no shoes, they are not wearing shoes, and he packs up and goes home, muttering, "What's the point of staying, the people don't wear shoes." The other salesman says: "Oh my! I'll stay for life and make a fortune." That's the sort of person that Liverpool needs. Not the sort who sees the mess, the abysmal quality of life in Liverpool and walks away, but the one who now sees the huge potential.' He told me that hotels were not money-spinners in Liverpool – not for the moment, anyway; he makes most of his money out of high-class catering for posh weddings. He said that since he was always dealing with posh people, he didn't like to admit that he came from Liverpool. Instead he said that Liverpool was merely a branch office. My face said it all. 'I tell you, it's true, that's what these people have done to Liverpool. If you don't believe me, I'll get some of my headed notepaper for you. I try and pretend this is just a northern branch office.' To make sure I got the point, the next day he sent me a sheet of his notepaper.

The last thing Liverpool needs is such an attitude. Instead it needs some positive thinking and some political stability. If there is one reason why Liverpool lags behind Glasgow and Newcastle – both fighting similar depressing economic situations – it is because those two cities have a political stability that enables them to do things, and Liverpool has nothing of the sort. There are of course other reasons. Liverpool's problems are more deep-rooted. It was a commercial city rather than an industrial city. It was a major distribution centre importing raw materials and exporting the products of inland industrial cities. It had few factories of its own; no manufacturing base, no skilled base; and nothing to plug the gap when containerization finally curtailed the need for dock labourers. In the 1960s, the Labour government tried to help by steering the car industry into Merseyside, but when the going got tough in the early 1980s, these plants, which were only 'branch offices' with no commitment to the area, pulled out. By 1985 unemployment in Liverpool had reached 27 per cent, twice the national average; by 1989 it had inched down to 25 per cent. Since the 1960s many politicians with their hearts in the right places have tried to help Liverpool; it has been the recipient of one worthy inner city scheme after another; each has concentrated on the symptoms of Liverpool's malaise rather than the *cause*.

Eighties thinking is trying another tack. Wise men suggest that investment in cities owes as much to fashion and instinct as it does to fine analysis. It follows then that psychology and perception can be as important as the injection of public money to break a cycle of economic and social decline. Thus each city in the first instance needs a flagship development, something to get the city talked about, something to make folk think that things are on the move. Liverpool has Albert Docks. Many cities have dockland development schemes: Newcastle,

Bristol, Cardiff, London. Modern Britain has re-discovered the delights of water, and all around the country pretty scenes are being carved out of derelict waterfronts. When we were a powerful nation, the seas at our command, along with everything else, our docks were awash with ugly clobber, scarring cranes and men doing a hard day's work. Now that we are no longer a powerful nation, our docks have become bijou, fashionable, like a Laura Ashley print. Albert Docks is a pleasant place to walk around; it contains Britain's largest group of Grade One listed buildings, a million square feet of warehousing converted into offices, shops and apartments. It houses the Tate of the North, which might well have gone to Manchester if the riots of 1981 had not focused attention on Liverpool. There are five-storey warehouses forming an enclosed square – the courtyard is water; the scale is large, the design simple and uniform. The warehouses are made of red brick and cast iron. The upper floors are carried by a colonnade of massive cast-iron doric columns. Albert Docks is nicknamed the Venice of the North, which is a little exaggerated. But it is a heartening sight and the plans for the area are grand.

And it's not the only admirable spot in the centre of Liverpool. There's only so much I could take of Beatles' corner, which has been commercialized for all it's worth, with a Beatles shop and the John Lennon Society Headquarters; a pub called Abbey Road, an Eleanor Rigby statue and the revamped Cavern Club. Cavern Walks, in Mathew Street, is a glossy shopping precinct with, of course, a series of bronze statues of the Fab Four. It's a fine tourist attraction and that is what it set out to be. The Japanese manage day trips from London to Liverpool just to see this tiny section of a once-great city. But there's more. There are pubs like the Philharmonic, and bookshops that serve coffee and carrot cake in the basement and a surprising number of wine bars and bistros, several of which I sought out and tried. They always seemed to be full of young people; the middle-aged with money to spare live over the water in the Wirral, and they don't tend to spend their evenings in town. Indeed I found much to like and only one thing to loathe – the litter, which is disgusting. It's much worse than in London which, God knows, is filthy enough. It's at its worst when there are basements. I spent an hour peering into basements, and each one was filled with layers of discarded rubbish, most of which had once contained food, or sweets, or drinks. The litter spoils Liverpool, but it doesn't ruin it. It's a city that commands great affection, and I can easily understand why Alan Bleasdale and Willy Russell have never thought of leaving.

Alan Bleasdale, who is often confused with Willy Russell, once said: 'Leave Liverpool? Why? I like living in Liverpool. It's like an old overcoat. I know it; I feel comfortable in it. I know where I am and I never feel in danger. My family and my friends keep me here.' Bleasdale's Liverpool is now the leafy suburb of Mossley Hill. But he was born on a 1930s council estate in Huyton; his Dad cycled to work because he couldn't afford the bus fare, and Alan was the first in his family to pass the 11-plus and go to college. He showed me the house where he was born. 'An ugly estate, isn't it? No one could call it attractive, and yet I didn't realize how ugly it was until I left at eighteen to go to college. Then I came back and said, Jesus Christ.' And he showed me the school on the Bluebell estate where he used to teach physical education: some of the windows were boarded up, others were broken. 'Perhaps if you put people in shit, they behave like animals. The downtrodden destroying the places they live in is a bit like self-rape, isn't it? They are Giro-fodder. In my father's day they were cannon fodder, and now they are Giro-fodder.' Alan Bleasdale had been called a Marxist revolutionary for writing a brilliant – a most brilliant – television drama called *The Monocled Mutineer*, in which he showed men, or rather boys, being used as cannon fodder and kicking against the idea to the extent of organizing a mutiny. He was accused of distorting history and turning a minor spot of bother in a place called Etaples into a glamorous mutiny. Historians and Old Soldiers crawled all over the newspapers arguing that the army had squashed the outbreak of 'disrespect' with ease and that it was other people's armies that mutinied, the French, the Italians, the Russians – not the Brits! I reminded him. We laughed. But Bleasdale was saddened by the outbursts against him. He'd written a television serial, not a documentary. And he knew full well what he was trying to say. His father's father had died at Passchendaele. 'He knew it was going to happen. He never saw his son.' None of this makes him a leftie revolutionary. 'We are all full of ambivalence. I've made a lot of money and I want to keep it. In five years' time I might not be able to write another word and I need that money for my wife and children. Yet at the same time I know that wealth must be redistributed.'

It had been my idea to revisit old landmarks and his idea to end up in a pub. We went to the Philharmonic. 'For all its problems, Liverpool kids are full of exuberance and vitality. I notice this whenever I am casting something; it's all teeth and smiles, is Liverpool. We all have elements of the entertainer in us; we like to show off. We're brash and warm. Liverpool people think with their hearts; if they thought with their heads, they'd leave.'

'Leave Liverpool! I've never thought of leaving Liverpool,' said Willy Russell, who is often mistaken for Alan Bleasdale. 'Everyone asks me that question. I'm a writer, not a performer; I don't need to leave. And where would I go? Where is glamorous? Nowhere is glamorous. You only leave if you have to leave for a job. I look around and see filthy streets, schools that are crumbling, houses decaying, shops boarded up and my car keeps getting broken into, but there isn't another city in which I'd live. You know, when we talk of Liverpool we are talking of a small place. Travel twelve miles and the Scouse accent has gone, you're into Lancashire and it's different. Liverpool was never crushed by mills and heavy industry. We were a trading place, a melting-pot, like New York. We've never looked south to London for leadership. We've always looked to America. At least, we did when I was young, and I suppose we still do now. There's an arrogance in this place which fuels people like Alan and me. This place believes in itself.

'There's a massively flourishing youth theatre. I get at least two letters a week from kids asking how they can get Equity cards. And I was at the theatre the other night when two kids I'd taught came up and said they'd written a play about drugs and were trying to get it put on.'

'Why should they be attracted to the theatre?'

'Why? Because this is a very oral city. Working-class culture is oral-based; the written word is not to be trusted. Schools are middle-class places because they concentrate on the written word, and that's irrelevant to most kids. I left at fifteen with one O-level and worked for six loathsome years in a hairdresser's shop. I got my A-levels at twenty-one and then went to teacher training college. And when I tried to teach English it was a nightmare. Those kids don't want to be taught; they'd got passive resistance down to a fine art. Then one day I started telling them a story, and the next week they asked for another story. This was better than having them fool around, I thought, and then the penny dropped. They want their information inserted orally. When you go to the theatre up here you'll find a different kind of audience to your London audience.'

I'd been to a play the night before. I'd been to see Jim Morris's *Pinocchio Boys* at the Everyman. It was about three boys growing up on an estate on Merseyside who wanted life to be as exciting as television. I had difficulty with some of the television references because I obviously watch the wrong programmes, and I had difficulty with the ending, which was gloomy. With Willy Russell's plays there's usually a sense of optimism. *Educating Rita* and *Shirley Valentine* are gloriously optimistic plays: down-trodden Rita and down-trodden Shirley *do something* to improve their situation. I like this attitude; or was he trying to tell me that it is only women who are foolish enough to be optimistic?

'Women are easier characters; they have a language and emotions and they communicate. They are easier to handle than male characters. Rita and Shirley sort something out for themselves; they want to make life better and that's the way it should be. I've never seen a political play worth a jot. Once politics takes over, the theatre is lost. The world is a better place for having *The Importance of Being Earnest* and the Sistine Chapel. And that's how I feel.'

And the world is a better place for having Willy Russell and Alan Bleasdale. And that's how I feel. And if Liverpool can produce such talent, then the world is a better place for having Liverpool.

I'd met Willy Russell at his office. On my way back to Feather's, I didn't pay much attention to road signs and although I wasn't lost, I thought it wise to check that I was heading in the right direction. I saw two girls chatting on a street corner and I asked them if I was on course for the Adelphi Hotel, my local landmark. One of the girls, who was extremely tall and stunningly beautiful, said: 'I'm going that way and I'll walk with you. It's not good to be walking around here when you don't know where you are going. It's all right for me, I'm Liverpool's first woman bouncer, yeah. Everyone knows me. I got a lot of publicity when I became a bouncer. I do karate and boxing and so I can take care of myself. That's why I can wear clothes like this.' Her skirt was the tiniest mini-skirt in captivity. She towered over me, and her skirt reached my waist. 'I come from Allerton, which is a dead quiet place, so when I became a bouncer I told them I came from Toxteth. They'd know I could look after myself if I came from Toxteth.

'I'm a D J in a nightclub, that's where I'm off to now. If you ever want a night out, come to Snobs, it's a great place. Turn up and ask for Niki, that's me. Look, do you know where you are now? It's dead straight from here; straight on up there. Ta-ra.' And she was gone. I swear that she had bubbled and chatted from the moment I met her until she delivered me in sight of the Adelphi. I guess she was about nineteen; she had style and confidence, she assumed that every word she uttered was of interest to me. She believed in herself. Niki is the spirit of Liverpool. I'd found it at last.

Chapter 11

Wales:
A Touch of Grass

I travelled to Wales by the slowest of routes; I boarded a narrow boat at Chester and spent four days with a handful of strangers, lazily floating along the Llangollen Canal. My days fell easily into a slothful routine: after breakfast when we began the day's journey, I would get off the boat and walk on the towpath. As I could walk faster than the boat, I'd make a rendezvous to meet the boat at a bridge or a lock several hours later. That walk was a pleasure. There was peace and there was beauty and yet often the noisy old world was no more than a bridge away; if I stood still I could hear the hum of the rest of the world, scurrying about its business. The weather was dazzling; the colours were copybook autumn: greens and browns and golds. Each morning a heatless white sun would stare at the dozy countryside, a countryside all but ready for winter sleep, and bathe it in the most gentle, soothing light. The leaves, so cheerfully close to the end of their lives and with nothing to lose, would cheekily wink at the white sun, and that slight movement would make the scene glisten and sparkle. Many find September a melancholy month; I find it glorious. Of winter I expect little and can sometimes be surprised. Spring and summer are whores, they tease and tantalize and sometimes lie. September is virtuous, honest, glorious and never disappointing; it offers only what it can deliver. Mostly it just offers a last chance to step outside, breathe deeply, and walk freely. So I did.

By the fifth morning October arrived. It was dark and dank; the whole day seemed like the inside of the lock. I felt damp, and half expected my skin to be green and slimy. The towpath, instead of enticing me to walk, looked sinister, looked designed for skulduggery and murder, draped as it was in swirling mist resembling theatrical dry ice. At that point I abandoned the narrow boat, found a phone box and sought a taxi to Llangollen.

I was in Wales. I felt a little uneasy. I could not pronounce the street names or the place names. It was worse when I went into a shop. The sales assistant was speaking to another customer in Welsh. They stopped talking. I bought a newspaper and as soon as the transaction was over the two reverted to their native tongue. I felt horribly English. Wales is a foreign country. A small foreign country of some two and a half million people spread over an area that measures a mere 140 miles from north to south and at its narrowest point a mere forty miles from east to west. Most of the English think (if they think at all) that Wales is yet another province of England, like Cumbria or Devon. There's an awful story, oft repeated, of the time when the entry for Wales in the *Encyclopaedia Britannica* said 'see England'. Wales is much ignored, probably more so than Scotland. Say 'Wales' to the average punter and he'll probably paint a quick sketch of the south Wales valleys. North Wales, to those too young to remember Llandudno as a flourishing seaside resort, is nothing more than a mountain called Snowdon and a castle called Caernarfon, where a prince called Charles had a dazzling investiture. Or they might just talk about the Welsh nationalists who like setting fire to country cottages owned by the English as second homes. The Welsh have been nursing a grievance against the English for some 700 years for conquering them and then for trying to smother their Welshness. The English can be unspeakable at times: during the eighteenth and nineteenth centuries they punished Welsh children caught speaking their own language at school; a piece of wood with the initials WN (the Welsh Not) cut into it, was hung around the necks of pupils. Such an attitude defies belief. The Welsh have all my sympathy, not just because of the much cherished dollop of Welsh blood in me, not just because such oppression is manifestly wrong, but because of my distaste for a homogeneous world that speaks the same language, listens to the same music, watches the same films, reads the same books and drives the same cars. How dull. The dreariness of it, I think, is one reason why the folk in Bradford (and elsewhere) encourage multi-culturalism. It is intriguing to think of that newish attempt to encourage people to be different and contrast it with England's attitude, in the past, towards the Welsh. How stupid we were to try and ban their language and to strangle their customs and their culture. It amazes me that the British government did not seriously acknowledge that Wales had a separate identity until 1951, when a Ministry of Welsh Affairs was first established. That minister was elevated to Secretary of State for Wales only in 1964. Well, at least they now have Sianel Pedwar Cymru (S4C), the Welsh fourth channel that broadcasts in Welsh (but not before Gwynfor Evans, Plaid Cymru's first MP, threatened to fast to death), Welsh studies in schools, road signs in Welsh, the right to ask for court proceedings and tax demands in the Welsh language. But it isn't enough and it's too late. The number of Welsh speakers has declined steadily this century, from around 50 per cent in 1900 to 19 per cent today. The dwindling minority feel so miserable about this that they have become all the more pugnacious. Pity we didn't see the wisdom of encouraging bilingualism centuries ago, and then perhaps the Welsh would have been a little more tolerant of English weekend cottages (only a little, because people do not want to sit by and watch the rich buying second homes at inflated prices while the newly married Welsh are unable to afford homes of their own). As it is the Welsh are not tolerant of English incomers. They still feel that every time the English buy a cottage or a business their Welshness is threatened. In north Wales they fear that they are slowly becoming an annex of Liverpool, and in south Wales they increasingly feel that they are becoming an extension of the M4 corridor. As in Scotland, Europe is seen as a potential saviour. In a united Europe, Wales could perhaps find a safe haven and the freedom to be Welsh; to be less fettered by the English. Surveys have shown that more than half those interviewed support the nationalist aims of excluding English influence and preserving Welsh culture, but the vast majority, fortunately, do not support the methods used; they are against fire bombings. Perhaps if the Welsh had not had to fight so hard to keep their Welshness, then I would not have felt such an intruder. I'm not saying that I was *made* to feel unwelcome; merely that I felt an outsider, a foreigner.

The Welsh, said Jan Morris in *The Matter of Wales*, a book that was to be my constant companion, are different. They are what is left of the original Celts who swept into these islands from Europe. They were 'Warlike, artistic, quarrelsome, ill-organized, showy, flighty, witty and headstrong'. Then the Romans came bringing a few roads and a little order. Fortunately, when England fell to the Angles and the Saxons, Wales managed to avoid that particular deadening hand, only to be harnessed once and for all by the Normans. After that there was only a brief period – ten years in fact, between 1400 and 1410 – when Owen Glendower, the national hero, had fun trying to kick the English out. For a handful of years it looked as though he might succeed in his attempt to establish Welsh statehood, but by 1413 the rising had been suppressed. Jan Morris's vision of what Wales would have been like if Owen Glendower had won the war of independence is a delightful fantasy. Wales is a republic, a perfect little neutral state, with strong ties to Europe and cordial relations with England. Property laws are very strict, and the number of English cottage owners has been reduced. The economy thrived once the English had gone, with cooperatively owned steel mills in the south and a dozen or so coal mines providing power for the country – not a nuclear power station in sight. There are small industries, flourishing as workers' cooperatives, and the most advanced health service in the western world, financed with ease because Wales no longer has to fund English royalty, nuclear weapons and other nonsense. There is a little army which has no military parades and no uniform and is committed to 'absolute non-violence'. There is no pomp, the policemen dress in dungarees and the dear little country attracts idealists from all over the world as a 'model of a non-nuclear, neutral, un-militarist, ecological state'.

The vision was so appealing that I decided to visit Machynlleth, where Glendower held court and where Jan Morris placed the capital of her fantasy republic: it is in the middle, at the head of the Dovey estuary on the west coast. That is to say, the furthest point from England. If Jan Morris's dream for Wales had come true, Machynlleth would have been easier to visit. I once again let my life be ruled by train timetables and found myself in Welshpool, attempting to catch a little train that would chug its way to the coast. The station at Welshpool was deserted. I found a sign saying 'Information' and knocked on the door. A voice answered: 'You'll have to wait two minutes. I'm doing the money.' I waited. He opened up and we tried to work out how I could spend a few hours in Machynlleth and then get back on the train and head north. It seemed impossible. The one thing that became clear was that wherever I decided to stop, I'd be spending two nights. Few trains run in Wales on Sundays. I decided for no good reason that I didn't want to spend two nights in Machynlleth, and that if I had to spend two nights anywhere I'd prefer it to be Aberystwyth. It was a daft decision; it poured with rain and all I managed to do in Aberystwyth was read the Sunday papers and go for a damp walk along the cliff tops. The Welsh have even duller Sundays than the English. The fact that there are no trains is a giveaway. John Wesley's Methodism was hugely successful in Wales in the mid-eighteenth century. In part, one could argue, the Welsh would have grabbed at anything that enabled them to reflect their disdain for the Church of *England*, and Wesley's rejection of the snottiness of Anglicanism, and his passionate desire to help the poor to rise above their boozing and their ignorance hit the perfect note. These non-conformist views transformed Wales. It's baffling in some ways. How could these 'showy, flighty, witty, headstrong' people take so readily to the funless, teetotal, self-improving stance of Methodism? But they did. And the influence of the egalitarian people's church – or rather, chapel – was so entrenched that no one did anything on Sundays, not even wind the clock. Pubs were not allowed to open on Sundays until 1982 and even then there was a lot of huffing and puffing from the pulpit. It's not surprising, then, that there are no trains on Sundays.

On Monday morning I headed north. I wanted to visit the heartland of Welshness, Gwynedd. The Plaid Cymru MPs are elected in Gwynedd. Here they see the development of an east–west road, which would improve communications with Liverpool, as just another ethnic threat. Here they view south Wales as beyond the pale. South Wales is English-speaking (many of the inhabitants came from the Midlands, as well as Ireland, to work in the mines), socialist and industrial. A world away, not the real Wales at all. These attitudes are important. They help to explain why the Welsh voted against devolution in 1979 by four to one, when you'd have thought they would have jumped at the proposal. But just as in Scotland, where the Highlands and Islands were (and are) suspicious of the populous Strathclyde area, so too in Wales: the north feared (and fears) being swamped by the populous south. And in return the south feared that devolution would bring preferment for the bilingual, Druid-loving people of the north. Who needs to fear England when the people themselves do not trust each other!

As well as savouring Welsh Wales, I also wanted to visit Llanys-tumdwy; this was to be a David Lloyd George pilgrimage. The short distance takes a couple of hours by train; from Dovey junction there are twenty-two stops to Porthmadog. It was the most delightful journey; the train hugs the coast all the way, disappearing into the odd tunnel and emerging to display another little village or caravan site nestling close to the water's edge. I looked for a heron on the flat sands of the Dovey estuary. Dylan Thomas made much of sad, flat estuary sands where he watched 'herons walk like women poets'. I have a poor memory for snatches of appropriate poetry or prose, but this is easily recalled: what on earth made him liken a heron walking to a woman poet? Months later I saw a picture of Edith Sitwell and convinced myself that Thomas had her in mind when he wrote that line.

At Barmouth a blonde bounced in. She was an American with a large knapsack. She allowed her large knapsack to bump the smaller knapsack of another traveller and that was the signal for an animated conversation between the two of them. The conversation, which was really no more than a catalogue of the places they had visited, was punctuated by the blonde jumping up and down and taking photographs out of the window. She didn't know the word 'estuary'. She got the point when the young man likened it to a fjord.

I wasn't sure whether Llanystumdwy was closer to Porthmadog or to Criccieth, so when the ticket inspector came along, I asked him.

'Oh, I haven't a clue, love.'

I decided to get off at Porthmadog. It was by then 12.30, lunchtime, and when I finally managed to find the Tourist Office it was firmly closed. I drank coffee and waited until it opened.

'How do I get to Llanystumdwy?' I asked.

I had missed the bus. By sitting waiting for the Tourist Office to open I had missed the bus by ten minutes. The next bus, a couple of hours away, would throw my timetable out completely. And I also discovered that if I had gone to Criccieth on the train I would have been able to walk.

'How much will it cost me to take a taxi? I want to make a brief pilgrimage to Lloyd George's house and his grave.'

Her face broke into a huge smile. I had obviously said the right thing. She picked up the phone and chatted away in Welsh.

'The taxi is on its way. He said he won't charge you much. It'll take about an hour and he'll charge you £6.' It was my turn to smile. And to learn why my request had pleased her so much.

'I once worked for Lloyd George. When he came here, he'd leave his secretary in London and call on me for help. He knew me because I used to work for his brother. He would write everything out in longhand in *pencil*, you know. And his writing was hard to decipher. I used to say it was just as easy to read it upside down! And when lunch time came, we'd just sit there and eat together. He was like that, he had no problem coming down to my level or anybody's. Did you see that television series about him?'

I told her that I had and that it had just finished when I went on a visit to Albania and, since journalists are not popular in Albania, I'd used the television series as a 'cover'. I told people that I was a Welsh historian, guessing that their knowledge of Wales would be so slight that they wouldn't pester me with further questions. That story amused her; the television series did not. 'We didn't like it. I know it was made by a Welshman, but no one around here liked it much. We all know about his mistresses. His wife knew all about it too, he grew away from her and from us, but it's a pity they had to drag all that up and spend so much time on it. It's a shame.' And she of course wanted to know the reason for my interest in Lloyd George. I told her that it stemmed from my years on the *Guardian* which was, or at least had been, a Liberal newspaper. Of course my interest went deeper than that. The Liberal party attracted some great minds in the last century, and produced some great reforming governments, and I was intrigued that the Welsh with speed and ease had become devoted to the Liberal party in much the same way as they had adopted Methodism. In my view the two displayed, above all, the strong spirit of egalitarianism in the Welsh. Just as soon as the Reform Act of 1884 had given a large number of working-class men (but by no means all) the vote, politics in Wales was transformed. What would the Liberal party have been without Wales? What would it have been without Lloyd George?

The taxi arrived and off we went. The driver whistled and hummed as though he were about to burst into a full-throated song at any minute. Llanystumdwy is the prettiest of villages. It has all the ingredients that we town-dwellers expect to find in villages: a large church, a beautiful bridge under which flowed the purest water, a small hotel, a post office, a café and an arts-and-crafts centre. There were rows of slate-and-stone houses, several of which were being lovingly improved with new-fangled windows not exactly in keeping with the architecture. We went first to the boyhood home to which Lloyd George returned from Manchester, to live in the home of his mother's brother, the village shoemaker. In those days the village only had some seventy houses for poor labourers under the thumb of the Tory Anglican squire. Between us, the driver and I shared out fragments of history and hoped we had got the story more or less right. The story of the village-school education, and how L G spent much of his time with the blacksmith; of how he became articled to a solicitor in Porthmadog and how, later in life, when he won a libel action, he helped fund an Institute for the village. We had a little difficulty finding the grander house to which he moved, and when we did, we found that it was being painted by the present inhabitant. The museum was closed and so our final stop was the grave; a most beautiful spot in the woods, by the river, where Lloyd George played as a child.

It was an enchanting hour. The driver, whose name I didn't know, asked no questions of me, and sped efficiently from place to place, commenting mostly on the roads and how impossible and impassable they had been in summer before the by-pass had been built. The roads were not full of Lloyd George fans; the cars were *en route* to Butlin's at Pwllheli. 'The pub wasn't too happy when the by-pass came, nor was the petrol station – it had to close. It's now the arts-and-crafts centre.' The signpost to Criccieth had been daubed with paint. The place name was spelled with two 'c's in the middle. The nationalists, the taxi driver assured me, had been along and blotted out the surplus 'c'. Criccieth is Cricieth in Welsh.

I caught the 5.08 back to Aberystwyth and the following morning the first bus to Cardiff.

I viewed my visit to south Wales as a treat, something special, a welcome pause in this relentless round of unknown hotels. In Cardiff I was staying with a friend. Ann Clwyd is now the M P for Cynon Valley but we had once been colleagues on the *Guardian*. She had covered Wales for the paper and been based in Cardiff before becoming a Member of the European Parliament and then a member of the House of Commons. The thought of her warm welcome pleased me as I sat in a cold, near-empty bus, making a list of what I wanted to see and do in south Wales. The centre of my interest was the valleys: I wanted to see what was happening in the aftermath of the miners' strike. I saw the valleys as not just male, but macho, and was glad that Ann would be able to help me over the hurdle of being a female outsider. I saw the valleys as a battered and beaten area where nosey questions from an English woman might not be welcome. Such were my fears on the bus that morning. Two weeks later I was to leave south Wales with a chunk of heart left in Cynon Valley.

The miners and mining communities had fascinated me for some years; since the election of February 1974. Edward Heath's government had battled with the miners in 1972. That year was the first occasion since 1926 that the miners had taken *national* action. In 1972 they were displeased to discover that they had fallen way down the wages table, to seventeenth position, and their fight that year was straightforward enough – the miners wanted to improve their material lot. They did well: they won and their victory hinged on the battle of Saltley Gate. Saltley was a coke stockpile in Birmingham. A miners' picket had failed to stop the lorries coming and going and Arthur Scargill had made an emotional plea to other unions to support his fight. Twenty thousand of them had marched upon Saltley and the chief constable of Birmingham was forced to order the gates to close: Scargill's dream, solidarity among the workers, had stopped the supply of coke. The miners were riding high. They were riding even higher in 1974, having watched the price of oil quadruple, and once again they confronted Heath, reducing the country to a three-day week. Heath felt cornered and decided to call a single-question election, asking: who runs this country – the government or the trades unions? I was working for the *Guardian* at the time and one afternoon my then husband, Norman Fowler, rang me there to tell me that an election had been called. He asked me to take immediate leave to go to Sutton Coldfield to fight the election. There had been much talk that an election was imminent, but I did not believe that it would happen. That night I had the first political row of my life. I thought the decision to call the election was stupid and suicidal. The Tories could not win. And I did not want to stomp the streets against the miners. I saw the miners as workers to be cherished; they did the most disgusting, unhealthy and dangerous job in order that I could live in a warm and well-lit house, using endless electric gadgets without a second thought. They deserved the highest wages for that. Of course I knew that coal was no longer king, of course I knew that many pits were uneconomical, of course I knew that it was wrong for any one group 'to hold the country to ransom'. Of course I knew all the counter arguments, but none of this eased my loathing of tramping the streets for votes against the miners, of tramping the streets for a clearly defined battle between labour and capital. It all seemed so distasteful compared to the election of 1970. Norman listened to my lengthy emotional tirade and answered in two sentences. 'I've listened to what you have to say. Now, are you coming with me or not?' I went. Heath lost the election. The miners had brought down the government.

It is hardly surprising that the Tories decided that it wouldn't happen again. The story is that they planned most carefully; they saw another battle with the miners as inevitable, and however long it took and whatever the cost, they were going to win. They would pick their moment and they would win. It came in 1984; it took a year; it cost a lot. The Chancellor of the Exchequer said it was 'worth the investment'. The great miners' strike was not about who heads league tables of wages, it was about something more fundamental. It was about the way society is ordered; it was about whether society should put profit before social need. The coal board wanted to close pits; demand for coal had been reduced and too many pits were making too great a loss. The miners knew this; Arthur Scargill knew this. But he wanted a fight; he preferred a world in which governments subsidized jobs. The miners lost because they were not of one mind and because the solidarity shown at Saltley did not reappear – other unions did not halt the movement of 'blackleg' coal and oil. The miners lost because violent scenes of police fighting miners and miners fighting police alienated potential supporters. Arthur Scargill was too confident; he miscalculated on the weather and on coal stocks and on the strength of the left. The Labour party floundered. The event was a watershed for this country; a seminal event in post-war political history.

I had never met a miner. I had never been down a coal mine, but I had been down a gold mine in Western Australia. I hated it. I hated the darkness and the damp and the wading through water. I couldn't understand why anyone wanted to do the job, let alone fight for it. Why in the fifties when many were refusing to do so-called 'dirty jobs' and were happy to see them taken up by immigrants, did the coal miners cling to the mines?

The area known as The Valleys lies in the hinterland between Newport and Swansea. In all, there are some twenty valleys, and Cynon lies squeezed between the more famous valleys of Rhondda and Merthyr. The collapse of coal and steel has had a devastating effect on the lives of the half a million people who live in this area. None the less, they have to be coaxed to speak with one voice. The allegiance of each valley is to its own; this encourages narrowness, parochialism and a large degree of jealousy between them. Their economic problems are hardly new and certainly not caused by the miners' strike. As far back as 1936, when unemployment in Merthyr was 51 per cent, a report said that 'there might be a case for systematic evacuation wholly or in part of such a derelict area as Merthyr'. After all, mines have a finite life and when that life is over it is time to pack up and move on, in just the same way as people packed up and moved in all those years ago. Well, the valley dwellers don't want to move, that much is clear, and it's not just because there is nowhere else to go. Many did leave, but the drift is now over; indeed, some who moved away are coming back. At first glance it is hard to understand why. The statistics alone are not enticing. The valleys are beyond doubt Wales's 'inner city' with all the problems with which I was now familiar. Cynon Valley has some of the worst housing conditions in western Europe. It might have a high percentage of home ownership, 68 per cent, but 19 per cent of the houses are classified as unfit, with no inside lavatories and sometimes no hot water. Unemployment in Cynon Valley is 21 per cent; 24 per cent of school-leavers have no formal qualifications; there is a large number of people with long-term sickness and disability, and perhaps as many as 60 per cent of the people live on incomes of £80 a week or less.

On my first morning in south Wales Ann drove me right through Cynon Valley, from Cardiff to the Heads of the Valleys Road, which as its name suggests runs along the top of the valleys within sight of the Brecon Beacons. The journey takes forty-five minutes. I was expecting, I suppose, a landscape of menacing slagheaps. My mind was conditioned by images of the Aberfan disaster, when in October 1966 a slag tip, disturbed by heavy rain, engulfed a school, a row of cottages and a farm. The disaster killed 144 people, of whom 116 were children. I did not find menacing slag heaps. They have not been removed completely, but, since Aberfan, millions of pounds have been spent scaling them down in size and grassing them over to resemble natural hills. My first impression was of almost claustrophobic narrowness; the sides of the valley are steep but not particularly high. There are one or two expansive sections, but for the most part I felt hemmed in as we drove along a winding road with houses rising on either side for no more than a handful of rows, sometimes running at right angles to the valley bed, sometimes in parallel. Occasionally the landscape became green and pleasant but on the whole, having come from north Wales, I would not call the valleys picturesque. They could be, now that the pits have gone (there is but one working in Cynon Valley). When the land is reclaimed; when the pit heads are removed; when the slag heaps are camouflaged with grass; when the land is levelled and planted with trees or new industries; then the valleys could be attractive. This is the worst stage. The drama of the industrial landscape has ended; the scenery is still partly in place, partly falling down and partly removed, leaving gaping holes, hollow reminders of what was and no clear view of what is to be. Ironically, it is where the industrial scenery is still in place that it is most hideous. At Abercwmboi, British Coal has a plant making smokeless fuel. In order that some parts of the country can have clean air, this little place is made filthy. There's a wretched old plant that has been operating since the early forties, before nationalization; it uses some German process which seems to work well in Germany but has never worked well in Cynon Valley. Its chimneys belch muck, soot and sulphurous yellow fumes all over the neighbourhood. Cars parked nearby collect a film of black dust; God knows what goes into people's lungs. When the valley was wedded to coal, nobody much minded if their daffodils had black spots. When coal began to leave the valley, people clung to the phurnacite plant. It meant jobs, and they were defensive when it was described as a dirty old eyesore and labelled the worst polluting plant in Europe. After much nagging the company has promised to do something to clean the place up. But some in Cynon Valley have come to realize that the plant is bad for their image; they'd like to see it go. Potential investors, they argue, driving up the road as I did on that day, would look aghast and decide that this was not a suitable environment to house a hi-tech future.

Aberdare is the valley's main town – that means it houses the civic centre and has one and a bit High Streets, shaped like a Y; other towns have only one. It's a gutsy little place, forever popping up in history books for being in the vanguard of radicalism. It was one of the first areas enthusiastically to embrace non-conformist religion, one of the first places to turn from the Liberal party to the Labour party after the coal stoppage of 1898 (along with the Trades Council of Merthyr it invited Keir Hardie to become Labour parliamentary candidate in 1900); it was from the first a home for militant trades unionism – that is, trades unionism that allows the ordinary member to have a decent say – and in later years it has been a pocket of strength for Plaid

Cymru. Strolling through its main street you wouldn't guess at any of this. It's sleepy now. It's lost out to Merthyr. But it still has its council chambers and a cinema that plays Bingo, little cafés smelling of chips, shops offering delightful service – a transaction as brief as buying a newspaper invites a conversation which is invariably opened by a reference to the weather. How English can you get! But then in north Wales they describe the south as Anglicized, and it is at least Anglicized in the sense that I ceased to feel aware of my Englishness. A school has been turned into a delightful restaurant and there is a leisure centre and an arts centre. The town's only statue commemorates Griffith Rhys Jones, a conductor famed for his choir of choral singers. He trained as a blacksmith and said that the tones of both hammer and anvil developed his musical ear, enabling him to become a violinist and conductor. There are also shops that are boarded up, shops that are tatty, with broken windows and grubby curtains; there are sad-looking men sitting on benches talking and not talking; badly dressed women slowly climbing the steps to Bingo; and a grim-looking bus queue where women stand ankle deep in the weekly shopping, their faces weary and worn.

Penrihiwceiber is a one-street village. It's the poorest part of the valley, the most deprived area. There is no sports complex, nothing for youth. Tuesdays and Thursdays there is Bingo at the battered Miners Institute. The Miners Institutes are the valleys' equivalent of stately homes, but no one knows what to do with them now. And if they have ideas, they do not have money. The main street is truly dreary; again there are boarded up shops, but those that are open ooze the atmosphere of southern Irish towns of today, or of England in the 1950s: stores that sell a wide variety of inexpensive goods and clothes; the sort of draper's shop where in the 1950s you could buy elastic and thread, vests and stockings and knitting wool. There's a chapel, and, opposite the Lee Hotel, there's a paddling pool for children, which was without water. It takes no more than fifteen minutes to stroll the length of the village. The pit head stood at one end. It's gone now; it went in October 1985 within six months of the ending of the miners' strike. It's been levelled and left, levelled in a desultory way and left awaiting the next stage of reclamation.

The rows of terraced houses look surprisingly perky. Money has been found to 'envelop' them: to pretty them up outside with new roofs and windows, and fresh paint. They may have no bathrooms inside, but the 'envelope' at least makes them wind and weatherproof and it also cheers up the look of the valley. Most of the houses were built in the 1880s and are privately owned. They are of course tiny:

two rooms and a tiny kitchen downstairs. Many miners have added a bathroom beyond the kitchen, and many have made the two small rooms into one. More often than not they are beautifully looked after.

Jim Evans lives in such a house, which runs steeply away at right angles from the main street, around the corner from the British Legion. He used to be secretary of the Penrihiwceiber Miners Lodge. Jim made me feel that Penrihiwceiber had suffered a bereavement and was still grieving. It *had* suffered a bereavement: it had lost its pit and with it the jobs of most of the men, and when the jobs had gone so too had a well established lifestyle. The period of mourning was not yet over. People were still empty and confused. Ann had already told me that her mail bag contained letters from men who were suicidal because they couldn't see a way out of their dilemma.

When the pit closed, the men were offered the option of moving to other pits or of being made redundant. The offer of a job in another pit did not necessarily mean the offer of the same job; most of the men would have to accept lesser jobs cushioned by the same pay for three years, and then that pay would be reduced to the level of the job. 'The public generally didn't understand this. They were told that all miners would be offered jobs if they wanted them. They didn't understand the loss of face and pride which went with taking a job that was below the one they had. Beyond that the whole concept of men working away from their villages was wrong. Penrihiwceiber was a family pit, father and son worked together. In the morning you'd just tumble out of bed and stroll down the street. Transferring meant getting up earlier, catching a bus that wouldn't wait if you were late and then at end of day, waiting for the last and slowest person to clean up before the bus left to come back. Many of those who chose to go to other pits regret it now. You don't fit in that easily and it isn't the same.'

It isn't the same because Penrihiwceiber was special; everyone says so. It was known as the Bolshie pit, but it was not Communist; indeed, for many years it was under the thumb of a Catholic attached to the right wing of the Labour party. The union was very, very strong and prided itself on putting the men's safety before productivity. Some say they went by the rule book and downed tools too easily if they found something out of line, that they were not flexible enough. No one denies that productivity was low; they merely argue over the reasons. The Coal Board says it was because of the men's attitude; the unions say it was because low investment had made the pit difficult to work. Anyway, before the strike the pit was known for poor results. The Coal Board came up with the idea of linking it by a tunnel to the neighbouring pit of Deep Navigation. The coal would then be brought to the surface there and save on costs. It was part of their policy of combining small pits. The men said *no*. They feared that their pit would be subsumed. The Coal Board abandoned the plan and invested £1 million in a new coal face at Penrihiwceiber, with a new productivity deal. The strike came. Six months after the strike the pit was closed. The Coal Board says that the men got nowhere near the target. The men say they were doing their best.

Jim was offered a job in Tower pit, in the washery, which was nothing to do with the pit itself, but a mile away where the coal was washed and graded. He had been an electrician, taking care of the winders, working in the pulse of the pit, and working regular day shifts. If he had accepted the job he would have had to work nights as well. Travelling would have added one and a half hours on to his working day and he said no. He was forty-seven at the time. He accepted a cheque for £31,000. The dole stopped after a year. He'll get a Coal Board pension when he's sixty-five.

'I'll get another job in the end. I haven't looked far, to be honest. I'm happy for the moment using my electrician's skills in the community. I wouldn't rewire a whole house, that's too much to take on, but I'll fix the odd point, like. I'm luckier than most. I have two children, a son working for British Rail who is married and lives up the road, and my daughter who lives at home and who works, alongside my wife, at the local textile factory. Both are machinists. I'm the housewife now. Everything is the other way. I get my wife up at 6.30 and I get the car started – it needs a bit of choking in the cold. I get it all ready for them to step into. Then I do a bit of housework and shopping. My wife does the main shopping on a Friday, but I top up each day with bread and potatoes or a bit of ham, odds and ends. I do the cooking: I have their dinner on the table when they come in just before five. They only have a half-hour break and a sandwich midday.'

My views on the macho coal miner were fast disappearing. Jim said he's happy enough with his new life. He'd been the breadwinner for years; he'd worked hard, often seven days a week, and he'd be content not to work again if that meant that young men, those who have never worked, could have jobs. He still resents the colliery closure and fervently believes that the miners' strike was right.

'We could have won that strike, you know. If all the miners had stuck together, we could have won. It was Nottingham that finished us by not coming out. I haven't got a good word to say for Nottingham. Yes, our pit was losing money, but there were reasons for that. We needed a new face to make it viable and we got that in return for new production targets, but we could never meet these targets because everything was so antiquated. The board would say, well, we can't invest any more until you prove yourselves with increased productivity, but we couldn't prove ourselves without the investment – it was putting the cart before the horse. It was a hopeless situation. Bad management and poor investment is what ruined our pit. Not the men. The men were second to none. I tell you, that pit could have been economical with the right management making the right decisions. After the strike, it was farcical. The costs at the colliery had started to come down and yet they closed us. We tried to fight it; we said no at first, but then they put rumours around that the redundancy payments would be cut back and we got running scared, which is what they wanted. We were blackmailed by rumours into accepting the closure.

'During the miners' strike there was a tremendous sense of unity in this community; everyone was helping everyone else. We were all in the same boat. South Wales was solid. There were no scabs at our pit.'

'But south Wales said no to the strike in the first place. They voted eighteen to ten not to strike,' I reminded him.

'Yes, that's because it seemed like Yorkshire's problem at first. We didn't understand. A year before, we had had a strike here over the closing of a Merthyr pit, and we couldn't get the other regions to support us. We ran around the country explaining things but we couldn't get support for south Wales. So when we thought it was Yorkshire's problem we thought they could stew.'

To get the mines closed, the pits that had agreed to strike picketed the other pits. At times there was only one lone picket. But that was enough. South Wales was out. We talked then of broader things, of the Labour party and of the Tories.

'I wish anyone who is thinking of voting Tory would come and live here for a while. The only salvation for people like myself, working people, is a Labour government.'

'But the Wilson government closed many mines, and Kinnock was not that supportive.'

'I know, and I'm not over-enamoured by his behaviour, but he was and is under pressure to be more central in his policies in order to get elected. Look, don't take that away from me. Don't take the Labour party away, or I'll have nothing. I know mines closed under Labour, but they make a greater effort to create new jobs. The Tories live in a different world. In the *Mirror* today there's a story about Edwina Currie spending £15 on a meal! What is natural and everyday to them is a slap-up party to us. We can't afford wine at Christmas in this street. And as for those who spend £20 on a bottle of champagne – they ought to be kicked up the arse.'

During the laughter which followed that remark, Jim caught sight of his watch. We'd been talking and gossiping for a couple of hours and although the chicken was in the oven we had forgotten about the rest of the meal. We hastily washed up cups, peeled potatoes and set the table. With everything ready to welcome home the workers I left, having agreed to meet again on Sunday. Jim was going to take me to the British Legion Club for a drink so that I could meet some of the miners who had moved to other pits.

On the bus down the valley, I mulled over Jim's loyalty to the Labour party. The Labour party he joined, the party of Nye Bevan, with its clear socialist programme and its clear views on public ownership, no longer exists. Ann Clwyd belongs to the so called 'soft' left, but she admits that it is in a state of confusion, lacking a discernible ideology. Ann is unwavering in her commitment to certain basic tenets, to universal benefits, to equality, to public ownership of some utilities, particularly gas, coal, electricity, water – not old style nationalization, but nationalization with local decision-making and an enhanced role for the workforce. And of course she remains a loyal unilateralist. Indeed, Neil Kinnock sacked her from the shadow cabinet for voting against the Tory's defence estimates because they included increased nuclear expenditure. For some bizarre reason, the Labour party's wishy-washy attitude was to ask members to *abstain*. When a party flounders around like that, it is hard to think it deserves Jim Evans's loyalty. By the next election, when all the policy reviews are in place, when the new model Labour party is revealed, it won't be the Labour party he first joined, but none the less it may well be worthy of his loyalty once more.

The next morning I was on the bus back up the valley to Penrhiwceiber. I wanted to meet Mary Davies. Much has been written about the effect of the strike on the miners' wives: how they became politicized; how their actions ate away at the chauvinist attitudes of the miners; how in one year they had achieved more for themselves than in twenty years of so-called women's liberation. Ann and I had discussed this. She believes much of it to be myth-making. After the strike the women retreated into their homes, they didn't rush to join the Labour party or any other group. If they had won the battle it might have been a different story.

Mary and Lyndhurst – 'Lyn' – Davies live close to Jim Evans, in an identical house on the other side of the main street. Mary was delighted to have the chance to relive that year.

'I was niggly at the beginning of the strike. I was behind the strike in the seventies because it was about money, and I hadn't realized that a factory girl got more than my husband did for working underground. But this time I kept thinking, what is this strike *for*? It isn't for money, and as we were getting older I wondered whether it was wise to use our savings. But my husband and my son and my son-in-law were very committed. At first I didn't get involved; they didn't want us to get into it. But as I watched the battles between the police and the miners on television, I thought, what *is* going on? So I joined a support group, which at first was just for collecting food. Then the women at the Point of Ayr pit in north Wales asked us to come and picket and I thought it was an ideal opportunity to go and see for myself what was happening. Lyn was away, so I left a note, telling him and saying we'd discuss it when I got back.

'At Ayr our busload of women had a police escort. We couldn't stop the men from going into the pit, but for us the visit was successful because the police were so vile to us that it pushed us into wanting to do more. In the morning it wasn't too bad, the police were local men, but in the afternoon they were not. I think they were from the Metropolitan police, because of their badges. The things they said to us! I'd been brought up to respect the police, but once I was on the picket line and heard how abusive they were to women, it didn't stretch my imagination to see how they could behave towards men. I always thought the police were there to keep the peace, not to incite things . . . Never in my wildest dreams did I expect to hear them talk to us like that.'

'What did they say to you?'

'Oh, some mild things like, "You should be at home cleaning up your dirty house"; and nasty remarks like, "Come behind the bushes and I'll show you what a real man is like." Or, "Tell your husband I've carpeted my house from top to bottom on the overtime I've had from this strike."'

'That all sounds rather juvenile to me.'

'I suppose it does now, but it shocked us at the time. And the worst thing was the threats. I had a rolled-up newspaper in my hand and a policeman said to me that he would run me in for having an offensive weapon. I tried to say it was only a newspaper and he said: "I know that and you know that, but I'll *say* that there was a weapon inside."

'I came home determined to get more involved. Lyn said, "What on earth got into your head? If I had been home you wouldn't have gone through that door!" I told him that times had changed.'

Mary Davies got so involved that she travelled abroad to explain the miners' case. She got so involved she regularly went picketing with her husband. She got so involved and so bold that she rang the *Daily*

Mirror, reversing the charge, and asked for Robert Maxwell's office. She told his staff about the kids in her valley who had nothing except a dirty paddling pool and suggested that the *Mirror* might like to provide some money to take them for a day at the seaside.

'The *Mirror* decided that there was great publicity to be had if they could find a way of taking kids to the seaside for a day, and they told me that I'd be first in the queue, but they forgot. Others went to the seaside. When I tried to remind them of the promise, they said that they were winding up the seaside trips. Oh, no you're not, I said. If you don't keep your promise I'll go to the *Sun* and tell them how the *Daily Mirror* broke the hearts of the kids in my valley. That did it! Three busloads went to Butlin's at Barry Island, and all the kids got great bags of things to take home.'

Lyn Davies had by this time returned with the morning shopping, and, having dumped several plastic bags in the kitchen, he sat down beside his wife and nodded and smiled as she told her story. He is transparently proud of her.

'If you had told me all this was going to happen to me I would not have believed it. We women never got involved. If Lyn went to the club first of an evening, he'd have to come out later to fetch me in because I wouldn't go through the door alone. That's how I was before the strike. By the end of the strike this "dumpy mum from the valleys" was sharing a platform with Tony Benn. And instead of just explaining what the support groups were all about, collecting food and tins and money, I found myself explaining why we were on strike; what would happen if our pit went and why our pit wasn't making a profit. I told them that if you buy a house and you don't keep it in good repair then it will get dilapidated and that was what our pit was like, full of stuff our fathers used. No wonder we couldn't make a profit.'

Lyn remained silent no longer. 'I've been down that pit thirty-nine years. And I'm telling you that if they had looked after it, we'd have had another twenty years left. We never had anything new, it was always make-do-and-mend, bit of machinery from here, patching up there. Bad management ruined the pits, they made bad decisions all the time. They had men coming from outside to tell us what to do, but they never asked local men; they would never consult us and we *knew* the pit; we knew what would work and what would not. Under private enterprise it would have been no worse. We had to fight the management tooth and nail. If they said good morning, we'd go outside to check. That was the nature of our relationship. I didn't ask for another job. I'd had enough. There's no contentment, no peace in the mines now.

'I'm not a Scargill man. South Wales went back first because we have got more bloody brains in south Wales than in Yorkshire! A good general takes his men in if he sees them getting slaughtered. He'll retreat and fight another day. With our general we were just cannon fodder. We were slaughtered. We were sold down the river, first by Nacods and then the other unions left us to it; those leaders will get knighthoods. They were bought; we were slaughtered. You wouldn't believe half the things I could tell you. The Coal Board were using a small port near Preston to get the coal in, and we went up there to picket, just ten of us in a van. Seventeen miles away we were stopped by the police, hundreds of them. "The first one out of that van, spends a couple of days in the nick", they said. What could we do? It was that well planned. I'll tell you, I went up to Durham and I saw this coal stockpile and it looked like a mountain that would last for ever, but I'm convinced it was hollow and wouldn't have lasted for two weeks. Now I saw that with my own eyes. Makes you wonder about the other stockpiles, doesn't it? What propaganda! Clever woman that prime minister. Clever woman.

'I'm sorry to see the pit go, but we've had enough. I'd like nothing better than to see my grandchildren work in God's fresh air. But there's a problem: why should new industry want to come to the valleys? What's special about us, when so many places, Newcastle and Liverpool, need new jobs? That's why we fought so long and so hard. We knew that if the pit went there would be nothing. There would be an empty village. My daughter has gone. She and her husband have gone to Brighton. But not everyone can do that; they get caught with the house prices. You can't get more than £4,000 for these, and it cost my daughter £27,000 for a bungalow.'

'Lyn's lucky,' said Mary. 'He's fifty-six and had nothing to lose. The older you get in the colliery the less pay you get because you get an easier but downgraded job as you get older. So he's fine. But what about our children? It's causing such tension. Marriages are breaking up; some youngsters are hopelessly in debt. While that strike was on, we had a purpose. It might seem strange to you to hear me say this, but I enjoyed the strike. It changed the country and it changed my life. We had no money, but we had a sense of belonging again, of thinking about our neighbours and the community. The children had the best Christmas of their lives. It's tragic in a way that the women gave up after the strike. We should have stayed together and gone to help those who had supported us, but it didn't happen. Transport is such a problem. In the strike the Lodge provided transport, but there's no transport now; it's hard to get to meetings in Cardiff.'

It didn't surprise me at all that Mary had enjoyed the strike; all tales of 'war' emphasize the 'spirit' that existed between men and women, interdependent and bound together by common ideals and goals. And it didn't surprise me that once the common purpose was removed the women used transport as an excuse for not staying together. What they had lost was a focus, a sense of direction, not transport provided by the Lodge. At the bus stop, by the empty pool, I was once more engulfed by images of bereavement, of loss; of a lost pit and, above all, a lost fight. It would take some time before this village got back its breath; got back its sense of purpose and the will to fight. Lyn asked why anyone should bring industry to the valley when they can go elsewhere. That's the talk of a defeated man. Such feelings will diminish in time. The end of the mines has got to be a good thing, I wrote in my notebook, and I underlined the word good.

The mood among the men at the British Legion on Sunday morning was one of disillusionment. Jim Evans had brought together a group of three men who were happy to talk, and in time others joined us, pausing long enough to add their comments before retreating from the anteroom, where women were welcome, into the men-only bar, which was their Sunday-morning habitat. The message was simple: the 'ceiber' pit was special. I could carry out a house-to-house survey if I wished, and everyone would say the same. It was home from home to hundreds of men who knew each other by name and who worked together to help each other. If one man needed to get away early for a funeral or whatever, everyone worked that much faster to achieve the aim; if someone died, they could rely on a whip-round to help their family through. Moving to another pit destroyed this feeling and without this feeling, this camaraderie, pit life was pointless.

'We are a load of gypsies now. Thirteen buses arrive at Taff Merthyr pit each morning; the men come from all over the place. For the first few days it was bloody frightening, and the atmosphere was ridiculous. After a year it got easier, we got to know the pit, but we still don't know the names of the men who work there, and the attitude is so different. If we go against the management we are threatened with the prospect of a downgraded job. If we are seen going to the Lodge (the union) with a complaint we are told we will be downgraded and we are afraid of losing money. They say to us: "Don't bring your 'ceiber' ways in here. You lost and *your* pit is closed."'

I asked them why they didn't put themselves forward for Lodge membership and change things to their liking, the way they had at Penrihwceiber. John and Norman said they already had to get up an hour earlier and get home an hour later, without getting involved. In other words, their sense of commitment was not that easily transferred. Norman was in Yorkshire when he heard that his pit was to be closed. 'I came off the phone with tears in my eyes and said, "They've shut my bastard pit!" I'm still emotional about it. I can't look at the site; I can't look at that nothingness.' He refused redundancy through fear. He was forty and had children of twelve and nine, and he looked at the houses on either side of his and saw that each contained unemployed youngsters. 'I said to myself, if they can't get work, what chance have I got at forty? I'd have got £23,000 which is a lot of money. My wife wanted me to leave. But you've got to be man enough to make your own decisions. What was I going to do all day – sit in the club here? I work regular and I drink regular and my wife knows that. I still don't know if I made the right decision. I sometimes wish I'd taken the money rather than work in this shit-hole. I sometimes wish I could turn the clock back. It cuts me to the quick.'

John feels much the same: 'I thought hard about it and discussed it at home, but I'd be in the club all day and that's no life. Sometimes I wish I had taken redundancy. All they care about is keeping the Black River flowing. We can take the risks, we have to. If we want a bonus, we have to take chances. If we went by the book there wouldn't be a profitable pit left.'

Stan had no doubts: 'I hate it. I'm at Penallta and the atmosphere is bad. The boys made me feel welcome, but we have so many troubles with the management. They just tell us to get on with it, or get out. The quicker the place closes the better. With a bit of luck I'll have a phone call tomorrow . . .'

'You won't find many who'd say different,' said Jim, who sat beside me and had said little. 'The government intended to break the unions, the only place where the working man can make his grievances known. Well, they've done it, or the Coal Board has done it for them. They have broken the strength of the Lodge and destroyed the affinity. The Board can do what they like now.'

Jim walked me to the bus stop. People were going to chapel. I said that I'd like to take a handful of pictures to remind me of the village. I wanted one of the pit-head and asked him to walk with me. He said nothing and walked alongside me, past the shelter daubed with the words: 'Nacods scabs', and past the Lodge. When we got to the site he pointed out where the gates had been and the position of the pit-head baths. Suddenly his voice tailed off and he fought to control the tears. 'I don't normally come down here . . . I can't . . .' It was my turn to fight back the tears. It had been insensitive of me to ask him to come with me, but I treasure the moment when we stood there in silence, our eyes roaming over the forlorn, grey, pitiful scene. He was no doubt lamenting the loss of his pit. To me the scene symbolized the limitations of human nature. My mind raced back to Northern Ireland, where I had experienced the same feelings of profound despair for a world in which men were set against one another for no good reason. A world in which bosses fight workers and workers fight bosses might, in the name of ideology, think itself noble. For a moment it is noble, for an hour, for a month, for a year, but in the end it comes down to what I saw before me: rubble. Rubble and blighted lives. We were right to shed our tears. Before us was an ideal gone sour; before us, the socialist dream of nationalization, of a better deal, of a world in which men worked together, lay amid rubble, razed. British Coal is to be privatized.

The task of reviving the valleys is enormous, so enormous that it may never be achieved without ruining the sense of community, of belonging, that I had come to appreciate. In the valleys thousands of men worked underground, in inverted skyscrapers. There is simply no room for them to be employed above ground, together in the same spot. Some of them will inevitably have to travel to one of the drab-looking – architecturally pathetic – trading estates which are fighting hard to attract new industries. They may have to go to Hirwaun at the head of the valley or to Cardiff, and the villages may become dormitories. The railway, cut by Beeching, has been reinstated. But there will be new jobs. Lyn's sad comment that he couldn't see why people would choose the valleys when they could go to Liverpool or Newcastle is unnecessarily pessimistic. Much is happening; much needs to happen. For too long people have assumed that the fortunes of coal are cyclical; that the bad times are to be tolerated because the good times will come again. They thought that the Chernobyl disaster would turn men's minds away from nuclear power back to coal. It isn't so. The south Wales mines passed their peak in the second decade of this century; the coal that is needed now will be extracted from modern mines needing fewer men. Never again will the valleys be dependent on one massive employer holding their very lives in the palm of his hand. Diversification should have been pursued with vigour years ago; it is being pursued now. Wales already competes with the north-east for the boast of having the largest concentration of Japanese manufacturing investment in Britain. Indeed, Wales received the first Japanese plant in the early seventies, when Sony went to Bridgend. Cynon Valley received the second when Hitachi went to Hirwaun to make television sets. That site is now also making microwave ovens. The Japanese tend to employ women, the cheaper sex and mostly young women who, coming straight from school, have no bad work habits and can be easily moulded to the Japanese style. This feminization of the work-force – the trend is for seven jobs for women to every three for men – is radically altering the structure of the economy and is not without critics. To many it is galling to see the Japanese come in and kill the remains of British endeavour to make such items as television sets and cars. It raises xenophobic hackles, it causes anxiety. But for the moment at any rate Japanese investment is only about 5 per cent of total foreign investment and is way behind American investment. From the publicity it attracts one would be forgiven for thinking it was much larger. In any event, at 5 per cent it is welcome; if the consumer is going to buy Japanese products, it is better they buy them assembled here with at least some input from local component makers, rather than add to our balance of payments problem. Furthermore, since the Japanese are intent on setting up in Europe, then it is better that they set up in Britain than in France and Germany. They do so, it is said, because it is quite hard enough for the Japanese to find engineers who speak English, impossible for them to find those who speak German and French. For the moment at least, we are reaping the benefit of language.

The Japanese are working well within Wales. It is no surprise to find that their egalitarian approach to the workplace – shared uniforms, car parks, lavatories and canteens – is particularly acceptable. But the Japanese alone are not going to revive the valleys. British Coal Enterprise is doing its bit to assist new ventures. The extent of its success is often questioned, and the miners in Penrihwceiber are scathing; they won't touch anything with a 'British Coal' label. British Coal are not fussed; they don't expect mining men to have entrepreneurial zap, and their brief, they argue, is to help provide jobs, not jobs for ex-miners. However, the real key to the future of employment provision lies within the principality's boundaries. It has become fashionable for leading Welsh figures to talk of the Welsh finding their own solutions rather than holding out a begging bowl to London or waiting for solutions to be imposed from outside. In January 1988 an Institute of Welsh Affairs was set up. Its founders were much influenced by Glasgow's ability to haul itself out of an economic trough. Its first report was a plan to revitalize the valleys, a detailed plan that covered improvements to housing, roads and railways, land reclamation, town-centre renewal, a major boost for tourism, as well as arguing for more fundamental changes to education and training to raise the qualifications of the workforce to meet modern needs and to introduce the ideas of self-employment and entrepreneurship. The valleys, just like Newcastle and other areas of heavy industry where father followed son without a second thought into musclebound jobs, have no history of self-employment. Peter Walker, Secretary of State for Wales, adopted some of these recommendations in his plan for the valleys. The money that came with the package has caused many an argument. Peter Walker claims to have provided £500 million over three years from 1988; others accuse him of making a pretty package out of grants that were already in existence and that the amount of 'new' money was half his boastful figure. Anyway, it's not enough. But the people of the valleys are not slow to appreciate that at last a Conservative government is paying some attention to their needs. And Peter Walker is not slow to spot a chink in Labour's armour, and wishes to capitalize on it. In 1966 the Labour party won thirty-two of the thirty-six seats in Wales. In 1983 the Conservative party won fourteen of the thirty-eight seats. Perhaps this inspired the setting-up of the Cardiff Bay Development Corporation, which aims to transform the city's docklands in the manner of London and Liverpool. It's a mammoth project, reclaiming 3,000 acres of waste land and transforming it into a lakeside city with waterfront shops, offices, restaurants, leisure and marina developments, a centre for the performing arts and thousands of new homes. The bulk of the money is coming from the private sector, and maybe 30,000 jobs will be created in the ten years or more that it will take to create this imaginative vision. The scheme has plenty of critics. The centrepiece, a barrage across the mouth of Cardiff Bay to create a fresh-water lake, has upset conservationists, which is a pity and a genuine problem. The bay, with its 2.5 square kilometres of mudflats, is a site of special scientific interest because it is the habitat of thousands of birds. The developers propose a new lagoon several miles to the east as compensation, but it is only a fraction of the size of the bay, and conservationists argue that some birds die if they are relocated. Aside from this serious conflict of interests, there are endless niggles: residents fear the new homes will be too expensive for first-time buyers; local industry fears dislocation; the valleys fear that the construction work will go to outsiders, not ex-miners. But all these problems are solvable; I'd ban outside labour and encourage every ex-miner and school-leaver to get building skills. The train journey down the valley is very pleasant.

The Conservative party's gains in 1983 were not sustained; how could they be after the miners' strike? In 1987 they won only seven of the thirty-eight seats. And as in Scotland, the Welsh nationalists, Plaid Cymru, are gaining ground. None the less, the Tory party cling firmly to the belief that Labour strongholds, the 'inner cities', could with effort turn blue. Whether social concern or political cynicism and opportunism motivate that effort and the signing of the cheques is a matter of much debate, but in the end it is of secondary concern. Penrihwceiber needs hope; the valleys need a future.

Chapter 12

Birmingham:
The Right Medicine

Birmingham is one of the world's unloved cities. It's always being slagged off, not only in a bored-taxi-driver way, but seriously, by university types who draw up league tables suggesting that the quality of life is awful in Birmingham. Glasgow University, in an analysis of desirable places to live, said that Edinburgh came top of the form and Birmingham bottom of the class: 38 out of 38 – the least desirable place to live. Well, is it true, or is it a fearful slander? It is of course neither. I wouldn't willingly live in Birmingham. I hate the accent for one thing: it is the sound of a headcold, of chronic catarrh. But as a place to live it is no worse than Bradford, only bigger. Much bigger. One million people live in the city. One million people imprisoned by a ring road and, if they try to fight their way out, they'll be caught in a figure of eight called a spaghetti junction. Birmingham sold out to the car years ago. By comparison, Newcastle's motorway, which caused me to get lost and to curse the car, is but a slight blemish on the cheek. This is a massive deformity, the kind that makes you want to stare and look away at the same time. Prince Charles, our future king, does not like Birmingham. I don't think his tongue has ever lacerated the spaghetti junction, but that's because he's a buildings chap, and he has been exceedingly rude about some of the city's architecture. He said that the new conference centre (to be completed in the nineties) was 'an unmitigated disaster', and that the public library looks like a place for incinerating rather than keeping books. Such *bons mots* tend to cling around the neck of the recipient for ever more. The game is fun: I like it. I think most of the Prince's subjects like it too. I don't think many of them have much visual sense, and I don't think many of them have a real feel for cities, and these two facts mean that we have some ugliness around us. We thoroughly enjoy Prince Charles having a go; it makes a pleasant change from endless pap about female members of the royal family. The Prince of Wales has raised the profile of the debate to a dizzy height but we must not lose sight of the fact that architectural mess is a worldwide and dogged problem. In some ways our mistakes seem mild compared to those of other countries; the glass pyramid outside the Louvre in Paris, designed by a Chinese-American, shows madness on a par with the spaghetti junction. What *is* happening?

Criticism of modern architecture, from the bleak, cheap stuff I saw passing as factories on estates in the Welsh valleys to grand development schemes, to piecemeal additions to art galleries, is widespread. But then there is nothing new in disliking contemporary buildings; the Victorians disliked Georgian neatness and uniformity, the sixties lot disliked Victorian offerings, the eighties dislikes the fruits of the sixties, and the result is confusion. What do we like and why? Our schools offer not a scrap of visual education; most of us don't have even the vocabulary to describe a building.

Throughout history there have been two basic schools of architecture: one school designs buildings that gently lie down with nature; the other designs buildings that proudly stand up in contrast. Then along came a third kind (so the writer Robin Boyd has taught me): one that is neither sympathetic to its surroundings nor challenging. It is evasive, a nervous chattering as opposed to a statement that is bold, straightforward and honest. And it is not lack of imagination or lack of sensitivity or lack of originality that causes this, but an overabundance of these qualities without the discipline of a common artistic aim. Architects are a supreme example of rampant individualism. Thus we are presented with buildings, each one crying, 'Look at me,' each one self-consciously different; all determined to be arresting; all showing off their isolated moments of conception. And when our eyes are finally drawn to one building, they are given no rest, but are forced to race across broken planes and interrupted lines. Technology has liberated the architect and he, poor thing, is floundering in his freedom. And fouling our cities.

Birmingham sees itself as a Victorian city, despite the fact that it existed before and has taken a hammering since. It is a manufacturing city, a city of a thousand trades; it makes buttons and belts, jewellery and firearms, steel pen-nibs and kettles. Joseph Chamberlain's family produced screws. Chamberlain was once mayor of Birmingham. He passed legislation banning the building of back-to-back housing, municipalized gas and water, planted many trees and inaugurated the building of 'a great new street, as broad as a Paris boulevard, to let light and air into an insanitary area'. For this he was much criticized. The redevelopment cost a fortune, all of which had to be borrowed and paid for on the rates. But Corporation Street in part still stands, and so does Victoria Square, built at the same time to be the city's administrative and cultural centre. The town hall is intact and so is the museum and art gallery, but alongside it is the reference library, rebuilt to resemble an incinerator. It is easy enough to find the remnants of the city that Chamberlain made famous, but it has been swamped by an ugly Birmingham. Everywhere the roads seem to be barricaded by buses, blue and white buses, three abreast, with noisy squealing brakes and shrieking banners saying, 'Smoking kills.' Birmingham likes banners. The motor show was on. It seems fitting that the city that sold out to the car with spaghetti junction should host the motor show and be inordinately proud of the fact that the centre's streets can be turned into a Grand Prix track. There were banners across the streets saying, 'Welcome to the Motor Show'. Perhaps it is possible to design beautiful banners, but I have seen no evidence of it. Banners are by definition downmarket and tacky. Birmingham, the city of garish banners; of loud advertising and of hideous shop fronts: Pizzaland and Pizzahut, Dayville Ice-Creams and Spud-U-Like, and Kentucky Fried Chicken. The city's advertising says: 'JR would feel at home in Birmingham.' He probably would. It's why I don't. Birmingham has a reputation for producing and liking the cheap and showy. There's a word in the dictionary to prove it: Brummagem. Brummagem is an article that is counterfeit, cheap and showy. The dictionary says it is an allusion to plated goods and to counterfeit groats made here in the seventeenth century.

The Bull Ring says it all. It was opened in 1964, a vast purpose-built shopping-centre. Walter Gropius, a German, one of the founders of the modern movement in architecture, whom some consider a great twentieth-century architect, spoke admiringly of the Bull Ring. He is said to have been some kind of socialist with a dislike of decoration and a contempt for styles from the past. The Bull Ring is a concrete bunker, a weather-stained coal hole. Those who have been to East Berlin say it reminds them of that city. The Bull Ring is earmarked for an expensive – £400m – face-lift. The gossip is that the planners intend to repeat the initial mistake by building yet another vast shopping-centre. This time it will be stone clad.

After an hour of the Bull Ring, I sought comfort in the art gallery. The art gallery in Birmingham is famous for its collection of Pre-Raphaelite paintings and drawings. Sir Edward Burne-Jones was born in this city, the son of a carver and gilder who, though hardly rich, was not poor. At Oxford he met William Morris, born in Walthamstow before it was cockneyfied and jerry-built over. Morris was rich. Together the two decided that they would establish a society dedicated to a crusade and holy war against the age in which they lived. They hated industrial Britain; they worshipped the past, particularly the creative labour of craftsmen, which led them to relish all things medieval. The two came under the influence of Dante Gabriel Rossetti who, also having difficulty with things present, became leader of the Pre-Raphaelite school – for those who believed that after Raphael art declined rather than advanced. Every age throws up men who hate the present. I have always been irritated by such men, and particularly this little group who did so much to turn our hearts and minds against industrialism instead of using their remarkable influence to improve the things they disliked. They were responsible, at least in part, for rich industrialists rushing off to buy country houses and sending their sons to schools where they learned to become 'gentlemen' and spurn industry. William Morris was the worst of the lot. He called himself a socialist and yet he worshipped the Middle Ages. It is said that the Normans introduced into England the feudal system; that they introduced the concept of the idle gentlemen and the aristocratic ideal; that they introduced class divisions. How can you be a socialist and a medievalist at the same time? Only by choosing selectively from the goodies in the past and blotting out the bits that don't suit your thesis, in which case you might just as well choose selectively from the goodies in the present, rather than arrogantly condemn the lot. The Pre-Raphaelites' exaggerated rejection of the world in which they lived was futile. I think that it is the most delicious joke to find this famous Pre-Raphaelite collection of paintings in Birmingham. It is the perfect irony to see works by men who hated ugliness and who fought for the return of creative labour hanging in the art gallery of a city that is well known for its ugliness and for the poor quality of life it offers its citizens. What would Burne-Jones, Morris and Rossetti have made of modern Birmingham? Perhaps they too would have seen it as an exquisite joke.

I tried to catch a bus to Acocks Green in East Birmingham, where I was staying; although there were many of them, I couldn't find the right one and so headed instead for the 5.25 commuter train, which was packed to the gills. A girl fainted, although there wasn't much room to faint properly. A woman got up and gave her a seat. The men pretended that nothing had happened – the medieval concept of chivalry is hard to find in Birmingham.

I had selected to stay in East Birmingham not because I intended to visit the motor show, but because I was going to spend several days in hospital. Fortunately, my visit to East Birmingham hospital was not as a patient. I was meeting Peter Freeman, a senior registrar. That weekend he was in charge of the accident and emergency unit (alias Casualty to those who watch television). He had said on the phone that when I arrived he would put a white coat on me and that for the following forty-eight hours I could be his shadow. And that's what happened. At 8.30 in the morning, I put on a crisp white coat and became a shadow. It is as good a way as any of seeing the health service at close quarters. I was sick of reading about it; sick of tales that Britain's post-war pride and joy was being crippled at the young age of forty by a government dedicated to cost-benefit analysis.

There's a small overnight-stay ward at the hospital, where A. and E. cases can be kept for observation. Peter Freeman's first task was to make a ward round and see who could go home. In the first bed there was 'a domestic injury'; a middle-aged woman had stitches in her head; she had been hit by a flower-pot thrown by her husband. She had been drinking lager and brandy at the time. Peter looked at the bump on her head and told her she could go home and report to her own doctor.

'Who is at home now?' he asked.

'My husband.'

'Do you need any help? Would you like a visit from the social services?'

'No.'

Peter walked to the next bed. I was dying to ask all sorts of questions of the woman.

'You won't want to get so involved by the end of the day,' said Peter laughing. 'A. and E. is for quick assessment. If it is a baby or a minor, it's different. But for adults I can pick up the gross things quickly. We see far too many domestic disputes. We leave it to the patient to seek help.'

This woman had no shoes, no handbag, no money and could only hope that a member of her family would come and get her. In the end, the nurse had to wrap her feet in plastic slippers and send her away in a cab for which someone at the other end would pay.

The next bed contained a lovable elderly man of seventy-seven who had a glass eye and who had fallen and hurt his heel and foot. We looked at the wound and the dressing and Peter decided to get a physiotherapist to assess his ability to cope at home with crutches.

Out of ear-shot Peter said: 'He's probably got a permanent disability, but there's nothing we can do but let it heal by itself as best as possible.' His voice seemed cold and I decided I'd never make a doctor. For the next hour I kept thinking about that old man and wondering if I could nip back to see how he was getting on. But Peter was right, by the end of the day something had happened. I too saw people as 'cases' and had lost my usual appetite for questions and involvement.

Bed three had a policeman sitting at the side. In the bed was a thirty-year-old male, an Asian taxi driver. At 2.15 a.m. three youths had hopped out of his cab and refused to pay. A brawl followed; he got beaten about the head and one of the youths had been stabbed with a Stanley knife. The man with the stab wound was in another ward. They had to separate them. It looked as though this thirty-year-old Asian taxi driver's next stop would be a prison cell. But for the moment he needed an X-ray to see if he had a broken nose.

By 9.10 we were in the plaster clinic – an excellent idea; those who have been plastered the day before return to make sure that the plaster is not too tight/loose. The first case was a perfect illustration. The patient's hand had swollen overnight. This clinic is a conveyor-belt in winter, with old people slipping and fracturing wrists. It was October and it was pretty full: there were young and old, there were sullen faces and smiling faces; there were black faces and there were white. For an hour we looked at yesterday's plasters. I was mistaken for a doctor. A young woman who'd fallen downstairs and badly sprained her foot had been put in plaster because it was more comfortable. She was a cashier in a Safeway's supermarket and had taken time off to serve drinks at the motor show. A plastered leg is not what is wanted of young women hired for decoration at the motor show. Her sprain was costing her money. 'Do you think I should go back to Safeway?' she asked me.

'You'd better ask the doctor,' I said.

'I thought you were a doctor.' she said, eyeing my white coat.

'But you are Dr Freeman's patient.' I was careful not to lie. Many, many times during the next forty-eight hours I was taken for a doctor. I loved it.

The Asian taxi driver's X-rays showed that he had a broken nose. We went back to his bedside to tell the policeman that he could now be moved.

'Please, please, will you stay in touch to see if I'm OK?' the driver asked Peter.

'No, the police have their own doctors. You'll be looked after.'

The taxi driver then apologized for the noise and fuss he had made the night before when he was brought in.

It was time for the hand clinic. Hands are a neglected field, and they are Peter's speciality. It fits in well with A. and E. work. For an hour we looked at hands. There was a building worker who had put his hand through a sheet of glass in a fit of anger. He hadn't done himself serious harm. There was a seventy-one-year-old who had spiked his hand on a pole. There was a woman whose hand had seized up while she was Hoovering. Four fingers had gone 'dead'. They seemed better, but stiff. She had to report to physiotherapy on Monday. There was an Asian who had been attacked in a spot of 'Paki-bashing'. He'd had stitches to his head where he'd been hit with a bottle, and his hand was swollen. There was a crushed thumb. Its owner asked for a letter saying that he was able to do light duties. He'd only had his job for a month and was afraid of losing it. Peter treated his cases speedily, pausing after each patient to fill in records. He didn't stop to chat. He didn't stop for anything for three hours and then we stopped for coffee.

We went back to see the old man with the damaged heel. He was to be discharged. His wife was at home to help him. 'Hospitals are for treatment. If treatment is not needed then it is best that patients go home. No, it's nothing to do with funds; I'm sending him home because he'll be better off there. It's been proved that people get better more quickly if they are at home, particularly the elderly who get confused in hospital. When you are old, being in hospital is associated with death, so it is much better if he goes home. I'd feel happier if the local social services department had more funds and could offer more support in the home. Let's hope his wife can manage.'

East Midlands General Hospital is old. It was once a TB hospital, and that became obvious once I'd wandered around the grounds – several wards still had large covered-in verandas. Since then the hospital had grown up piecemeal, blobs of red brick on a campus. The accident and emergency block was small, and reasonably welcoming. It conformed to my image of an NHS hospital: basic, no frills, no comforts, scrubbed clean. This unit treats 60,000 new patients a year. It is due to be rebuilt; it's about fifteenth on the list and Peter said that if Birmingham had been chosen as the site for the next Olympics, it would have shot to the top of the list. A. and E. has been the Cinderella of the hospital service, which is surprising. Most people's experience of hospitals is as an out-patient and it is from this experience that they form their impression of hospitals in general. But for many years the effective treatment of those injured or taken suddenly ill has been a problem. When the NHS was inaugurated in 1948, it inherited casualty departments that were 'round the back of the hospital', staffed by young doctors. Most of the treatment was handled by nurses. There was a consultant in charge who rarely visited his patch. No one gave much thought to all this until the fifties, when road accidents increased. Then it became obvious that casualty departments were not designed, equipped or staffed to cope. A report in 1962 rejected special 'accident hospitals' along American lines, and instead argued for a twin system: some hospitals could handle minor problems, but general hospitals were to handle major problems. Orthopaedic surgeons were put in charge of the newly named accident and emergency departments, and much of the work was to remain in the hands of young doctors. The Platt Report said that 'Accident surgery is unlikely to provide a satisfying career for a consultant.' Such a comment angered those who knew this not to be the case. They had to be patient. Platt's proposals didn't work. A report in 1970 found that standards were still low and that there were 'insufficient junior doctors with inadequate senior cover'. In 1962 it might have seemed a good idea to put orthopaedic surgeons in charge, but it hadn't worked out. While that branch of medicine had seen its workload diminish, with fewer cases of rickets, polio and TB of joints, it had only been a temporary lull, for new technology meant that there was a growing demand for new hips and new knees. Orthopaedic surgeons had their hands full again, and had little interest in A. and E. work beyond 'fractures', which, while an important slice of the work, was only part of it; there were other areas – heart cases, overdoses and acute asthma – in which they had no expertise.

It was back to the drawing board, and in the early seventies a committee under Sir John Bruce decided that the time had come for A. and E. to have its own consultants, with their own training programme and career structure. In time it was also clear that all medical undergraduates should have some training in emergency work. A new speciality was born, and it has been a huge success. The absentee landlord was banished and the brightest young doctors were tempted to look anew at an area that in the past had received their attention only while they were in training. Choosing a career in A. and E. meant the chance of becoming a consultant at a much younger age: within six months of our meeting, Peter Freeman, then thirty-four, was to move to Wolverhampton as a consultant.

I relate the transformation of casualty into A. and E. with a purpose. It is a perfect illustration of how the NHS workload has grown; each decade throws up new problems, like road accidents; each decade throws up new possibilities, like new hips; each year knowledge becomes greater and skills become specialized. To this must be added the fact that the lowering of infant mortality now means there are many more elderly people in the population, an age group which makes great demands on the service. And they live longer; a bout of pneumonia no longer signifies a quick release from old age. Nor are we anywhere near the end of medical advances to keep man alive: each year younger premature babies survive; each year tiny babies born with multiple problems are subjected to multiple operations. Each year a man badly smashed up in a car accident has a greater chance of survival; each year costly and complex intensive-care equipment prolongs life. It then becomes perfectly obvious that each year more money is needed. Ten years ago, under the last Labour government, the health service absorbed just over 11 per cent of public spending in real terms. In 1989–90 the equivalent figure is 14 per cent. The question remains: where is that money to come from to meet all our needs and our rising expectations? The founders of the health service were wrong when they anticipated that in time a healthy nation would make fewer demands on the service.

Our coffee break and chat about the history of A. and E. went uninterrupted. The 'bleep' did not summon us. There were plenty of accidents, but no emergencies. A little girl awaited our return. She had glass in her foot. Peter extracted it with the aid of a local anaesthetic. Another slightly older girl had a cyst on her head which had become infected. A woman had been stung by a wasp while working on her allotment. A tiny girl had fractured her arm. Then came a young man whose case was particularly interesting. He was a teenager with a pellet in his head. He'd had a gash stitched the day before.

Afterwards he remembered that something hit him before he fell. Then his mate found an empty pellet case. That made him think. Peter removed the pellet. The fifteen-year-old boy did not like needles. He and I had a friendly chat about our hatred of needles. I thought I might hold his hand to calm his fears, but then since he was fifteen, I thought perhaps I had better not.

We managed twenty minutes for lunch before being bleeped to give advice on a man who had cut the top of his finger. The food, risotto and carrots, was not the sort to linger over. Anyway, Peter was taking a break in the evening and going home and I was going with him. The afternoon was routine. The department was not busy; for one thing there was a bus strike on and in this poor area of Birmingham people would not think of using a taxi; and some hesitate before calling out an ambulance.

Peter lived in Sutton Coldfield. His wife manages to combine part-time nursing with running a nursery school and bringing up two children. They are both levelheaded in their assessment of the health service. The shroud waving and panic statements of which we have heard so much in recent years serve no purpose. The public no longer know what to think, with figures and opinions being flung in anger by the service at the government and vice versa. The Freemans' view is clear enough: the system is not falling apart, but standards are falling. 'We are,' Peter Freeman argues, 'being asked to accept lower standards than those instilled by our training.' Much had been done to make the system more efficient, trimming fat was painful but necessary, but, as any surgeon knows, going too close to the bone is risky. The district general manager had insisted that the hospital was wasteful and extravagant; that patients remained in East Birmingham longer than they did in other hospitals in the area, sometimes twice as long. 'I agree that the system needed tightening up – most big organizations could benefit from a tightening of procedures. There was waste, I'll admit that, but we have to be careful how far we go. Apart from anything else, shortening bed stays does not save money; it means you treat more patients, and that costs more money.'

Three wards had been closed. The closure of two children's wards had been accepted without too much huffing and puffing. There had been four children's wards, and figures proved that for much of the time the four were only three quarters full; closing one did not affect services. Closing an adult ward was another matter. Any cutback in beds would affect A. and E. because emergency cases could be held up for hours while a bed was located. These are considerations that no doctor has had to contemplate in the past. The hospital now had a red-alert system when beds were in short supply.

'Red alert has been activated several times. I remember an asthma patient who needed intensive care and couldn't be admitted at East Birmingham and had to go to the General Hospital seven miles away. A senior nurse and an anaesthetist went with him. It could have been crucial. But most of the time it means that new patients are hanging around on trolleys in A. and E. for longer than is necessary; sometimes four hours or more.'

During my weekend visit there were fifty beds available. But the fear of a shortage puts added stress on doctors and puts them at odds with the management. Doctors in the past have felt that management's role is simply to argue for more money, but the new breed of hospital managers, brought in after a report suggested that the NHS was poorly run, are wedded to notions of cost effectiveness. And so they should be. In the past hospitals were not asked to cost the services they gave. They had no idea *how* to cost an operation so that Hospital A's costs could be examined against Hospital B. Several pilot schemes now in place could highlight large differences and help hospitals to learn from each other. Doctors could have much to gain from the upheaval of the eighties once the new management structures, new systems of budget control and vital computers to aid this work are all in place. Meanwhile they fear they have much to lose. Above all, they do not want men who understand balance sheets interfering with their clinical judgements. The answer to that is to involve the doctors in the running of their units, make them responsible for budgets. The days of the blank cheque and doctors not wanting to bore or bother themselves with costs have gone. Peter Freeman is happy enough to be involved in budget management. 'It's not in the interest of the NHS for us to get bogged down in budgets, but I think it is reasonable enough for someone to come to me and say, "Item X costs £1 and Item Y costs £2. Is there any reason why we should not stock the cheaper item?" That makes sense, and it means that the money saved can be spent in other areas. In recent years we've had to sharpen up and we have benefited from having our medical decisions questioned. For that reason I'm glad that GPs are now facing changes and are being made accountable. If they provide a better service it will be of great help to A. and E. departments. It could mean that I don't have to handle the young man who comes in asking for a wart to be removed: a GP can do that. Just as it will be some time before we can really evaluate all the changes in the way hospitals are run, so it will be some time before we can evaluate the changes to GPs. On the whole I think good doctors have little to fear. There are areas where there could be problems, but it all comes back to adequate funding.'

We went back to the hospital at 11 p.m. The atmosphere had changed. The patients tended to be noisy. Peter's first task on our return was to sort out a Mrs X. Mrs X was known to the department. A regular pest. She sat now in the waiting room and was refusing to move. With her was her daughter, who was about eleven, long-haired and white-faced and strangely silent and detached. Mrs X, who was thirty-four, had a urological problem. She claims that surgery had made matters worse because 'an incision was made in the wrong place'. Since then, Peter said, she kept turning up and demanding attention. Whatever the rights and wrongs of her case, A. and E. was not the place for her to air them. The doctors on duty refused to see her. I curbed my desire to ask a score of questions and stood silently at Peter's side.

'I repeat: you should not be here in A. and E. Go home. Hospital is no place for your daughter at this hour.'

She began to answer him, saying she needed to see a doctor.

Peter got agitated. 'You have an obsessional condition. You do not need this department. You need the help of a psychiatrist.'

'Bullshit!' she screamed at him. 'Bullshit! I work in a psychiatric hospital. Just because I am behaving in a way you don't approve of, doesn't make me a psychiatric case.' And then she launched into a stream of abuse, laced with quotations from Karl Marx, and ended up saying that there were psychopaths running the country, while the meek and mild were in mental homes. Up to this point, and not knowing the rights and wrongs of the case, I thought that Peter had been rather tough on her. I could now see he had no option. There were others who needed his attention. He told her once more to leave. For some time she hung around quietly. I offered to go and talk to her, but Peter advised me not to get involved. We let her be and finally she left.

The fuss from Mrs X was a suitable curtain-raiser. Saturday nights in A. and E. are known to be noisy. Most of the noise is caused by drink. For the next few hours I was to feel sad and sickened by what I saw. I was saddened by a sixteen-year-old boy who drank half a bottle of whisky and was groaning, in some discomfort; he had banged his head while being sick, which had not helped. Before too long he was asleep and it was decided to keep him in overnight; there was much chat about what could be given to help his hangover. 'Bloody hell, I'm not giving him anything,' said a strident female voice. 'I'm not even giving him Paracetamol when he wakes up tomorrow.'

'Oh why, oh why, do they do such things?' said a nurse loudly in the corridor as she walked away to get some form or other. The drunken boy had just started a new job. His brother had committed suicide a year ago.

Two drunks were in each of the next two cubicles. They had been drinking together and had been assaulted as they left the pub. So they said. One could not stop shaking and had double vision. The other had a swollen eye and cuts on his knee.

'How did it happen?' I asked.

'Don't worry, we know who done it. We'll sort it out in our own little way. Let's leave it at that, shall we?'

My sympathetic curiosity was thwarted – and wasted. X-rays were taken of their skulls. Drunks can be a real problem for doctors. There was once a drunk who fell or who was pushed off a bridge. Next morning he woke up paralysed and his family were suing the hospital. They argued that if the right X-rays had been taken, he might have been helped. You can't get much sense out of a drunken man. As a safety precaution, costly X-rays are taken.

There were many more drunken patients. At one point screams attracted me to a curtained cubicle.

'Oh no, don't cut my hair. Not my fucking hair! Not my hair! Not my hair!'

I peered in. The drunken youth thought he spotted a potential ally. His shoulder-length hair had been bleached and permed. He had a wound on his head that needed stitches. A nurse was trying to clear the way for the needle.

'Doctor! Doctor! You're a woman, you understand. Don't let them ruin my hair. I don't want a bald patch.'

I told him that the patch was going to be tiny and no reason for him to behave like a baby. It was not what he expected to hear. And then I fled before he could see or hear my helpless laughter. There was another boy with a tattoo on his face that had gone septic. He called it a Borstal spot. It was nearly 1 o'clock when a father brought in his son, who had a high temperature and a cough. He said he had seen his GP in the week and was not happy. The baby was checked for pneumonia and meningitis and then allowed to go home.

Around 1.30 my notebook records the arrival of 'tarts with wounds'. There were two of them, with tiny black skirts and messy blonde hair. They had been drinking, and one had slashed her wrists. She had slashed her wrists before; she was known to the department. The other girl was her friend. Half an hour after they arrived, I found them giggling and laughing with a couple of drunken boys who were also waiting for attention. I was tired and running out of patience with self-abuse victims. I thought I'd go to bed. Peter had already gone home. He was 'on call', but did not need to be in the hospital. Just as I had gathered up my coat, there was a real emergency. A seventy-seven-year-old woman had been driven from Warwick. Coventry would have been nearer, but there had been a problem with intensive-care facilities. She was prepared for surgery in silence and with speed. She was operated on for an aortic aneurism and died in the night. A motor accident followed soon afterwards. He was rushed into intensive care. I stood on the sidelines and watched admiringly as the department sped into action to save lives.

I went to bed well after 2 o'clock. I had been allocated a doctor's room. I didn't sleep. I was too tired and too easily distracted by the sound of car doors slamming and by feet as they scuffled past the door and thumped down the stairs. I met Peter the next morning at 8.20.

I wanted to talk to the nurses. It takes a special kind of nurse to cope with A. and E. work. A senior sister explained: 'Most of us would be bored on the wards. We don't like routine. We like going from cruising to top speed very quickly. We like the pressure – we work best under pressure. We also have better relationships with our doctors and consultants: we work as a team. And we are able to do more things; we do 95 per cent of the stitching and plastering.'

All the nurses agreed, although I did find a student nurse who seemed confused by it all and who told me that she was disappointed with her lot. She had not realized that she would have to spend time clearing up mess from the floor. She seemed a bit pathetic. She said she wanted to be able to spend more time with the sick, but shortages of staff meant that there was no time.

'What would you like to do that you haven't got time to do?' I asked.

'Comb their hair, and things like that.'

She did not belong in A. and E.

The senior sister analysed the department's workload for me. I wanted to be certain that what I had seen the night before, particularly the self-abuse and the drunkenness, was representative.

'The system is sorely abused. I reckon the biggest group are the fifteen to twenty-two-year-olds. The majority of those come in with problems related to drink. Many of the others just wander in because they can't be bothered to go to their GP. We are open all day and all night and they treat us just like a bus service. That fifteen to twenty-two-year-old age group has been spoiled. Whatever they want they want immediately. I know my words are harsh, but you have seen for yourself what we have to put up with. At times, I'm full of sympathy for them, there are some very poor GPs out there who do everything to avoid home visits. There are Asian doctors who make their patients pay £5 for a home visit.

'But on the whole it is alcohol abuse that's made our workload rise so much in the last fifteen years. Those with problems are getting younger and younger. If they are not actually drunk then they are under the influence of drink.'

By now there was a group of us sipping coffee and chatting. We talked about the social cost of drinking. None of them passed judgemental comments – only the nurse who the night before had said she refused to worry about the hangover of the young boy who had drunk half a bottle of whisky. None of the others betrayed any anger at having to mop up the mess people made for themselves. So I'll be angry for them. Before I had spent the night at East Birmingham hospital I had not realized the extent to which the system was under strain because we are all so stupid and thoughtless and selfish. Excessive drinking has become a major, major problem. Research has shown that alcohol consumption per head has doubled since 1950. Research has shown that something like 8 million working days a year are lost through alcohol-related illnesses. Research has also shown that much violence is related to drink. The NHS is left picking up the bill: one figure, so gross it is hardly believable, suggests that hospital admissions for alcoholism have risen by 2,500 per cent since 1950. The media regularly draw our attention to drug problems; rarely do they look at drink. Mrs Thatcher's government has done much to focus on the drink-driving issue, but not nearly enough to make people aware of the hidden costs of alcoholism. The Beveridge Report of 1942 contained these words: 'Restoration of a sick person to health is a duty of the state *and the sick person.*' The youngsters I saw the night before were not even sick. Beveridge knew only too well the difference between liberty and licence.

Peter took me to intensive care. I wanted to see what it was like and he wanted to see how the overnight accident was getting on. It was a spacious room, silent, and laden with hi-tech grey boxes covered with circular clock faces and sprouting wires. A consultant anaesthetist was sitting by a computer. The ward was designed for six beds and needed twenty-nine nurses, but they were five short. There were four beds in use. One was occupied by a thirteen-year-old girl who had a virus and who, after two days of constant observation, was about to be moved to a ward. She was sitting up in bed talking to her mother. There was an elderly man with complex problems and a middle-aged Burmese man on total life-support. He was tiny and stick-thin; he looked like a little bird. His eyes were closed with tape and his body was wired up to machines that winked and blinked. He had been like this for some time. When he was found he had pneumonia and had been starving himself. His wife had been suing him for divorce. She now spent part of most days sitting by his bed. The nurse in charge said that if he lived now there was certain to be brain damage. Why then did they continue with all this expensive effort? The answer was confused. The general view was that you can't let a middle-aged man die.

The road accident victim was unconscious. He was to remain unconscious for three days. Peter was needed back in A. and E. and left me talking to the senior nurses. They explained how their job had changed and why it was so difficult to attract nurses to intensive care. The work is unsatisfying; there is little patient contact and plenty of machine-minding. Nurses prefer the former. Intensive-care nursing has become a job for a technician.

'The sort of patients we care for nowadays would have died ten years ago. We still have a high death rate, which makes it depressing work, but on the other hand it is very rewarding when people live when we had expected them to die. That gives us job satisfaction.' My hunch is that in time intensive care will be the province of male nurses; men are happier having relationships with machines and they do not seem to need the patient contact that female nurses require. My hunch is that before long we are going to have to ask ourselves some awkward questions. In a perfect world the National Health Service ought to be funded from taxation to do everything and anything; there ought to be bright, shiny new hospitals everywhere and no waiting lists and no lazy G Ps and no arrogant consultants. To write such a sentence is easy; it adds nothing whatsoever to the debate. There is no perfect world and therefore we need to ask ourselves whether or not we are trying too hard to keep people alive. Ought we now to slow down and *think* about what we are doing? What effect does it have on very premature babies to be kept for months in incubators? No one knows. What effect does it have on babies with multiple handicaps to spend their early years in and out of hospital? No one knows. Does anyone care? Is it right to condemn a brain damaged man to live? And what about the very old? In the geriatric ward of this East Birmingham hospital I saw a woman of ninety who could neither see nor hear who was spoonfed by a male nurse. She never received a visitor.

Did Beveridge envisage a 'free' health system for boys who paid to have their bodies tattooed and then expected the N H S to come to their rescue? Did Beveridge envisage a service for infertile women? Such questions are unpalatable. They are being asked in the universities. Academics with an interest in health policy are daring to suggest that some treatments should not be offered on the N H S; others are daring to ask clever doctors and scientists to stop and think about the *quality* of life they are offering to those they keep alive. I found it difficult to ask the male nurse in the geriatric ward why he was spoonfeeding the little old lady to keep her alive, so that she could spend another day in bed. I found it difficult because such thoughts are not to be spoken. I got the words out in the end. He looked at me with contempt. 'Are you asking me to play God?' he answered. It's a cop-out answer for those who are not prepared to examine what they are doing and for those who do not wish to make difficult decisions.

The A. and E. department was busy on Sunday morning. There were a fair number of sports injuries: chipped ankle bones, sprains and broken limbs. 'I think we should contemplate banning Sunday-morning sports,' I quipped to Peter. A father overheard the remark and, not being used to my sense of humour, gave me a lecture on all the money he had collected for the children's hospital and the donation he had made to funds for a body scanner. In the afternoon Peter was performing two hand or, rather, finger operations. He invited me to watch and I accepted. And then fretted. I had once disgraced myself by fainting in a hospital in Russia. We were being shown fancy work with eyes and lasers and one minute I was watching intently and the next minute I was on the floor. I need not have worried. Watching Peter slice into a finger did not make me queasy. I was more interested in the an-aesthetist. Peter had said to me that they were far more important than any surgeon; that is to say, they had the potential to do far greater harm. In the end, the most upsetting moment was listening to the two men coming around from the anaesthetic. One huge man groaned and groaned. 'The pain; oh, the pain. The pain's too much.' Over and over again he said this. I gather it is commonplace.

At 5.30 p.m. we were called to look at a young man of twenty-five whose head, throat and eyes hurt. His neck ached and he had a temperature. Peter was fairly certain that the young man's tonsils were causing the problem, but he was worried about meningitis.

'It terrifies me. If you miss it you can be in real trouble. You can have a vegetable on your hands, as well as a lawsuit.' He left the cubicle to check bed space so that the young man could be kept in overnight for observation.

'Look, please, I don't want to stay in. I'm frightened of hospitals. I once had a lumbar puncture that went a bit wrong. They apologized but look, I'm very unhappy in hospitals. I can go home, can't I?' I was beginning to think that Peter and I made a good team. Whenever he left, the patient would start talking and providing valuable information. He had to stay in. His temperature rose and in the night he started vomiting. It was a tonsil problem.

Our next concern was a man with breathing difficulties. Two of his brothers had died, at forty-two and forty-eight, of heart attacks. His wife had brought him in. She thought his blood pressure was too high. She called me over to her side and began to whisper: 'Come here, doctor. I can talk to another woman. Look, he smokes too much, around fifty a day. He'll tell you lies; he'll say it's much less. Could you have a chat with him about his smoking?'

Peter returned and began his questioning. He asked the man how much he smoked and the reply came: 'Oh, about twenty-five a day, doctor.' The wife winked at me.

'You'll get more sympathy from doctors if you stop.' Another wink came my way. I hadn't had a chance to say anything to Peter; perhaps she thought we benefited from telepathy.

At the end of my weekend I felt so at home in the East Birmingham hospital that Peter suggested that I could walk on to the ward and give instructions to nurses without them querying my authority. I felt like playing the game, and only one thing stopped me. I was too tired. I needed to sleep. One young doctor said to me as I was leaving: 'You don't look too good. Take the advice of a doctor – go and get some rest.'

Once the tiredness had left me, I felt despondent. I'd seen the problems, and where were the answers? I believe that the NHS needed the shake-up it is receiving. There are many discrepancies in the service around the country. Why is it possible to have a hip-replacement operation within two months in one area and have to wait two years in another? Why do the figures that are emerging vary so much from one area to another? Why do some areas make good use of day surgery and others not? Until convincing arguments to the contrary are revealed, we must assume that the answer lies in the fact that some areas are more efficient than others. The NHS needed to examine itself, to be forced into thinking about new ways of doing things; new ways that save money, as well as new ideas which make the system more accountable to patients. Much has been made of hospitals allowing their laundry and cleaning to be done by outsiders at a lower cost. But at East Birmingham I talked to the cleaners, who said that the only reason private companies could do this was by paying their employees less. East Birmingham's cleaners said they were paid up to £28 a week less by their new 'private' employer. They accepted this situation, they argued, because the alternative was the dole.

The birth of the NHS was accompanied by well documented resistance and cries of pain from those who feared the worst, so it is not surprising to find that there are many who dislike the present upheavals; they'd hate anything except a bigger cheque each year. When it was first mooted that hospitals should raise funds through their own income-generation schemes, there was a chorus of disapproval. The unions, particularly NUPE, disliked the idea on principle; the state should fund the system. Full stop. Others howled because they did not want to have to waste time thinking about money-raising ideas. A couple of years on, many hospitals have realized that they can in fact improve services to patients, staff and visitors through carefully chosen schemes *and* make extra money for themselves. With this discovery, it became intellectually respectable to think of hiring someone to take charge of income generation; someone who could easily cover the cost of his or her salary through schemes that lease out hospital land to provide space for banks, hairdressers, shops and cafés, through schemes that allow hospital premises to be hired out for conferences, and through amusing little enterprises like providing pregnant mums with photographs of their 'scans'. In the end of course the money raised is peanuts compared with total budgets, but they are useful peanuts and they bring additional benefits to patients, staff and visitors.

Once the efficiency drive has trimmed the fat, and once these new ideas are in place, then what? Two things: a campaign to make people feel more responsible for their own health, to stop them being so selfish and so careless with the health service (not another word about drugs until the social cost of drinking is well understood), and a hard look at just how far the wonders of modern medical science should be available on the health service. And after that the most vital question of all: how are we to pay for our increased needs and rising expectations? The answer is, quite simply, via state funding through taxation. The growth of a divisive two-tier system of private and NHS medicine should not be encouraged. Giving tax relief on private insurance is not the answer. Private medicine has *nothing* to offer other than speedier service and it is not beyond the NHS to improve its appointment system and its waiting lists. Fortunately, I think there is little danger of private medicine taking hold because the public have made it clear that they don't want it. Private insurance may have grown from 5 per cent to 10 per cent since 1979, but most of that has been through companies doling out private insurance as a perk, and even that figure has peaked. There are now private hospitals with empty beds. The private sector over-estimated our desire to quit the NHS. The result is that the private sector no longer sees the future as a straight competition between the two. Instead it sees the future in cooperation; building and sharing facilities in much the same way as they share the skills of doctors. No government has been able to face the prospect of outlawing the private sector, which says much about political stamina. If it was not possible to outlaw it in 1948, there was certainly a time in the mid-sixties when the Labour party could and should have grasped the nettle. Instead, Mrs Barbara Castle fought against pay-beds in the NHS. That was wrong. If she had wanted to kill pay-beds she should have killed all private medicine. Her halfway house started a spate of private-hospital building and was responsible for the uptake of private insurance. If no one has had the guts to kill off the competition, it is better that the two sectors work together. And Mrs Thatcher should not be allowed to starve the health service of funds. The money is there if we choose to spend it. I'm not impressed by figures that suggest that other countries spend more than we do. No other country has a system that is worth apeing, and higher spending does not necessarily mean a better service. I'm still puzzled by figures that suggest that we have eight beds for every 1,000 of the population, compared with America's six, when America's spending well exceeds ours. I'm still puzzled by figures that suggest that the NHS employs eighty nurses per 10,000 of the population compared with America's fifty and France's forty-five and West Germany's thirty-five. We must be misusing our nurses. In other countries orderlies do the bedpan-emptying and nurses do many things that are done here by junior doctors.

We can afford to fund the health service from taxation if we desire to do so, of that I am certain. When Mrs Thatcher came to power she was determined to cut public expenditure. And despite giving billions more to the health service, this she has managed to do. In 1975–6 public expenditure ate 48 per cent of the gross domestic product. By 1988 public spending was below 40 per cent of the GDP for the first time in twenty years. I don't know what is magical about this figure, but if it brings happiness to the Treasury and the Chancellor, so be it. I do know what is magical about the National Health Service: it is the sight of nurses putting stitches in the head of a tiny child; it is the sight of a young doctor eating a Mars bar at 1 o'clock in the morning as he copes without murmur with a succession of drunks; it is the sight of Peter Freeman in the operating theatre, proudly explaining his every move to me as he fights to ensure that a middle-aged man can live the rest of his life without the hindrance of a stiff finger.

Chapter 13

Norwich and the Cost of Learning

I felt like a character in a David Lodge novel as I arrived on the outskirts of Norwich. A Lodge character, an academic, at Rummidge (Birmingham) University would be coupled with another academic somewhere on the eastern side of the country, and much commuting would be necessary. They'd have met at Cambridge and their pursuit of university posts would have forced them in opposite geographical directions. The journey between Birmingham and Norwich is not speedy: the roads are not fast and, in my case, the long-distance coach was routed through Cambridge.

I can hardly bear to mention the problems at Birmingham coach station. Suffice it to say that the coach was late and, once again, I found myself running around to find out (a) why it was late, and (b) why we were not told, and ending up with (c) an impolite exchange with an irritable coach driver. This one overheard me questioning the inspector and interfered, with his mouth full of sandwich, to tell me that he was having his meal break come what may. I assured him that it wasn't my intention to rob him of a well-deserved feed – which, in all fairness, he appeared to be having standing up and at a speed that could not have been good for his digestion – all I was asking was for Tannoyed information so that I knew what was happening. The system was weird anyway and guaranteed to provoke anxiety: you had to stand in a long queue marked A, B or C and wait to be told which bay the coach or bus would be leaving from. The station was huge and noisy, which made it altogether possible to miss a call and be standing patiently in a queue while the bus slipped silently away. As it was the journey was going to take me six hours, and it wasn't a ritzy coach with lavatories – I think they must keep those for a couple of the main inter-city routes. We started twenty-five minutes late and our stop at Cambridge was reduced to ten minutes to catch up on the late start.

David Lodge's characters wouldn't be using the bus of course; they might have low salaries compared to merchant bankers and always be complaining about lack of money, but they would all have cars. When they weren't discussing personal poverty their conversation revolved around a four-letter word. And when my sloppy old bus finally reached Norwich my conversation, I was certain, would be dominated by the same four-letter word: cuts.

Most of the country's forty-four universities have been put on a compulsory diet. Just like the hospitals, they too had been told to streamline their operations in order that public spending could be curtailed. They like it not: they bewail their fate. But the impact is nothing like the same; the state of the universities is very much a minority concern. It should not be, but it is. The whole of higher education is a minority concern; only 14 per cent taste education beyond the age of eighteen, and only 7 per cent study at universities: far too small a percentage. Within that figure a mere 21 per cent come from the homes of manual workers. The current aim is to lift the total of 14 per cent to 20 per cent, but 50 per cent would be a worthier target. Alongside these unappetizing figures, the public perception of academic life is at best poor, and at worst distinctly unappealing. And here the universities are their own worst enemy: most of the unappealing portraits are painted from inside. The vice-chancellor of Cambridge, Sir Peter Swinnerton-Dyer, as he retired in 1981 said he was aware of those 'who merely give the same ageing lectures from the same ageing lecture notes . . . Here, as in every university, there are academics who draw a full day's pay for half a day's work.' One academic made a study of the image of his profession as seen through television, films and the novel. The conclusion was most amusing: the last British professor to get a good press was Professor Higgins in *My Fair Lady*. In the main we are drenched with images of academics, if youngish, as lazy, lusty and left wing, and if old, deaf, daft and out-of-date. (In America, of course, dons are dashing, but that's another story.) Since it is academics, in their writing, who provide these images, it can't be argued that ignorant outsiders are to blame for this state of affairs. From Kingsley Amis's *Lucky Jim*, through Malcolm Bradbury's *The History Man* to David Lodge's *Nice Work*, the dons of fiction have fared badly; they've become figures of fun and targets to tease. I wondered what would greet me in Norwich: my destination was the University of East Anglia, with 4,500 students and a budget of £21 million; a 'new' university, but that now means twenty-five years old. I might with luck be spared too many of the deaf, daft and out-of-date, although I doubted if I'd be spared the sound of folk feeling under-valued, under-funded and under attack.

I'd been invited to stay on the campus, and I accepted with relish. My months in boarding-houses had well prepared me for the spartan student life and I felt instantly at home in my neat and tiny room. At least it had a table which I soon covered with mineral water, yoghurt and fruit (from the campus shop) for my breakfast. There was a communal kitchen close by but I wasn't staying long enough to get the hang of all that. The bathroom was close by too: it was the size of an airline lavatory. And it didn't have windows. Windows were, however, the main feature of the neat and tiny room – they provided a stunning view across acres of lawn to a man-made 'Broad'. That the university was a product of the sixties, I could tell at a glance. Red-brick, that derogatory description given to older, non-Oxbridge universities, does not apply here. There is no red brick to be seen. UEA is a concrete university. UEA was designed by Sir Denys Lasdun, who was also responsible for the arts complex on the south bank of the Thames (now being revamped to make it more pleasing to the eye). Some people like concrete: I have a problem with it – I've tried and I can't like it. It's austere and forbidding, the weather stains it, making it sadder looking with each passing year. It's anti-style and desperately functional, like plastic gloves, or wind jackets. They each do their job, but they never adorn. Concrete is so intensely practical that I want to walk on it, not look at it. Whatever the merits of the design itself, the effect is ruined in concrete. Two of the student-accommodation blocks, including the one in which I was staying, are pyramid-shaped terraced storeys which remind me of the Barry Island Butlin's that I'd seen in south Wales. Lasdun says they are meant to resemble a temple. The shape is officially known in architectural circles as 'ziggurat', after the pyramidal Sumerian temples. Who knows, perhaps Butlin's at Barry Island was meant to resemble such a temple! The buildings look their best at night; then the bland, boring, stained concrete surfaces hide in the darkness, giving prominence to the lights twinkling from each room and forming a tableau of lanterns. Inside, because of the tiered storeys, there are stairs and stairs and more stairs. Concrete and uncarpeted of course. Outside there are walkways and walkways and walkways. The accommodation block is linked to teaching buildings, library and restaurants by high-level walkways. Walkways have a bad name in council-house building and are being removed on the South Bank. They are without cover and are cold and draughty. On the best of days the breeze plays havoc with your hair and on the worst of days I found myself instinctively bending to the shape of a banana in order to combat the gale. How anyone could have thought it was a good idea to have raised and exposed walkways in this exposed and windy part of the country is something of a mystery to me. But there it is, concrete buildings with walkways, surrounded by 270 acres of parkland.

The University of East Anglia has a low profile. To the people of East Anglia this is not so; they are well aware of a clutch of distinguished academics like Malcolm Bradbury and Christopher Bigsby who appear regularly on television and radio as well as in print; they are well aware of several distinguished schools, most notably English and American studies and Environmental Sciences; above all, they are much pleased with the Sainsbury Centre for Visual Arts. Sir Robert Sainsbury and his wife have given the university their private art collection spanning prehistory to the present day and including African tribal sculpture, North American Indian and Eskimo arts and oriental antiquities. With the help of an endowment from David Sainsbury, this eclectic collection is housed in a building, designed by Norman Foster, that has won numerous awards for 'the use of aluminium', for being 'low cost' – which means cheap to build – for being a tourist attraction and for being a decent museum. The building is thoroughly modern, a huge hangar, a simple tin shed, which I find neither attractive nor unattractive. Inside, however, the space is used cleverly, with cosy corners and objects viewable from all angles – nothing is merely dumped on walls. At first the collection was seen as an adjunct to the history of art department, its main purpose to introduce students to non-western art. Now its claims are much broader. It has become the public face of the university, an invaluable town–gown link. Outside East Anglia its fame is restricted, mainly because Norwich is seen as isolated, an outpost on the eastern side of the country. Most people above a certain age confuse UEA with Essex, which was a hot bed of radicalism in the seventies and was constantly grabbing newspaper headlines for demonstrations and 'sit-ins', which were then the vogue. You don't hear much of Essex now. And you don't hear much of UEA. Universities have never had to sell themselves, either to potential students or to the rest of us. That is all changing. Glossy brochures are the order of the day. UEA has to compete for students and it has to compete for private funds. As government support diminishes, vice-chancellors have stopped chatting among themselves and started a new line in rivalry: competing to see who can whip up the highest percentage of private funds. There's no point in blaming Mrs Thatcher alone for this. 'Cuts' (which has become the sort of word that demands quotation marks) were a feature of the seventies. A UEA chronology notes: 1974: cuts; 1975: freeze on appointments; 1976: freeze re-imposed. By 1981, 'cuts' are no longer worth a mention; they are a fact of life. No party it seems is willing to write the cheques;

and the Conservative government has been fearless, not to say savage, as it looks at the cost-effectiveness of the unpretentious polytechnics and compares their figures with those of the universities. In 1981 UEA was presented with a 12.5 per cent cut in its grant. It responded by what it describes as selective cheeseparing across the university, and by increasing the number of overseas students, particularly from the Far East, where governments are only too happy to pay students' fees, and from America, where both parents and students are well used to shouldering the cost of higher education and come to Britain because on the whole the price of a degree is less. Home-based students were reduced in number. Overall the university felt it had done well. It was rewarded with a further cut of around 16 per cent to be achieved by 1990. UEA, along with eleven other universities, received the largest cut in its grant. From the outside it looked as though UEA was being cuffed across the ear for poor academic performance. The assessors had taken a look at the quality of research and found UEA below average in three disciplines, including physics. The university accepted this criticism, pointing out that it has an outstanding research record in three areas (applied mathematics, economic and social history and art history), and claiming that the real reason why its money was docked was because its teaching costs are high. Its teaching costs are high for three reasons: it offers a wide variety of inter-disciplinary courses, which in translation means a student can pick a combination of courses and end up with something akin to a tailor-made degree. To give students such options is an expensive business. The university also leans heavily on the seminar system rather than lecturing students in large halls. This is an expensive business. And the university assesses its students continuously, rather like the new GCSE examination, and the final examinations count for only 50 per cent of the degree. This is an expensive business. In other words, the university was being penalized for trying to give its students a better than average deal. No wonder I expected to find folk feeling under-valued and under attack.

The vice-chancellor, Professor Burke, who was appointed in 1986, did not give me a lecture on a philistine government with no commitment to higher education. He seemed resigned and pragmatic. Resigned, no doubt, because he came from Canada knowing that his first task would be to engineer cuts totalling 16 per cent, and pragmatic because of his background: he is aware of the world beyond the university. A native of Birmingham and a graduate of Birmingham University, he is internationally known for research work which led to the discovery of Interferon as an anti-cancer agent. He became vice-president and scientific director of Canada's largest biotechnology company, Allexix, where he initiated seven joint programmes with universities. It's an impressive track record, and his experience in industry and his ability to see the potential for closer links between university and industry make him seem an ideal vice-chancellor for the nineties. Furthermore, he is reluctant to winge; he'd rather look forward to the future.

Listening to Professor Burke outlining his blueprint for making cuts in a way that didn't destroy the university was a great deal more interesting than I had expected, and emphasized how little we understand of the process. And if we don't understand the process, how can we assess whether or not the government is wrecking the system or making it leaner and fitter? Burke inherited a draft proposal for cuts which had to be abandoned in part and which, he says, taught him much. It contained a proposal for closing the music department. It's a small department of six, and at first it was thought that if it took its share of the cuts and was reduced to five, it would become non-viable and have to go altogether. The proposal produced an outcry in the department which promptly proved that a department of five could indeed be viable, but more importantly it produced a bigger outcry from the people of Norwich and Norfolk, who claimed that the presence of the music department had done much to enhance the level of music performances available to the region. The professor of music, Peter Aston, had conducted the Aldeburgh choir for seventeen years, and the thought of losing him provoked letter after letter. Professor Burke realized that to take the university down a path that damaged its relations with the region was not the way forward. The music department survives with five people and an appeal was launched to raise £150,000 for performing scholarships for students. And it survives by working harder, warmed by the knowledge that it is valued both inside and outside the university.

Development studies also faced part-extinction: there was a proposal to abolish undergraduate degrees, but to keep the postgraduate programme. There was some feeling that the undergraduate course attracted students with low A-level scores and therefore could be abandoned. Apart from the fact that it was soon realized that this would erode the graduate programme, another impressive campaign was mounted. The vice-chancellor received 800 letters. 'It was a highly orchestrated campaign among those who misunderstood our proposal and who thought we intended to kill the whole department. None the less the Third World lobby got together, and we had letters from the House of Lords and from MPs. They argued that if UEA abandoned its course then the country would lose something of value, since there is only one other similar course in the country, at Cardiff. So once again we came to realize how much something was valued, and we decided to keep the undergraduate course, but reduce the intake by 15 per cent, which went some of the way to answering those who said the A-level scores were too low. We then asked the department to raise some money of its own. Many of its members act as overseas consultants, and in the past this has operated at break-even level because we didn't want to make money from the Third World. However, since it is largely international agencies that fund this work, and they operate by making a small profit, the ideological obstacles were overcome. Thus, with income generation and a cut in students we have kept the department, and I really do think they have come though the experience a lot stronger than they were before.'

Physics was not so lucky. It was a small department and its answer to this deficiency was to expand in order to compete with the civic universities of Sheffield and Birmingham. Burke did not think this a good idea. He did not feel the department was strong enough academically to argue for expansion, and anyway, he thought it a strategic mistake to try and compete when Norwich was so far from the major employers of physicists. His answer was to go in another direction – not to offer a single physics honours degree, but to offer instead a new degree in physics and its applications. He admits it led to a showdown in which he said it was either a new structure or closure. Inevitably, some academics left, reducing the department from fifteen to nine.

All the university's 'schools', which divide into one third science, one third social sciences and one third arts, have had to bear a share of the cuts. The aim was to lose twenty-eight members of staff, mainly through early retirement. Some areas were cut more easily than others: sociology has been reduced from twelve to four. History and biology proved the most difficult, and outside advisers were asked to help solve the problem. Professor Burke's conclusion is that this process of rationalization, a word often used in business and which means selling fewer lines, has curbed student choice upon which UEA prided itself. Others of course argue that by offering so much choice quality suffered, and whereas no one wishes, say, all history students to be studying exactly the same areas, the curtailment of a few options is no great loss.

Professor Burke also feels – rather like the hospitals – that he is now running his university much closer to the edge, and that he cannot take further cuts. He dreads the thought that having coped with this round of cuts, the university will once again be rewarded by another squeeze. Having said that, however, he is generous enough to point out that the whole exercise has concentrated minds on strategic directions for the nineties. The nineties present problems: the number of eighteen- and nineteen-year-olds in the population is going to drop by 30 per cent. The largest drop is going to be among social classes four and five, who take up a mere 8 per cent of university places. Social classes one and two, which take the bulk, will drop by around 10 per cent. I thought this might provide an excellent moment to improve the numbers of working-class entrants, but Professor Burke dashed these hopes in a second. He argues that it will worsen the situation. With school-leavers in such short supply, they will be courted by employers and thus have no incentive to struggle through sixth form, let alone university. In Norwich itself, Norwich Union could absorb all the O-level students produced in the area in the coming years. The answer to the demographic change is for the universities to break the pattern of dependence on A-level school-leavers. They will still form 60 to 70 per cent of the intake, but entrants must be sought from those with less conventional qualifications. One idea is for the university to work hand in glove with Colleges of Further Education so that it is possible for HND candidates to move to the university for a two-year course. The two are already cooperating on course content to make the transition easier. There is also increased demand from people in jobs who want to do part-time courses such as a master's degree in electronics or management. To increase the number of part-timers doing first degrees appears to be difficult: they are subsidized by the university since it is impossible to charge such students the going rate of around £1,500 for tuition fees – the market wouldn't stand it. It would seem an ideal moment for a campaign to persuade the government to pay the tuition fees and prove their commitment to continuing education.

Professor Burke is not optimistic. He sees student loans as inevitable. 'We already have *de facto* loans. Student grants have been frozen over the last ten years and are now 20 per cent less than in 1979, so that students have had to take loans.'

'How do you feel about this?' I asked. He parried the question, so I asked again.

He paused and then said: 'Bad. It's short-sighted. Britain is going to need all the brain-power it can get. But higher education is not as highly valued here as it is in other countries. In North America it is seen as the way out of the ghetto.'

'What then are we going to do to make it more highly prized? Analysts have said time and again that Britain's economic future depends on having an educated workforce. What more can be done?'

'Somehow or other we have got to *prove* to people that it is worth the money. One of the ways is to get the community involved, so that they can see, and another is to do something about our public image and improve our public relations. We have been complacent about this in the past, but we now need to explain what we are doing. I think it will take a generation.'

Improving public relations will also help the task of fund-raising which the government has urged on the universities. UEA has appointed its first development officer, held gatherings of former students in the hope that they will make donations and run two successful campaigns, one for the music department and the other to raise £100,000 for the Centre for East Anglian Studies.

'I feel that the government is over-optimistic in what it thinks the universities can raise by themselves. Right now they see us as unwilling to work hard for our own future, so we have tried to raise money just to show that we are doing all we can. In the end, of course, you can't run the skilled manpower needs of the nation on charity. We are prepared to do our bit, but such efforts will only provide money at the margins. Seventy-five per cent of the university's budget goes on salaries, which doesn't leave much to play with, so any extra raised by the university gives us a measure of independence.'

The mood on the rest of the campus was not quite as cool and pragmatic. Half the senior staff have been there since the beginning, which is not altogether a good sign. One can feel the mental cobwebs. There isn't enough movement between our universities, but now that tenure has been abolished for newcomers to the system, perhaps that will change. Several of the long-stayers recall the heady days of the sixties, when public spending was not seen as a monstrous Russian vine that would grow at huge speed; when they would not have stood accused of threatening our economic well-being. They are nervous of a future where industry is encouraged to fund research, not only because this might change the nature of research projects, but because the independence of research may be jeopardized. Research coming from universities has always been seen as impartial. Would this be so in future? Universities are places where people can have visions; where people have time to think, and this might well be curtailed with heavier teaching loads and under the constant glare of purse-string holders. University staff are not well paid. I think they should be more highly regarded and rewarded – as should all teachers. Academics relish their lifestyle, but they should not be penalized for being lucky enough to have jobs they enjoy.

I managed to find the head of the physics department before he quit the country for Texas. His views were understandably sharp and defiant.

'I'm happy to be leaving this country. I don't like the social mood. I think things are appalling at all levels. The whole attitude towards the future is unproductive. I get the feeling that the government is running the whole enterprise down. Some measures were necessary, but they have gone over the top. I feel desperately sorry for young people; all they can look forward to is a series of training schemes where they move boxes around – that's going to be their future.'

Dr Roy West left school at fifteen and came late to higher education. He intended to be a chemist and finally settled on physics. He has fought hard to maintain and expand his department. The research record was poor, he argues, because the department was too small and teaching took up too much time. His problems started in the early seventies, when student numbers fell because there was general disillusion with what science had done and could do. This, he argues, was a world-wide phenomenon, but whereas in other countries, most notably America, the soul-searching gave way to the excitement of Star Wars, in Britain scientific potential beyond the level of *Dr Who* does not excite the public's imagination.

'My salary in Texas will be two and a half times better than here, but I'm not going for the money. I earn twice the national average anyway: I make around £20,000 and that is OK by me. I'm going because I've spent a long time training myself, and I want to make the best possible use of the next fifteen years. I don't want to go on fighting the philistines. My university changed my life and I know hundreds out there who could get more out of life if they had the chance. In Texas they are determined to get an education. No, I don't know why they have such a different attitude to us. I don't know what has hit this country. I don't find myself in tune with the population. It won't make much difference when Labour gets back in; it will take twenty-five years to recover from the last ten.'

Most evenings I called in at the campus pub in search of student conversation and in the end managed to get a group together, having promised to provide a couple of bottles of wine in exchange for their views. The university has a high percentage of women, nearing fifty-fifty. When it was set up, UEA went out of its way to attract women students, perceiving this to be a gap in the market. My group reflected this mix, and reflected genuine affection for the university and the city of Norwich, even though none claimed UEA as their first choice. Most had chosen a civic university, gone to look at it, been disappointed and then chosen UEA unseen, fearing that a visit might prove just as disappointing. Those who had made a prior visit had been impressed by how friendly and eager the staff were. They were particularly impressed that they had been treated like adults, made to feel sought after and offered a glass of wine! What impressed me most after a couple of hours of chat was their ability to live on very little money – their grants have been cut by some 20 per cent since 1979 and a full grant is around £2,000 for living away from home at a university outside London. They are eligible for some welfare payments, and they make much effort to supplement their grants with work both in the vacations and during term time. One girl worked in a Bingo hall three nights a week and one boy told me that his parents – his father is the head of a northern art college and his mother a teacher – had tried to raise a second mortgage on their home to send their children to university. The Building Society had refused, so his parents had taken in students from the local university to provide the necessary funds. The young man said that he felt guilty at taking his father's money. All of them said that they wished grants were non-means-tested and available to everyone, since they were well aware that some 50 per cent of parents who should have contributed to their children's maintenance did not do so, either because they could not afford it or because they would not. On balance the group preferred not to be tied to the parental purse; they preferred independence. And the lack of parental support was so common that it was taken for granted. I was the only one that was shocked by parents' meanness and selfishness; I was the only one who felt that parents had a duty to their children to help them through a first degree. The introduction of loans demonstrates an inconsistency in government policy; the whole thrust of that policy has been to cut taxes and give individuals more money to spend as they choose. Since many adults have been given massive tax cuts, it would seem logical to ask them to pay more towards their children's educa- tion. Means-tested grants for higher education were the one means- tested allowance that had a good name. It was calculated on residual income (income after allowing for such payments as mortgages, pension payments and life assurance) and no contribution from parents was sought until this figure reached £9,000. Once the government realized that 50 per cent of parents were not paying towards their children's maintenance costs, it should have realized either that this figure was too low and needed to be increased, or that it was fighting a losing battle with parents and, for the sake of the nation's future, it ought to find the money to fund higher education. To dump the problem on young people seems a cop-out.

The students did not approve of grants giving way to a loans system even though they would have left university by the time proposals were in force. They were well versed in the arguments for and against student funding, and one neatly encapsulated the various parties' attitudes.

'The Tories say we are here for individual gain and therefore we should pay towards the cost because we will get higher-paid jobs at the end; the Labour party says we are here for society's benefit; the Democrats say yes, but . . . and waffle, and the hard left say it is wrong for the working man to have to subsidize us!'

They all felt that first and foremost they were at university for their own benefit, for their own fulfilment, leaving me to argue that society would benefit – they'd all end up paying higher taxes and being better fathers and mothers, better citizens, perhaps. I wasn't playing the devil's advocate. It is what I believe. Health and education are better dispensed by the state and the state should find a way of paying for young people to consume as much education as they are capable of digesting. It should start by paying them a small allowance in the sixth form and it should pay them to live – not handsomely, but above the breadline – at universities, polytechnics and colleges. I can't find one good argument for accepting the government's proposal for students to take out loans to part-fund their journey to a BA or BSc. It could keep young people away from university and it could drive young people into the arms of their nearest university so that they can live at home, as they do in Australia and America. Parents too mean to pay towards grants are often happy enough for their children to stay at home for a few more years. That way they can exercise power and influence for longer.

The 'future' was the topic on which they were least impressive. They seemed to have no clear idea of what they wanted careerwise, and defended this position by suggesting that most arts students were similarly undecided. They acknowledged that life at UEA made them feel wrapped in cotton wool. The outside world was 'horrible'. 'The idea of having a boring job is horrible. A friend who graduated last year had to get a job in a bookshop. She thought it would be for a couple of months, but she is still there and she hates it. And so many of our parents and their friends retire and say, "Thank God that's over."

'All of us dread that. We dread having to take jobs where Monday is something we'd rather not talk about and Saturday is the big night out.'

The school of English and American studies is famous. Many members of the faculty review books in Sunday newspapers, appear regularly as critics on radio arts programmes and claim friendship with real writers.

They enjoy interviewing writers on video to give their students a glimpse of the real thing: the live writer. Sometimes they prevail upon the writer to visit the campus. It means much to students, or so it seems, to say that they have seen Doris Lessing or Harold Pinter in the flesh. Arthur Miller is another favourite. There is now an Arthur Miller Centre. Malcolm Bradbury is probably the best-known of the professors. He says, quite rightly, that our most successful world product is the English language, but that the English language would be like Welsh without America. That is an uncomfortable thought. If the pilgrim fathers had shunned English, adopted or invented another language, English would be like Welsh. I shall never again carp about the way in which the Americans have messed around with the English language, I shall just be grateful that they chose it. Within the school of English and American studies, Professor Bradbury is convenor of an M A course in creative writing – indeed, he was the founder of the course, in 1971, together with Sir Angus Wilson. At the time English departments were drunk on ghastly words like 'structuralism', and hooked on high theory, and Bradbury felt inclined to remind folk that literary creativity was of value for its own sake. There was also a lot of talk about the decline of serious fiction in Britain; there is still much talk about the decline in serious fiction, but at least Bradbury had the courage to try a new idea. Twenty years later such a course is still an oddity in this country. There are plenty of them in America at under-graduate level, where they teach composition and claim to teach the art of writing. We do not believe it is possible to teach anyone to write. The course at U E A is for postgraduates and students are chosen on the basis that they have talent and show promise, and that a year to write and talk about writing with other writers and cross-examine each other's work in progress will help the best to the bottom rung of the ladder to publication. They must be doing something right: previous students include Kazuo Ishiguro, Ian McEwan, Clive Sinclair, Rose Tremain, Adam Mars-Jones and Maggie Gee. Some argue that such talent would have succeeded without the course; it seems fair to answer that the course at least accelerated that success.

Part of the course demands study of the nineteenth- and twentieth-century novel, which is designed to encourage awareness of the history of fiction and of narrative and critical theory. The rest of the time students undertake their own creative writing and once every four or five weeks they must be prepared to submit it to the rest of the group for analysis. Professor Bradbury warns students that this is tough: it is not meant to be destructive. I was intrigued. I asked Malcolm Bradbury if I could attend a workshop and he said yes, provided I was willing to read the work submitted for analysis *and* join in the discussion. I hesitated. I am well used to dissecting journalism and non-fiction, but not fiction: my comments might not be helpful.

The group was mixed, four male and four female, and ages varied from early twenties to middle forties. The work to be discussed that afternoon was by Mark Innis and Michael Brown. Mark Innis submitted nineteen pages of *A Chinese Summer*, which might turn out to be a novel or a novella. Bradbury encouraged him to outline the plot so that we could glimpse the context of the nineteen pages. Innis, a self-confident and mature young man in his early twenties, said that his work was one of mood rather than action. His central character was a youth who was in despair at the ending of a relationship; he would be involved in some kind of accident and that by the end he would be mentally restored but there would be a question-mark over his physical condition. Professor Bradbury, puffing away on a pipe and filling the room with delicious sweet smell, said he found the writing of the first nineteen pages to be superb, the central character was firmly in position, but he was anxious about the central incident: the individual scenes were marvellous, but where was the narrative drive? At the end of nineteen pages he had begun to think that nothing would happen. Now if this sounds hard-hitting, it is the fault of my précis, because that was not how it came across; Bradbury could not have been more supportive. He spun out his words, decorated his phrases, questioned Innis patiently, dragging from him a few of his intentions that had clearly not crystallized in the writer's mind. It was a masterly performance: I got the message and much admired the diplomatic and constructive way it had been delivered.

The group pitched in. There was discussion on the use of mixed tenses, and the merits of short sentences, on the novella – how many characters it could sustain and what was the ideal pace – on the use of specific phrases in Innis's work and the purpose of certain descriptive interludes. The sad youth was much given to walking in the park and looking at children, which the author said he had learned from Salinger: when people feel alienated, when they feel outsiders, they often turn their attention to children. The group was very praising. I began to feel a web of approval being woven around Innis. There was no competitive nonsense, although one older student's tone was a touch abrasive, and he niggled about the double use of a nice line describing how the letters on a plastic bag changed shape when the bag was full. No, said the rest of the group, using the idea twice is splendid! It came to my turn, and I stuck firmly to the notes I'd made the night before when I had first read it. It was a fresh and youthful piece of work –

unlike the others, I had not known in advance the age of the writers – but I was bothered from time to time by missing details: a paragraph would raise questions that I would have liked answered. The characters around the youth, particularly the parents, were too sketchily drawn, I felt. Mark Innis became defensive. He said he wasn't interested in the parents, they were going to disappear from the story and he didn't want to give further details. The group closed ranks: answering my queries would definitely spoil the delicacy of the writing. Professor Bradbury took the reins and pointed out that writers could withhold information deliberately, but not leave out information unwittingly. He preferred the reticent approach. At first I felt my comments had been unhelpful, but then I changed my mind: at least we now knew that details could and should be left out. Innis had been reassured and readers like me could stop being inquisitive.

If I was beginning to feel that the group's ability to secrete a protective shell around itself was too cosy, detrimentally cosy if it precluded tough comment, I was soon proved wrong. Mike Brown had submitted the opening pages of a film script. The group ganged up on him; they didn't bother to analyse the script, they merely queried why he was bothering to write it. It was abundantly clear that they thought their own attempts at novel and short-story writing were infinitely superior to his attempt to write a film script. As it happened, Brown had positioned himself at one end of the room, facing a horseshoe of other students. I felt a wave of superiority floating across the gap. Bradbury, who knows about these things, having turned Tom Sharpe's *Porterhouse Blues* into a television series, pointed out that there were drawbacks: when writing a novel the author can paint on a huge canvas, encompassing the Napoleonic wars, but as the writer's pen touches the paper with a film script, the first question is, how much am I spending? Michael held his ground.

'I'm not here to write a novel. I want to make a film.'

The assault continued: one member who had something to do with film-making warned that it wasn't a writer's medium, the script writer would be faced with rewrite after rewrite to suit the whims of others. Film-writers were not important. Film-writers were 'invisible', said an Irish girl. Michael held his ground: he said the idea of working in a team and having close relationships with those involved on the same project appealed to him. As long as the director understood the aims of his script, rewriting would not be a problem. I was rooting for him; I wanted him to go on arguing his case.

'Can we discuss what I have written? I haven't got too much out of this discussion so far.'

I said a silent, 'Hear, hear!'

The mood worsened. A girl said that when she read the reference to 'a big building' and a Porsche car she said to herself, 'Oh, shit, this reminds me of Dallas.' At this point I wrote in my notebook: 'This is appalling.' The previous evening when I had read the film script, I'd made up my mind not to make a contribution to the discussion because I have no experience of reading film scripts. The previous evening when I read the film script I did not know that Michael Brown was an American. I cannot help but feel that this influenced the group's attitudes. For an American, to want to write a film script is a worthy ambition: America has a film industry. We do not have a film industry of much consequence, so we look down our supercilious noses at the medium. I did not feel that Malcolm Bradbury had done enough to ease the tension, and afterwards suggested that he should seek out Brown and make an effort to massage his mangled morale.

It is said that Michael Brown is a man of 'great enthusiasms'. He eventually abandoned the film and started work on a novel. At the end of the year he returned to America to take another course, in law and business. Mark Innis's *A Chinese Summer* was published by Bloomsbury. The book is autobiographical. This was not evident from the first nineteen pages, but was evident when completed. The sad youth suffering madly and badly from a lost love also lost his leg through cancer. Mark Innis lost a leg through cancer.

The city of Norwich was a magnificent surprise. I saw it first at night, in the rain, and it was beautiful. I'd been advised to see it at night; Norwich is special by night. The city has fallen in love with the spotlight. Many of its historic buildings and a sprinkling of its numerous churches are stunningly lit. The city claims thirty-two pre-Reformation churches, a number it can no longer sustain and which it expects will in time decline to twenty. Meanwhile it is caressing the best with floodlights – not the garish white light of football pitches, but more appropriate, gentle, warm beams. And it isn't just majestic buildings that benefit, but open spaces like Market Square and streets like Elm Hill. To stand at one end of Elm Hill, by Stamp Corner, looking down a cobbled street bathed in lantern light is so pleasing it made me smile, even though a fine drizzle was falling on me. The scene had a Christmas-card perfection, unreal but not artificial, and deeply satisfying. I thought of J. B. Priestley who on his thirties journey commented on the chill gloom of Norwich, on the feeble light of the occasional street lamps and, just to underscore his view, he added: 'Norwich is not brilliantly illuminated at any time.' Perhaps it was this gibe that goaded the city council into devising its award-winning lighting scheme.

After this night-time glimpse, I rushed back the next day to see what else would be revealed by a city of which I'd had no image apart from thoughts of prosaic insurance companies and Colman's mustard. I went straight back to Elm Hill to see if the magic had disappeared in the morning light, and found it equally pleasing; the golden glow had given way to colour-washed prettiness. The oldest house in the street, a thatched fifteenth-century cottage, is now a coffee-house. It had once been the home of worsted weavers, and of leather workers and shoe-makers. It mirrored the history of the city. All the pre-Reformation churches indicate how prosperous and important the place once was and, indeed, in the fourteenth century Norwich was awash with crafts-men and entrepreneurial wool and cloth merchants generating wealth. The word is that in 1450 it was the richest town in the land. Certainly by 1700 it was the second city in England, a centre of trade with Europe's northern cities, dominated by the weaving of worsted. It was on the right coast, facing the right way. But Norwich lost out to Yorkshire during the Industrial Revolution: Yorkshire had the fast-moving streams and cheap coal needed to power looms. People and wealth moved northwards. It's odd how much we hear now of people and wealth draining from northern towns to the south, with little thought of how this operated in reverse in the first instance.

Norwich and East Anglia's greatest advantage now is that it was bypassed by the Industrial Revolution. Never having had heavy in-dustry it has not had to face urban decay, nor the vast task of adjusting to a diverse and service-dominated economy. It had to find the answers much earlier; it had to learn the importance of flexibility and adapt-ability by diversifying into silk and paper and, of course, leather and shoes. In time shoe-making was to suffer from foreign competition and something else had to take its place. The service sector, upon which so much of modern prosperity is based, has been strong in Norwich for decades. Its largest employer is a financial institution, Norwich Union. The little coffee-shop knew its place. I wanted to linger, to sit in the coffee-shop and be lazy, but curiosity propelled my feet forwards through the narrow, winding alleys and streets free of traffic. I glanced at two of the six bookshops and walked through the 200-stall open provision market, with its brightly coloured awnings. I spent an hour merely wandering without purpose and marvelling at how Norwich had managed to avoid the worst effects of twentieth-century development. Practically the whole of the city centre is a conservation area: tower blocks are few. How on earth did Norwich manage to keep its head when all around were losing theirs? Some argue that it is more by luck than judgement, since the place is slow to change and decidedly untrendy and therefore, by the time it caught up with what was happening elsewhere, it could *see* that the modern fads were not for Norwich. Others give credit to political stability: the Labour party has dominated Norwich for as long as anyone cares to remember, and continuity yields consistency. While others were building supermarkets on the outskirts of their towns, Norwich remained faithful to city-centre traders. It needs more shops, since it is the centre of the fastest-growing region in Britain but such expansion is not going to be allowed to ruin what has been so carefully preserved. Instead there's a visionary plan to put a new development *underground*, beneath the site of the old cattle market. A landscape park will be created at surface level. I wished it well and headed for the past.

The castle and the cathedral dominate the skyline. The castle, which for 500 years was a prison, is now a museum housing among other things a fine collection of paintings by John Crome and John Sell Cotman. Crome, the son of an innkeeper, was the founder of the group that revelled in painting the local countryside and who adopted the phrase, 'Nature is still our Goddess and our Guide,' as their motto. One of his pupils was the brother of George Borrow, who was a clerk in a lawyer's office. It is said that Borrow spent much time in the cattle market, with the gypsies, listening to their tales, some of which found their way into *Lavengro*. Norwich is the only city in England to claim its own school of painting recognized at a national level. And that school was undeniably influenced by Dutch painters, demonstrating the close links between Norwich and the Netherlands which existed since the medieval period, partly through an influx of immigrants fleeing religious persecution. Both the Dutch and the Flemish found Norwich a haven. I have a weakness for Norman cathedrals, and Norwich's is more enchanting than most: it is surrounded by houses, which help to soften the usual image of a cathedral being above and aloof from the intimate dwellings inhabited by man. I decided I'd like to live in one and was told that I'd have to wait at least a hundred years. So, fickle as ever, I continued my walk and found an alternative. Alongside the River Wensum at Anchor Quay, rehabilitation and development has produced a batch of town houses (both council and private), in an idyllic setting; the idea was to encourage folk to contemplate life in the city centre rather than in the countryside. I don't normally find myself attracted to the thought of living in new buildings, but these were deeply appealing. The way in which cities have developed their riversides in the eighties is cause for celebration.

By the time I had finished my walk I could see why Norwich had been nominated as Britain's most attractive city in a report commissioned by the EEC and undertaken by Reading University. Norwich was the only British city in the top twenty-five of the European league table that based its assessment on four main areas: the income of the citizens, unemployment rate, people moving into the area and the attractiveness of the city to tourists and business travellers. In 1971, Norwich was thirty-seventh, below London and Leicester, but by the late eighties London and Leicester had slipped, and Norwich had been placed just below Paris and just above Rome. Well, it's a jolly PR line and I went off to lunch with Patricia Hollis, the leader of the council, ready to ask her how much she'd had to bribe the researchers to achieve such an accolade! I finished lunch, some hours later, with reluctance. Patricia Hollis is – quite simply – one of the most impressive women I have met in years. In her late forties, she is a senior lecturer in English history at the university. She revitalizes both the image of the don and of the local councillor, and she demonstrates how the city has benefited from the presence of the university. She came to UEA in 1967 and became a councillor in 1968. When she joined the council she was the only graduate. Since she joined, she has chaired housing and finance and been leader since 1983. She has also been on Norfolk County Council, East Anglian Economic Planning Council, the BBC Regional Advisory and so on and so on. She is married to a philosopher, has two grown-up sons, and has also written books and been a Parliamentary Candidate. Her enthusiasm for Norwich is boundless. She calls it a pint-sized Great City; she believes in *local* government: the city council should decide what is best for Norwich without too many orders from the County Council based in King's Lynn, let alone interference from central government. She dismisses charges that lengthy control by Labour has in any way made the place complacent, and proudly points out that the average age of Norwich councillors is thirty, and that 35 per cent of its members are women.

'We are accountable to the electorate and they clearly like the way we run the city. The city has always had radical leanings and we all know that we have to work hard to maintain our success. We are constantly looking for new growth areas in the economy; for new firms and factory spaces to provide more employment. We are constantly looking at ways of improving our communications, and traffic flow in the city, and new pedestrian areas, as well as enhancing our leisure facilities and new ways of attracting tourists.'

It was education, however, that dominated our conversation. Patricia Hollis was the founder-director of the university's part-time degree programme and a passionate believer in the need to widen access to further education. Our present system she claims is divisive. The expansion of higher education in the 1960s benefited the middle classes and women in particular, but not the working classes as a whole. Her solution was that no one should enter the workforce until they are eighteen. An allowance should be paid to those over sixteen, and all education over that age was to take place in tertiary colleges rather than in sixth forms. Working-class students find it easier to be in colleges of further education than in schools, where they don't feel comfortable. Such colleges should provide much improved vocational education where students could sample a variety of trades from painting and decorating through plumbing and car maintenance, as well as majoring in one. The much derided YTS scheme would be a dead duck overnight. The tertiary colleges would also provide A-level studies, but with much wider courses and with all students taking both arts and sciences. Those that went on to higher education, whether immediately or later, full or part time, whether in polytechnics or universities, would be offered mixed arts/science degrees. All through the system teachers should be highly valued, highly paid and given frequent retraining. We mulled over vocational education for a while: the numbers concerned are vast, and we have failed and failed and failed since the middle of the last century to get the recipe for training right. There are 2 million people unemployed, and yet the building industry is short of craftsmen and may well be driven to recruit in Europe. Industry has a very poor training record: it doesn't seem able to plan its manpower needs. One day it decides it needs skilled men, and hasn't allowed time to train them. The Thatcher government has put considerable effort into improving this area, and has succeeded in going round in a circle. In the early seventies the Tories, realizing that employers failed to give adequate training – apprenticeships had been abandoned rather than modernized – introduced state intervention in the form of the Manpower Services Commission. That was hardly a resounding success. First attempts to revamp the scheme ran aground when the TUC played up and important sections of the membership decided to boycott the whole thing. The government had to think again and turned once more to the employer: two thirds of the members of the Training and Enterprise Councils (Tecs) will be employers from the private sector because 'it is they who are best placed to judge the skill needs'. Maybe employers have changed; maybe, frightened by the prospects of a shortage of school-leavers, they have seen the error of their ways. Maybe.

Chapter 14

The City of Bristol and the Duchy of Cornwall

I left Norwich by train and decided that, for once, I would ricochet with all speed from coast to coast. In London I paused to fill my suitcase with warmer clothes and accepted a lift to Bristol. I sat in the back and pretended I was J. B. Priestley; at the end of his time in Norwich, Priestley's mind turned to the law, and he nagged about the way in which our libel laws prevented journalists from uncovering corruption, whereas in America the law of libel was much less strict and corruption was forever being uncovered. Our libel laws are still strict, but going to court is so expensive that few can afford to fight and very few bother. There's no legal aid for libel, so the courts have become the province of the rich and famous, and beyond libel they have become the province of the rich or the last resort of the poor on legal aid. That means they are no-go areas for the majority, and much needs to be done about it. But no one is much bothered by the plight of the press: no one seems to think their hands are tied and should be freed. It's just the opposite in fact: there's concern about the way in which sections of the press abuse their rights – the way in which they invade people's privacy in order to print details of sexual peccadilloes; the way in which they print inaccurate reports without giving the subject the right to reply. The cry now is to curb the press, not free it, and they have only themselves to blame. Unfortunately, the honourable scribe will suffer; curbs on the hunter of salacious titbits are bound to inhibit the best kind of investigative journalism.

For the moment my thoughts were less concerned with the state of modern journalism and rather more concerned with the state of the legal profession. The very words evoke the world of Jarndyce *v.* Jarndyce; a world of ossified tradition, a world of Masonic secrecy, which the consumer enters at his peril. At worst the law stands for all that is wince-making in England: arrogance, complacency, conformity and conservatism. And snobbery: solicitors are seen as players and barristers as gentlemen. Gentlemen become judges, although a few solicitors are allowed to join the club. Judges fascinate me; they have such power, real power, to play God, deciding who and what is good and bad. How are judges picked? How do they know whom to believe, when all too often the truth seems secondary to a legal jousting tournament? Do they fear making wrong decisions, or do cases evaporate with the end of each day? Why do sentences vary so much? Since most judges come from professional backgrounds, how do they understand the plight of the guy caught brawling outside a pub? And how does a person view the world when day after day he sees nothing but those accused of lawbreaking?

I have a friend of twenty years who is both a QC and a recorder – a part-time judge – and I suggested to him that it would be fun to visit Bristol when he was sitting as a recorder. I could watch and listen to him at work by day and then in the evening we could gossip by the fireside. I could discover what makes a good judge and rake over the arguments in favour of a two-pronged profession of barristers and solicitors and discover why both wings have doubled in the last twenty years: in 1971 there were 2,500 barristers and 25,000 solicitors, and now there were 5,000 and 45,000 respectively. What fun, was his first reaction; his second was more cautious. And then it became clear that it couldn't be fun at all. My request had to go before the Lord Chancellor and the Lord Chief Justice personally for endorsement. Yes, a recorder – a part-time judge for a mere four weeks a year, presiding over the least serious of Crown Court cases – had to seek permission from the highest authorities before he could talk to me. Six months later came the reply: the Lord Chancellor said in writing that as it was his duty to preserve the integrity and independence of the judiciary, he could not allow the recorder to talk to me about the cases he was involved with; nor could he talk to me about sentencing policy, nor could he talk to me about particular points of law on which he might have to decide in future. I dare say that still left a few things to talk about besides claret, but none the less I dropped the idea of focusing on judges. I suppose, knowing a little about the workings of the Lord Chancellor's department, I ought to have been flattered that he didn't just say *no* to any conversation: there exists some kind of code that states that only the most senior members of the law are allowed to talk to the 'media'. The Lord Chancellor then was Lord Hailsham, and undoubtedly he had been made nervous by Judge James Pickles speaking out so fearlessly and claiming that judges were 'scared to death of the Lord Chancellor and his minions'. Pickles felt it was time judges left 'the monastery in which they lived and meet the populace from time to time and tell them what they think about the monastery'. It looked for a while as though Pickles was going to be the first judge to be sacked for anything other than for criminal behaviour.

We have a new Lord Chancellor now. Lord Mackay of Clashfern is thought by some to be one of Mrs Thatcher's most brilliant appointments. Apart from anything else, it showed, they said, that she wasn't all that anti-Scottish if she could invite a breath of Scottish fresh air to ruffle torpid English feathers. And Lord Mackay is certainly doing that. He's brushing aside some of that complacency, conformity and conservatism. He's busily promoting ways in which the law can be made cheaper, more accessible and more efficient. Others have talked of doing such things before, they talked and talked and did little. Lord Mackay has chosen to assault several areas: he favours the introduction of a 'no win, no fee' system, similar to that already operating in Scotland, where lawyers agree to charge their normal fee only if they win. While some argue that this is immoral and will encourage lawyers to be dishonest in search of victory, most people dismiss this as an insult to the profession, believing instead that lawyers will become more diligent knowing that if they lose a case they will be out of pocket; and clients will feel more inclined to seek justice rather than nurse grievances, knowing that they cannot end up out of pocket. It is an excellent notion. There are drawbacks in that lawyers will obviously be eager to capture the obvious 'winners' and anxious to be rid of the borderline, but against that one must place the thought that lawyers now are known to take borderline cases because *they* have nothing to lose. Lord Mackay also favours ending the barristers' monopoly of higher court work by allowing some solicitors to become qualified to plead in those courts. He also favours widening the net from which judges are chosen to include all advocates, and putting an end to the system whereby a barrister can only be briefed by a solicitor and not by a client. In return for all these gains, solicitors will have to accept further competition for the lucrative business of conveyancing. A few years ago their monopoly on this work was removed by the creation of a new profession of licensed conveyancers. This innovation made the buying and selling of houses cheaper for property owners, and now building societies and other institutions are to be allowed into this field.

These proposals are not as radical as they seem at first glance. Some favour a system whereby all lawyers have the same training, and all practise as solicitors for a number of years, after which those who wish to become barristers would be selected by examination. In other

CHOPPING DOWN THE CHERRY TREES

words, they fancy a fusion of the two wings into one. The present
proposals are certainly a step in that direction and the bar has made it
clear that it is not happy. The howls of protest are hard to ignore.
Barristers launched a campaign to raise a million-pound fighting fund
to guard their patch, and hired a flashy advertising agency to argue
their case before the Green Paper – a discussion document – turns
White and becomes law. Does the most cossetted of professions see its
privileges of centuries being whittled away and like it not? Or are
barristers genuinely worried that the proposals will not achieve their
stated aims; will not make the law cheaper and more efficient? It is a
mixture of the two. There are genuine worries, particularly about how
the independence of the bar could be harmed: there's a suggestion that
an advisory council dominated by lay-people would be given a greater
role in regulating the profession. But there's also a strong whiff of self-
interest emanating from an elitist breed of men inclined to pomposity
who also know that their influence in both Houses of Parliament is
significant. Most judges seem against the new proposals, but I can't
help thinking that it is Mrs Thatcher they are against. A House of
Lords select committee examining life sentences discovered that in
60 per cent of the cases the judge's recommendations (and they are only
recommendations) for the minimum length of sentence to be served had
been increased by the Home Office. In other words, the government
thought the sentences too soft.

The prime minister said on 18 January 1984 that she would like the
governments which she had led to be seen as governments that tackled
the vested interests which had been immune for years – the trades
unions, the nationalized industries, local government *and* the monopolies in the professions. One by one she has done just that; perhaps
barristers thought they would be immune.

Bristol has a reputation for being radical, of promoting change in
legal proceedings to make life easier for the client. It claims a number
of firsts, including the introduction of a duty solicitors' scheme and a
conciliation scheme, to take the sting out of matrimonial proceedings.
The idea that divorce courts should abandon traditional adversarial
procedures in matrimonial and family matters has been talked about
for more than a decade. So has the suggestion of family courts, where
the welfare of those involved is seen as of greater importance than merely
pronouncing on who is 'right' and who is 'wrong'. Nothing has
happened in England, except in areas like Bristol where solicitors
encourage couples to cooperate in sorting out their problems instead of
racing them to court in search of a fat fee and a spot of *Kramer v.
Kramer*. I went along and eavesdropped for a morning on one such

session; it is sad enough listening to the to-ings and fro-ings of 'sensible' divorcees. 'He says he wants to take the child away on holiday at Christmas. What do you say to that?' 'I say No. He can keep the child for a bit longer, but the child goes to school. *He* takes her to school and that's it.' It's the stuff of documentaries rather than the cinemascope.

The duty solicitors' scheme was introduced when it was discovered that too many people were going through the courts without legal representation and that such people got a rougher deal than those who were represented. Now if someone appears in court and is not represented, the magistrates can adjourn the case and refer to the duty solicitor. There is a rota, and solicitors eagerly join; it is after all both a service and a means of getting work. I went to court to witness the scheme in practice and also to get some idea of the kind of cases magistrates had to face; it was some time since as a young reporter I spent days in court covering a stream of minor offences, and I wondered how the pattern had changed. My guide was Dudley Thomas. The doorman said: 'You want Mr Thomas, do you? One of the best, he is, one of the best.' He was young and stocky and wore heavy brogue shoes. He has a splendid sense of humour and regaled me with numerous legal anecdotes which well illustrated the fallibility of even the best solicitors. Above all he made it clear that solicitors were no longer staid and slow and given to sitting in mahogany-lined offices charging whatever fees they liked. Competition had cleared the cobwebs; solicitors jostle for legal-aid work; paying clients demanded fixed quotations in advance and businesses invited firms to tender. After the riots in St Paul's district two young solicitors had moved in and cornered all the black business. A very smart move, said Dudley. The numbers of solicitors had increased because legal-aid enabled more people to be represented. The duty solicitors' scheme ensured that people knew their rights. The number had also risen because people had become more assertive; they no longer swallowed what fate dished out – if they thought they had been sacked unfairly they went to tribunals in search of compensation. Here as everywhere people's expectations had risen and here as elsewhere the professions no longer commanded automatic deference.

The magistrates' court was new, pine-panelled, bright and light, and designed so you could hear with ease. The lady magistrate wore a tweed suit and a cameo brooch, which is just what you expect a magistrate to wear. The first cases were straightforward theft: a girl was accused of having stolen a sweater from Marks and Spencer, and several cartons of cream and a hair-dryer from John Lewis. In the second case a couple were accused of stealing a Honda motorcycle and riding it without insurance. Then there was the committal of a well-dressed and good-looking young man charged with living off immoral earnings. I was beginning to think that the nature of crime had changed little when along came a young man caught in possession of a chocolate bar containing cannabis. He explained that he used cannabis for medical purposes. He was an asthmatic and cannabis helped his breathing difficulties. Another youth was charged with stealing an Access card, and yet another was charged with destroying a pane of glass worth £13 belonging to Bristol city council. He was drunk at the time. And I didn't have to wait long to see the duty solicitors' scheme at work: a middle-aged man of no fixed abode was accused of breaking windows, car headlights and so forth. As the charge was read out he looked contemptuously around the court and then said: 'I've already been in prison for that!' There was confusion; no one seemed to know what was going on and the magistrate adjourned the case until the duty solicitor could sort it out.

Bristol's reputation as an innovator intrigued me. I was given a number of reasons for it: size – the place was big enough to be interesting and small enough to be cohesive; it had a very active law society and, above all, the city is dominated by solicitors and not barristers. London, they argued, is dominated by barristers. Until recently all the big cases went to London. Now there is a local bar, but it is small and there are only four QCs. The message was clear: solicitors deal with the public at first hand, therefore they are better able to see where changes are needed; they are practical and less conservative and enjoy exploring changes. It seemed only fair that I should hear the other side.

Nicholas O'Brien is a barrister. He argued that at local level solicitors and barristers get on well; there was no need for antagonism between the two. A royal commission had decided that it was in the public interest to have a split profession, and as far as he was concerned that was correct. It was relatively easy for a solicitor to become a barrister if he wished to do so, and in any event solicitors over the years had eased into areas previously reserved for barristers, without any serious problems. Solicitors could plead in magistrates' courts, in county courts, in some crown court cases and, in certain remote areas like Barnstaple and Truro, they could even appear in a jury trial, but they tended not to use this right to the full. More often than not they used a barrister for a difficult case, or where it seemed more cost effective. It was indeed true, he admitted, that barristers are cut off from clients, that they tend to deal with them at arm's length, but the proposals for clients to have direct access to barristers, while it would end this detachment, would not achieve its aim of making the law cheaper and more efficient. At the moment Nicholas O'Brien's overheads are about 30 per cent of his costs. They are low because his needs are few; a shared typist and someone to take case bookings. If direct access were to come into being, his overheads would increase and his fees rise. 'I understand why people ask the question, should you use two people, a solicitor and a barrister, when surely one would do. But solicitors do a lot of preparatory work, finding witnesses and taking statements, and if I have to start doing that it is going to mean that I can handle perhaps one case a week. That is not going to be cheaper for the client. And I don't think it will be good for the client. It will mean that I am using my court skills less, once a week instead of every day, and any skill has to be used as much as possible to keep it up to the mark.'

O'Brien also feels that it is not in the best interests of the client to encourage (as the proposals do) firms of solicitors to take on in-house barristers. As the system stands he sees a barrister as something of a 'second opinion'. 'A solicitor brings a case to me and I look at it afresh and spot things that have been missed and pick out cases where the solicitor has made a mistake, and I can say that the case is not worth proceeding with. If a barrister within a solicitor's firm were to take on this role, he'd be more inclined to cover up the solicitor's mistakes and proceed with the case regardless.' But surely not if there were a system of contingency fees: no win, no fee?

'I don't think such a system is the answer to making the law cheaper and more accessible. In the end, someone has to pay. I agree that going to law is expensive. I couldn't afford it myself! But I really don't know what the answer is. Perhaps a better answer would be for people to take out insurance to cover litigation. They could pay £50 a year, or whatever.'

Nicholas O'Brien was about to handle a most unusual case; the sort of case that doesn't often get to court; the sort of case that is hushed up. I followed him to court to sit and listen.

As the magistrates' court is modern, so the crown court is old. Court One had high-backed red-leather chairs; everyone was dressed in black and white, many with gowns and wigs. My jade-green scarf was the only splash of colour. The atmosphere was sombre. I sat back and admired the stained-glass windows with their mixture of shields and emblems and spotted one for John Cabot, navigator, who sailed from Bristol in 1497 and planted the flag of England on the northern coast of North America five years after Columbus discovered the continent. And another to Edward Colston, 1636–1721, whose chief pleasure was spending his great wealth for the benefit of his native city and whom that city has subsequently greatly honoured with statues and plaques. While I admired the windows, I eavesdropped on fragments of conversation: a female voice near me was explaining how her ninety-two-year-old aunt had known Gandhi. O'Brien was prosecuting. The accused had been charged with the attempted rape of a twelve-year-old. The defence lawyer was arguing that the accused was on drugs and didn't know what he was doing. The young girl was the accused's daughter.

The man in the dock wore a suit, a shirt with a button-down collar and a blue tie. He was thirty-five; he'd been a bus conductor and then a carpenter and had been unemployed for long periods of time. He'd been given suspended sentences in the past for possessing drugs.

Nicholas O'Brien stood up. His robe slipped and slithered. 'The child's mother was at work at the supermarket at the time of the first offence, and the girl's younger brother was watching TV. The girl's father called her upstairs. He was in bed. He said, come and give me a cuddle. The child did and he touched her breasts. Some weeks later he asked her again to get into bed and told her to take her skirt off. He pushed her legs apart and attempted to push his penis into her. She resisted and the attempt failed. The girl did not tell her mother because she was frightened. The second rape attempt relates to an incident some time later when the girl went with her father to a recording studio in the docks area. He showed her two wooden rings, large curtain rings, and said they'd make nice bracelets. He told her to lie on the floor. He tied one wrist to the leg of a desk and the other to a chair and one leg to another chair. He tried . . . It was painful and she screamed and he apologized. She discussed the matter with a girlfriend who told her to tell her mother, but she did not. Then one day when she told her father she didn't feel like going to school he slapped her face and told her to go to bed. She ran out of the house and found her mother at her place of work.'

The accused's lawyer said his client was in urgent need of hospital treatment. The woman whose aunt knew Gandhi was a doctor. She told the judge that when she interviewed the defendant she found him confused; she thought he was affected by drugs; she thought he needed psychiatric treatment.

The man in the dock stared at her. His blink rate was very high.

The judge: 'You say he took drugs to stay awake?'

The doctor: 'Yes, he had just bought his house from the council and he needed to do a lot of work on it, so he took pills to stay awake.'

There was much talk about something called a 'fugue' state, and amphetamine psychosis, which all seemed to add to the fact that the man – or so his defence would have us believe – did not know what he was doing. The judge remanded the man in custody for three weeks for psychiatric reports. He said: 'I think at the end of the day I might have to send your client to prison.'

The *Bristol Evening Post* reported the case on page one. 'Girl, 12, tied to chair in sex ordeal.' They named the man but then in order to protect the child they could not say it was his daughter. The option, which I would have chosen, would have been not to name the man but make it quite clear it was his daughter. The report as published represents a hidden statistic. This was the third time on my journey that abuse of daughters by their fathers had filled pages of my note-books. On the first occasion it was in Liverpool, in Toxteth; a black girl told me that the story of her appalling life began when her father sexually abused her. My face must have showed disbelief. She said, 'It's not that uncommon, you know. I do counselling work with child-abuse victims now, and I know it's not uncommon.' The second time was in south Wales. I was at a dinner-party where the subject of incest was discussed as though it were nothing more or less than drug abuse. I said as much. 'Oh, we don't know anything about drug abuse here, but we know about incest.'

The Cleveland affair means that many people who knew nothing about child abuse know about it now. In Cleveland in the spring and summer of 1987, 121 cases of suspected sexual abuse of children were diagnosed by two paediatricians, Dr Marietta Higgs and Dr Geoffrey Wyatt, using a technique known as anal dilation; a diagnosis which was approved while it belonged to forensic pathology, but contested once it was applied to paediatrics. After bitter legal battles, twenty-six of those children from twelve families were said by the judges to have been wrongly diagnosed. (In the other cases the children's alleged abusers either left their homes, or the parents agreed to 'protective plans' with social services, or the children were removed from their homes.) The furore surrounding the Cleveland affair resulted in a judicial inquiry which acknowledged that sexual abuse of children was a serious social problem, gave cautious approval to the diagnostic techniques used and criticized in some way almost everyone involved with the Cleveland crisis. The press had a field day. As Beatrix Campbell says in her book *Unofficial Secrets*, somehow the press managed to give the impression that most of the abuse cases were cleared by the courts, which was not so, and the two doctors suffered a witch-hunt. Campbell points out that even the *Guardian* had a headline saying 'Cleveland: The doctors were wrong', on a 'leak' of the judicial inquiry. I certainly had formed the opinion, after careful reading of several newspapers, that the doctors were over-zealous and I needed to read Beatrix Campbell's book before realizing that it wasn't that clear cut. The press reporting had not been accurate. An attempt by the colleagues of Dr Marietta Higgs to make this point and to get her reinstated ensured that Cleveland had two years in the public eye. And after all the noise, where are we? The *response* to sexual abuse has been debated at length – in future, those who detect abuse will know they must act cautiously – but are we any the wiser about why children are abused? Only in that we know it has nothing to do with poverty; it crosses all income groups and all classes and races.

There was a time in our history when incest was widely practised. Giraldus, writing of the Welsh in the twelfth century, states, very simply, 'The Welsh are much given to incest.' Are we today unearthing the remnants of cultural practices we thought were long dead? Or are we unearthing a pristine problem, a problem thrown up by the failings of contemporary family life? Is it as some feminists suggest, that if we involve fathers more fully in fathering they will not abuse their children? Or is it merely telling us something unpalatable about male sexuality? Could it be that the British attitude to children is all wrong? One consultant paediatrician, Dr John Partridge, wrote these words: 'The attitude towards children in Britain is too often rejecting. Children seem of little value, rather a nuisance, to be treated irritably.' Children are low status objects, to be used and abused, who in turn use and abuse their own children and dismiss and discard their, by now elderly, abusers. A report from Brunel University, unconnected with child abuse and designed to discover how a man's job affected his attitude to his wife and children, stated unequivocally that those in boring, regimented jobs with no responsibility had impoverished relationships compared to those in flexible jobs demanding initiative and responsibility. The research cut across class lines and dealt with blue collar, white collar, any jobs where men felt bored or undervalued – the researchers called them 'slave jobs', jobs you had to put up with in order to pay the mortgage. 'The fathers in slave jobs did not help in the home, never cooked or washed up, were less involved with their children and less fond of them.' Could there be a link between dehumanizing jobs and bad man-management and child abuse? There are only questions; there are no answers.

Bristol is an interesting city. It is a pity that when I think of it, I think first of one particular court case that reveals the darker side of life. It was in Bristol that Coleridge wrote 'The Rime of the Ancient Mariner' and that Defoe met Alexander Selkirk and learned the story of his adventures, upon which the writer based *Robinson Crusoe*. Bristol was a merchant city; it acquired prominence and wealth on the profits of the slave trade and on sugar and tobacco, as well as wool and soap and leather and fish and wine. It has always been seen as an energetic city: history records that it was particularly badly battered by the Black Death, but that resourceful men fought back and built anew. It was badly battered during the Second World War, and once again men fought back and built anew. For the most part, post-war redevelopment was not a success; but Bristolians were sensitive to the mess and have since put much effort into retrieving their city by planning with care and with beauty in mind. The development of the sides of the river which runs right into the centre of the city is splendid. Once, such was the planners' low opinion of the value of the waterfront, a hotel was built with its back to the view. That lost opportunity has now been corrected: the hotel and the city have both realized that a watery outlook is an asset. Tackling the environmental mistakes of the past is only one of Bristol's problems. It has, like other cities, its share of bad housing and of homeless families; of racial prejudice, and the ghetto of St Paul's, which erupted along with other cities in the early 1980s. And it faces the same challenge as the rest of the country: finding new employment to take the place of dying industries. To this end it has been busily chasing the future by attracting its share of insurance, banking and other service sectors.

Bristol is also a gateway to the West Country and one misty morning I passed through that gateway on a bus, via Exeter to look at Cornwall. I was heading for a conference in Perranporth, south of Newquay, but such a distance is not possible in one day, so I broke the journey, first at Bude, to admire the coastline. In many ways, the coast *is* Cornwall. The county may stretch inland for twenty miles or so, but nothing inland – at least not in November – not even the barren and beautiful moors, rivals the coast. In the summer Cornwall's climate allows it to boast of many beautiful gardens attached to historic houses and castles, but the winter traveller can be forgiven for hugging the coast. By the time the bus reached Bude there were only three passengers on board. Two Americans, mother and daughter, had been told by their US travel agent that Bude would make a nice little overnight trip from London. It was either that or Edinburgh, they said, and they'd accepted Bude. In the evening light the two fretted about the narrowness of the country lanes – they'd never seen such tiny roads – and worried about what would happen if another bus came around the corner from the opposite direction. We arrived in darkness at 7 p.m., and they told me they would be leaving the next morning at 9.15 to return to London.

They'd shrunk England into little more than a day-trip, which offered me a valuable perspective on size. But what puzzled me most was why an American travel agent should even know of Bude's existence: most British people have never heard of the place.

I asked the driver of the bus for advice on a small hotel. 'I know just the one,' he said. 'I'll drop the other passengers and then drive you round.' He did that, only to discover that his chosen hotel was closed for the winter. I took pot-luck on the Burn Court Hotel. Within seconds I found myself faced with more riddles. The hotel reception was full of men wearing cowboy boots, checked shirts and jeans, with accents to match, broad accents of the southern states of America, of Texas and Tennessee. Ten minutes after checking in I returned to the hotel foyer in search of a telephone and realized that there was a queue. The phone was the only one for miles around that accepted one-pound coins, and the men from the southern states were making their weekly phone calls home. The hotel owner let me use his portable phone for a quick local call. 'You'll be waiting for hours otherwise. They each stay on the phone for twenty minutes. I reckon I get £500 a week through that box.'

I tried asking one of the men what they were doing in Bude.

'Satellites, communications, that kinda thing.'

'Is there an American base here?' I persisted.

'No, British.'

It wasn't the fullest of answers. In the bar after dinner it was clear that the Americans had been given the run of the place. They fixed their own drinks and one man showed two girls pictures of his sons of eighteen and twenty-three. The girls begged him to bring them over. 'We'll pay the fares,' they giggled.

The next morning was Remembrance Sunday, and wrapped up against the wind and the rain I walked for an hour by the sea watching the huge waves topple over one another to form a white sheet at the water's edge. I could see that it would make a surfing beach in summer. Just before 11 a.m. I went in search of the war memorial, wondering if there was to be a service. I found the memorial; at its base lay one bunch of chrysanthemums, white paper wrapped around the stems. A message had been written on the paper, but the rain had blurred the words and all I could see was, 'died 1943'. Eleven o'clock passed. The shop said that the guides and scouts would be having a march that afternoon. But I'd already decided to wander off down the coast to St Colomb Major, because I liked the name and because I'd heard about the rectory, a building dating back to the fifteenth century and drenched in tales of ghosts and smugglers. It was now a hotel with log fires, and the rain made me feel in the mood for a log fire.

The taxi driver was most forthcoming. I learned that the Americans were working at the Composite Signals Organization Station at Morwenstow. 'Up there they can listen to any telephone conversation anywhere in the world. They listened to Jane Fonda's telephone conversations when she got into the peace movement. I'm only giving you gossip, mind, but that's all we have to go on. No one talks about the place, especially not those who work there. The place was chosen because it's high up and provides a granite base. We tell ourselves that it's OK. It provides jobs, which is good for the locals, jobs from cleaners upwards, and it is especially important in providing a middle-class professional base. There's nothing else around here except tourism in the summer.'

He'd been an industrial chemist and had quit Cornwall for Birmingham in pursuit of his career, but he returned to take over his father's taxi firm. Cornwall was a better place to bring up children. His wife, who was born in Surrey, had taken eighteen months to settle down, but on the whole they were pleased with their decision. The schools were good and the only things they missed were the shops, and they put that right by spending a few days in Croydon once in awhile.

The coastal drive was glorious, the cliffs were covered in gorse and bracken and the lashing rain seemed appropriate and in keeping with the wildness. My first sight in St Columb was of a large RAF coach blocking the road, but the driver did at least direct us without hesitation to the Old Rectory, whose owners the minute I arrived began to apologize for the lack of *en suite* bathrooms and telephones. My attempts to reassure them that it was the absence of these things that had made me seek out the place were to no avail. 'We'll be putting in showers soon. It's the Americans, you see, they won't stay here unless we provide these things. We get lots of Americans coming here for dinner and for big parties. Their base is down the road, at St Mawgan, but they need these extra things if they are going to stay.' On the mantel shelf, over the fire, were two flags, one American, one British.

Up to this point I had accepted the way in which Americans had edged into my life on the bus and at Bude. Now I became truly curious. They seemed everywhere. I hadn't connected Americans with Cornwall. I knew that there were more than a hundred bases in this country, but I had not associated them with Cornwall. I knew that the US Air Force was the second biggest industry in East Anglia; that some 25,000 service men were dotted around the country; that the US ambassador had argued that these men, and their families and the USAF in general, added $1 billion to our economy and created, directly, 255,000 additional jobs. But I hadn't associated any of this with Cornwall. I decided to try and visit the base and, with the help of the hotel owners, I phoned the executive office of the US Navy. A polite voice told me that the US Navy were only 'guests', and that I should call the RAF. Several phone calls later I was told that the base needed six months' notice of a visit unless I could get special permission from 'on high', which meant the Ministry of Defence in London. I turned instead to the Campaign for Nuclear Disarmament: its local members would be able to enlighten me. I took a bus ride to Falmouth and met Betty Levene. I learned that the station outside Bude has been in operation since the early seventies and is part US National Security Agency and part GCHQ, the Government communications Head-quarters, Cheltenham. Before 1979, nerve gas had been manufactured at Portreath. And at St Mawgan since 1965 thousands of acres of Cornish soil has been used to store US Navy nuclear weapons – B57 nuclear depth charges – and that they were guarded by a special contingent of US Marines. The local paper might say that St Mawgan is 'alleged' to be a nuclear weapons store, but CND has no need to be so careful. They know that American nuclear bombs are housed there. Betty has Snowballed for several years. The Snowball campaign started in 1984 at the Sculthorpe base in Norfolk, where three people cut a single strand of fence in non-violent protest. St Mawgan is now annually snipped; Dora Russell took part in the 1986 Snowball. The fines are modest, but Betty used part of her annual holiday one year to spend eight days in prison for refusing to pay the fine. It was good publicity for the cause.

When Bruce Kent gave up the secretary-generalship of CND in 1985, he said that though membership figures were high, he felt tempted to say that CND could boast of no tangible gain. No weapons have been sent back, no bases closed, nothing had been agreed. In September 1988 Cruise missiles began to leave Britain. Earlier in that year, in February, the Russians had pulled their missiles out of East Germany. The long years of arms negotiations, first to limit the weapons and then to reduce them, were beginning to bear fruit. The American ambassador said: 'We are witnessing the removal of Cruise missiles because we, the Nato allies, have been strong and united.'

Nato came into being forty years ago, after the Berlin blockade in 1949, when Europe became suspicious of Russian intentions and fearful of Russian military might. It was thought that given half the chance Russia would invade West Germany, then Italy, France, Norway and Sweden, and then come to Britain. The only thing that seemed capable of calming such fears was for Europe to get together under the American nuclear umbrella. Nato came into being. Since then Britain has spent a large proportion of its national income on arms – funding an independent nuclear deterrent as well as contributions to Nato. Since then, thousands of American troops have been stationed on British soil; since then, American and British foreign policies have been closely linked, and it was because of this link that Mrs Thatcher allowed American bases in Britain to launch an attack on Libya. Some people, most notably the left of the Labour party, have never accepted the American-umbrella line of thinking. They say it is based on a false premise: Russia has no intention of wandering into western Europe; the Russians lost 20 million people in the last war, and they have no intention of repeating the experience. In any event, they continue, the Russians realize without constant and visible reminders that any war in Europe would involve America, just as it did last time. These differing theories about Russian intentions have kept parties, politicians and people arguing for years. Then along came Mikhail Gorbachev, a Russian the West could begin to like and trust, and suddenly years of arms talks took on real meaning. It became possible to believe that Russia did want to negotiate an end to nuclear weapons and a levelling off of conventional weapons. Gorbachev, with the help of Ronald Reagan, began breaking down the old cold war divisions: people began talking of a future without a Berlin Wall and the dissolution of Nato. It is easy enough to dream of a brand new start to the twenty-first century. But many voices are raised in warning; what exactly is Gorbachev up to? Is it a desire for peace that motivates him or is it that faced with an arms race of Star Wars proportions he began to shiver? He knew the Soviet economy could not cope, and plumped instead for the opposite tactic: ridding himself of nuclear weapons altogether, in order to have more roubles to spend improving the state of the economy. Perhaps, the cynics suggest, he wants to cripple Nato, and, even if his desire for peace is sincere, what would Russia's stance be if he were no longer leader? Ronald Reagan has gone and his successor, George Bush, is less inclined to flirt with Russia. And anyway, even if the superpowers were able to agree on denuclearization, what about other possessors of the bomb? What about India, Israel and South Africa, who already own the thing and Iran, Iraq, Brazil and Argentina, who may soon join them? There are too many unknowns and therefore it is not surprising that Mrs Thatcher still favours prudence and a strong Nato, with bases in place to ensure another forty years of peace.

In St Columb Major the pavements are very narrow: it is not possible for two people to pass each other. I stepped off the pavement many times to let an American voice pass – since there are no married quarters at St Mawgan, many find homes in this tiny town. If the servicemen were to go, the impact on this town would be noticeable, but it would matter little to Cornwall as a whole. At the weekend conference on Cornwall, at Perranporth, no one mentioned the bases. America was mentioned only once, when a delegate suggested that he would rather see an American in charge of Cornwall than an Englishman, because the latter's record in recent years as entrepreneurs and adventurers has been poor.

And because Cornwall resents English domination. It is Celtic and a nation, not an English county latched on to Devon. The Celts were bothered by other invaders, the Romans and the Normans, but it is the Anglo-Saxons for whom they reserve most of their ire. They put up a good fight under a strong leader who may or may not have been King Arthur, but in the end the English colonized them and made good use of their mineral wealth, particularly tin. They reckon the English are still making good use of them: Cornwall is their playground, and a provider of second homes.

The conference was attended by fifty or so people who care about Cornwall and about being Cornish. It was not a conference of Cornish nationalists, Mebyonn Kernow, although some were present; it was a gathering of those with the laudable aim of keeping their culture alive in a world that is becoming increasingly homogenized. Their agenda was wide-ranging. It covered the railways and the health service and the need for a Cornish resource centre and a Cornish development agency, and there were reports from working parties on education, devolution and tourism. Throughout their discussions ran one message: Cornwall does not wish to be ignored and does not wish to be hyphenated to Devon, as though 'Devon and Cornwall' were like Gilbert and Sullivan, nothing without each other, devoid of a separate identity. Cornwall is fed up with border blurring, with having more and more decisions that affect daily life decided on the other side of the Tamar. In the name of economies of scale, many of Cornwall's services are run by Englishmen in Devonshire. The final insult is the postal service. The postmark for north Cornwall is Exeter and for south Cornwall, Plymouth. The conference's attenders refused to use such codes: they marked their envelopes 'Kernow'.

The problems of a smothered identity could not be resolved without a firmer economy, and their solution is to emulate Scotland and Wales by having a Cornish development agency that would attract industry and investment. Their unemployment rate, around 20 per cent, is one of the highest. The Methodist church's community programme was the third biggest employer. (John Wesley was as popular and successful in Cornwall as he was in Wales.) The Cornish are no longer content to see china clay being dug out of the ground and taken to the Midlands: why couldn't pots be made in Cornwall? They were no longer happy to see potatoes dug out of the ground and taken to England to be put in plastic bags and sold back to them via Tesco. Why couldn't the value be added in Cornwall? Tourism has been a big earner, but tourism is seasonal and provides only low-paid work. And tourism is no longer a certainty, with numbers dropping as more and more people go abroad for holidays and with more and more competition from other areas of Britain. They told the story of how Cornwall's stall at British Travel Week had been surrounded by Hull, Bradford and Greater Manchester. They would like to find a way of attracting the kind of tourist that is interested in Celtic Cornwall; the kind of tourist that comes to appreciate Cornish culture, who is interested in historic buildings and who walks on the moors and admires the wildlife. The lovers of sea and the surf are no longer enough.

Ideas were plentiful and so was the realization of the magnitude of the task. They were all too aware that their biggest difficulty was apathy, engendered by too many decisions being taken miles away by faceless officials; by years of feeling that there was nothing anyone could do – except talk. And that was another difficulty: the well-known Celtic ability to argue and disagree, to talk and get nothing done. They appreciate that both Wales and Scotland are harder-nosed commercially. All in all the Cornish path to self-determination would not be easy. None the less, it would get easier as more and more people came to resent the fact that the best jobs still went to the English, and as more and more resented the fact that 'outsiders from up-country', having made their money, retired early to Cornwall, buying up houses and in the process putting property prices beyond the reach of local people. In fifteen years they'd seen a change; for a start the conference on Cornwall had become an established twice yearly event, and schools had become more interested in introducing Cornish studies. But this was a long way from the moment when Cornwallians would be confident enough to believe that they could become, despite their small population, a viable unit and turn their backs on London in the same way that the Bretons had turned their backs on Paris. After all, the Bretons, they said, were once weak, lily-livered and pusillanimous, but no longer. One day they could hope to have their own Cornish assembly; one day they could dream of being completely self-governing and part of a Celtic federation looking to Europe and not to London.

When I arrived at the conference someone suggested that I was yet another English journalist come to have fun at the expense of a principality of 400,000 people who wanted to be big when they were small and who bore grudges for events that had happened centuries ago. But how could anyone who had travelled through the United Kingdom, through the Highlands and Islands, through Scotland and Wales and through Ireland, feel anything other than a sense of embarrassment towards the overbearing English and their insensitivity towards Celtic feelings? The Cornish themes were familiar to me; their resentment well understood. I had come to be thankful to the Celtic fringe for being part of the United Kingdom. England without the Highlands and islands, without Scotland and Wales, would be a dull place. We should recognize that we are a partnership of nations, not just one nation comprising different people, with those in Brighton thinking that those in Birmingham and Blackpool are 'different', and never giving a thought to non-English regions. Regional diversity and community identity and Celtic culture should be encouraged just as it is with Asians and Afro-Caribbeans. Devolution should be encouraged; the dead hand of assimilation and the dead hand of Westminster should loosen its grip. No one can say that dependence has brought riches to Cornwall; she might just as well be poor and make a few of her own decisions as be poor and told what to do. Diversity and choice are supposed to be Thatcher themes. Well, let them reach Cornwall. Technology makes for easier communications; the fashion is for smaller firms, smaller schools; people working from home can work from Cornwall as well as Croydon. The fashion is for people to take more responsibility for themselves and for the community in which they live; for that to happen one must first give them back their identity.

Chapter 15

The South and the Sleeping Giant of Conservation

A number of Cornwallians live in Bristol. Paul Laity was born in Falmouth but now lives in Bristol. He gave me a lift to Exeter when the conference ended. He was a solicitor who became a barrister because he fancied appearing before a jury. But now he's gone back to being a solicitor. He joked about how difficult it was to get established as a barrister; how a clerk, who organizes the work of barristers, can earn £100,000 a year while the barrister runs around on a bicycle. I think snobbery played its part too. Laity's university was the lower decks of the navy, and that sort of thing is unusual at the bar. We drove over Bodmin Moor, past the Jamaica Inn, once known for smuggling and made famous by Daphne du Maurier. It's just a pub now. In Exeter we got lost and I settled for being dropped at the White Hart Hotel, because we'd passed it twice and it looked cosy, which was something of a contrast to the huge, half empty 'family' hotel at Perranporth. Then over a solitary supper I decided that I ought to feel kindly towards Devon, after a weekend of being cross with her for swallowing Cornwall. Although the county has many mouth-watering advantages over Cornwall – a university, towns like Exeter and Plymouth, a variety of employment – it still has many a problem. It's too dependent on tourists: 3 million of them pour into the place, clogging up the roads. Attempts both to improve the roads and to develop other industries involve scarring the landscape. The price of progress and of economic survival is a serious issue. Three sites were under attack: Dartmoor, the Dart Estuary and an area between Barnstaple and Tiverton, and they are of sufficient importance to attract the attention of campaigners. The Campaign for the Protection of Rural England (CPRE) had mounted a brilliant exhibition of photographs of threatened spots, taken by leading photographers. In all the exhibition featured twenty sites where intensive farming techniques, oil exploration, nuclear-power developments, industrial development, road-building and housing all demonstrated our indifference. Three of the sites – a county record – were in Devon. Lord Snowdon took the pictures of Dartmoor before the battle was lost.

I went to look at blighted Dartmoor with Pam Parker. Mrs Parker is a member of CPRE, and she was going to explain to me the business of the Okehampton by-pass. The roads to the West Country, through Devon into Cornwall, are a nightmare in summer; they are choked with traffic and queues, or tailbacks, are legendary. Out of season they are often little better, as the summer's heavy volume of traffic makes repairs ever necessary. A by-pass was much needed to avoid the little Devon town and speed cars on their journey across Dartmoor and into Cornwall. Everyone would benefit, but where could the by-pass go without damaging the environment? The fight over the route lasted well over a decade. It was the Channel Tunnel rail link of its time: needed, necessary, but where? And of course there was no thought then of underground tunnelling. To site the road north of the town would slice through farmland; to site the road south would slice through a corner of Dartmoor National Park. The government favoured the latter, because it would take only two to three years to build and would, they said, cause less damage to the environment. CPRE favoured the northern route because there is a policy which states that no trunk roads should be built through national parks when there is an alternative available. The northern route might well take longer to build, but not as long as the exaggerated figures suggested. The government held firm to the southern route even when a select committee favoured the north. The Okehampton by-pass goes through Dartmoor National Park. For CPRE it was a shocking defeat: the policy of protecting national parks had been breached.

Pam Parker showed me blighted Dartmoor and then the proposed new deep-water commercial port at Noss Bay, in the Dart Estuary. The distances in Devon are such that we couldn't comfortably include the site of the north Devon link road from Tiverton to Barnstaple. Mrs Parker was born in Devon, and after a spell in Berkshire returned to Devon and offered CPRE a slice of her spare time. For seventeen years she has been running the Devon branch and is a fine example of that breed of people, mainly women, who form the backbone of the voluntary movement, often seen in derogatory terms as either the rich assuaging their guilt by helping the poor, or as a section of the under-employed middle classes fretting over middle-class issues. In fact it is becoming obvious that we owe a great deal to the Mrs Parkers who, while the rest of us are preoccupied with our daily lives, have the time and length of vision to see the damage that is being caused by the demands of increased prosperity and enhanced expectations.

'An awful lot of people don't care what happens. Conservationists are looked upon with deep suspicions, as a lunatic fringe. But someone has to take a stand. We lost the argument over Dartmoor even though a Parliamentary committee took our side; Nicholas Ridley did not. People make decisions for the oddest reasons, and I suppose until more people take an interest in these affairs it will go on. One minute local councillors will say no to someone wanting to build a porch on to their house, and the next they are agreeing to a holiday development on the coast. Why? Horse-trading? Graft of some kind? Who knows. But I take heart from the fact that people are slowly becoming more aware of the importance of environmental considerations. We now talk about the "green vote" with some seriousness, and it is becoming easier to say no to farmers who want to rent out an odd bit of land as a waste tip.'

As we talked she drove her car with great care, hating traffic lights, which bring traffic to a halt and preferring roundabouts, which keep traffic moving. I said that roundabouts forced me to stop: she negotiated entry into the streams of traffic with great skill and without stopping. The Dart Estuary that afternoon looked sleepy and imperturbable; it seemed inconceivable that any one would think it feasible let alone laudable to turn this backwater into a bustling port with hundreds of lorries battling along the narrow roads we had just driven on. The area could do with more jobs, but where do you draw the line between growth and progress and peace and quiet? Pam Parker is more certain than most of us. And most of us when asked in surveys put 'the countryside' at the head of our conservation concerns. We may do nothing, but we care more than is supposed: it is thought that in the next few decades one in ten city dwellers – some 5 million people – will move to the countryside. The popularity of the city, whose bright lights were once a magnet, is on the wane; many will happily reject the anonymity of the city, where the individual is isolated and becomes alienated, and seek again a place in the country where people and friendship are important and where the word 'community' asserts its rightful and fundamentally important place. Man fears isolation from the moment he is born; from the moment he first realizes that he is dependent upon others for his well-being. For a time, maybe, when he has the option, he feels like flirting with the self-contained state, each for himself and God for us all, but in the end he prefers interdependence and a sense of belonging. It is natural. The big city is no longer synonymous with employment. Modern technology means an increasing number of people can operate effectively away from centres of population. Country matters will increasingly concern us all. Conservation in general will increasingly concern us all.

The environmental debate got off to a bad start in the early 1970s. A report from the Club of Rome contained a doom-laden message that the world would run out of resources and be unable to feed and warm itself by the end of the century. It said we ought to adopt a policy of zero growth if we were to survive, and was dismissed as exaggerated and alarmist by all but a few alternative thinkers. It has taken twenty years of a slow drip of ideas to move 'the environment' from the margin into the mainstream of political thinking. The Greens in their various shades, from the conservative 'light' who focus on the fate of the odd building, to the radical 'dark' who want nothing less than to overthrow the whole polluting, plundering system, are ready to replace fears of nuclear holocaust with fears of biological holocaust, an ecological disaster. It's easy enough to see why the movement has become mainstream: the evidence of our ignorant ways is staring us in the face, at a level we can understand: sick children and dead seals. Children have caught polio and meningitis viruses swimming off our beaches, some of which are the dirtiest in Europe: millions of tons of sewage are dumped into the sea. Some 12,000 seals died in the North Sea, probably as a result of industrial chemicals attacking their immune systems. Optimists say that the killer substances, PCBs, have now been outlawed and the seals' deaths were caused by an old enemy rather than a new one. None the less the effects of the chemicals will be with us for some time. But even if we can comfort ourselves a little with the thought that the North Sea is getting cleaner, the Irish Sea is getting dirtier and is still being used as a dustbin for industrial and domestic toxic waste.

Beyond the emotional, the proposals to privatize water have brought into the open arguments that have been swilling around for years. Time and again lack of spending on 'infrastructure' has been raised in Parliament and we have been warned that our sewers and sewage-treatment plants are in need of repair and replacement, but such investment is not vote-catching and such pleas have been ignored. Now we have woken up to water and realized that we must pay to clean ourselves up. The privatization of water is unpopular. It is seen as a natural monopoly and best run by the state. But the state, through underfunding, has made a mess of it. Our rivers need to be protected from industrial polluters who in the past have found it cheap enough to pay the fines in the unlikely event that they are caught discharging chemicals into rivers. And, closer to home, our domestic water supply needs attention: lead from pipes and tanks is entering the water, possibly damaging the brains of young children; aluminium in water is possibly causing senile dementia; and nitrates, which may cause cancer, are now at levels above those allowed under EEC rules. The nitrates get into the water from artificial fertilizers put on our farmland, and it's a fine example of how solving one problem can lead to another. Artificial fertilizers were introduced so that farmers could increase their food production. Fortunately, we no longer have a food shortage, and therefore there is no need to continue to use nitrates; the problem is that nitrates, like PCBs, do not disappear overnight, even when they are no longer used.

From water to air. For years we have been told that lead in petrol is a hazard to all of us, and particularly to children, whose IQ levels could be affected. The Japanese and the Americans have been using lead-free petrol and catalytic converters to control emissions from cars since the mid-seventies. Only now are we seriously phasing out leaded petrol. It is only when self-interest slaps us in the face that we are prepared to act. Otherwise we seem happy to listen to the Archers issuing their bite-sized mouthful of propaganda and believe that it is nothing to do with us. Propaganda has to be scary and sensational before we listen. It has taken all too long to see the link between these incidents, the realization that scientific progress brings problems and those problems are endangering our planet. And suddenly such phrases as 'global warming', 'greenhouse effect', 'ozone layer', wander into common parlance. We begin to understand that man's mistakes are causing the planet to heat up and, whereas this might mean pleasant things for these tiny islands – warmer, drier summers and warmer, wetter winters – it also means that sea levels could rise, putting south-eastern England at risk of flooding. Elsewhere in the world the pattern would be repeated: colder areas would benefit and be able to grow crops now denied to them, but desert areas would increase and there would be more famine-prone belts. This warming is caused in part by chemicals that are tearing holes in the ozone layer both at the South Pole and the North Pole, and in time this will also mean that the sun's damaging rays will no longer be filtered through a protective layer, and will cause increased skin cancer, eye damage and crop destruction. The damage is blamed on chloro-fluorocarbons (CFCs), chemicals widely used in industry as a cooling agent for fridges and air-conditioning units, but also in the making of take-away hamburger cartons. Britain has promised to cut the use of CFCs by at least 85 per cent by the end of the century. But ozone depletion is a global problem: what is going to happen when China and India decide that their massive populations deserve fridges too? One can only hope that cheap CFC alternatives will be found quickly.

Controlling ozone damage will not end the greenhouse effect. An increase in the amount of carbon dioxide in the atmosphere is also causing global warming. Burning down forests is partly responsible for this, and so are the emissions from coal- and oil-fired power stations. The daily belchings from these monsters also produce acid rain, which is damaging trees and sterilizing lakes and rivers. Billions of pounds will now have to be spent putting this right.

It is sad indeed that this list had to become long before concern about the environment moves to centre stage and governments take action. Mrs Thatcher made her first green-tinged speech in late 1988. She said: 'No generation has a freehold on this earth. All we have is a life tenancy – with full repairing lease. This government intends to meet the terms of that lease in full.' The conversion was met by genuine surprise, genuine relief, scepticism and sneers. David Hare had a play at the National Theatre, *The Secret Rapture*, which had a female Tory minister poking fun at Greens and Green issues. Damn it, she's done it again, he said, as he changed the lines in the play – to suggest that the Tories are only playing with the ideas. Whether Mrs Thatcher's coat of green paint is durable remains to be seen. I think it is because once such issues command public attention, they demand action of politicians. It is up to us to see that environmental issues do not slink back into the box marked 'for cranks only'. It is a ludicrous paradox that as we get rid of dirty smokestack industries and replace them with modern electronic and service industries, clean industries, we discover the extent of hidden dirt. The problems are serious and voters are ready for action. Mrs Thatcher enjoys stealing the clothes of other political parties and she enjoys watching them squirm naked; by harnessing Green issues to the Tory cause, she takes much away from the middle-ground parties like the SLD (and before them the Liberals), who have quietly been arguing the cause for years. There is also our future king. Prince Charles has been depicted as a loony for his concern about the environment. He is said to have banned aerosols and fur coats from Kensington Palace, and it was his mother who used the forecourt of the palace for the release of balloons promoting lead-free petrol. Prince Charles is going to be with us for much longer than Mrs Thatcher, and that is one reason why I think that Green issues will stay centre stage. Prince Charles will help to keep them there, aided by a growing army of supporters, from Pam Parker in Devon to the continuing success of the Body Shop, to Green capitalists offering shares in companies which care about the environment. And the reason why this army can be depended upon to grow is because affluence allows people the luxury to think twice about what they are doing.

Much has been said and written about the materialistic mood of the eighties; a mood in which people openly enjoy getting and spending money. What is often overlooked, however, is the fact that most of the people filling new shopping malls are handling surplus cash for the first time; they have ceased to struggle to make ends meet and are thoroughly enjoying their new spending power. For most people this getting and spending will be a phase through which they must pass before they see 'consumption' for what it is – a pretty pointless merry-go-round. When enough people have enough money, then Green issues can become fashionable; publishers can market books under the logo: 'Green Book Fortnight' and radio programmes can offer prizes to a miner who spends the money he earns in overtime buying a meadow and filling it with cowslips. The Green movement needs affluence before it can do more than mouth concern for the world its children will inherit. We are now at the stage when political parties will fight over the issue of who will do most for the environment and that is excellent – if hardly before time.

With Green issues now on the agenda of all political parties, it is a fine illustration of the dilemma faced by Mrs Thatcher's opponents. One of the saddest stories of the eighties is what has happened to the centre of British politics, and since I was on the doorstep of one of the main protagonists, I made a pilgrimage to Plymouth to see the constituency home of David Owen. Plymouth is the commercial centre of Devon, and Plymouth Devonport is David Owen's constituency and the reason why the place exists at all. For three centuries the huge Royal Naval Dockyard, commissioned by King William of Orange, was the largest repairyard in Europe. Just like the industrial towns of the north of England, its prosperity was based on one industry, which found its skills less and less in demand.

Fortunately, the picture was clear enough in the sixties for Plymouth to set about attracting footloose industry that would diversify its employment and form the beginnings of a manufacturing base. Under Mrs Thatcher, the naval dockyard came firmly under the microscope, and its costs were discovered to be excessive and its workforce somewhat pampered. The yard has been forced to become commercial: the workforce shrank, unemployment rose and the city had to battle along with the rest of the country to attract new industry. At least it had a start, with a handful of American companies already there, lured above all by sentimental links with the pilgrim fathers. The fact that these religious refugees had already left these shores and were living in Holland, and that Plymouth was just a stopover on the long journey from Holland to the New World, seems to be of little importance. The pilgrim fathers remain just as useful in the hands of copywriters. The town publicity material aimed at America argues that to visit England without visiting Plymouth is like going to India without visiting the Taj Mahal, or visiting Moscow without seeing the Kremlin! And when they succumb to such exaggeration they are rewarded by a wonderful view from Plymouth Hoe, a glimpse of the past through the alleyways of the Barbican, a postwar town centre with very wide streets and the overall impression of a working-class city adjusting to a white-collar future; a future that includes a new four-star hotel, up-market shops and a theatre. When I read further publicity which said that Plymouth's setting 'stands comparison with the locations of San Francisco or Sydney', I began to think that the city's sense of importance rivalled that of its MP! They certainly stayed loyal to him when he left the Labour party to found the Social Democratic party. Maybe their pronounced sense of history made them fancy a quarter share of the birthplace of a new party.

It was an exciting time in 1981 when four senior members of the Labour party decided that Michael Foot's left-leaning ship was not to their liking and quit to form a new party. Their names were Roy Jenkins, David Owen, Shirley Williams and Bill Rodgers. David Owen is considered to be the man who masterminded the Big Exit of the Gang of Four. It all seemed so simple: a realignment at last. Mrs Thatcher could have the right and Labour the left and the new party, smiling sweetly at the Liberal party, looked a promising occupant of the middle ground. I remember covering the SDP conference in Torquay in 1985. Everyone was saying how the shambles of the first three years had given way to a well-groomed image of a party with real promise. The sun shone, David Owen played cricket, the press took pictures and the delegates were pleasant and did not shout at one another. This image was important. The SDP wanted to be the party of cooperation, not conflict; they said they were fed up with the bickering and the contrived antagonism of Tory and Labour. This was the party that would put the nation first, not vested interests and petty-minded differences. The differences were there, alas. David Owen from the beginning saw Roy Jenkins as insufficiently radical and as the SDP formed an alliance with the Liberals the differences multiplied and became public. Roy Jenkins wanted an alliance to be a partnership of principle and Owen wanted it to be a temporary liaison lasting long enough for the alliance to get proportional representation on to the statute books. Then the Liberals could be dumped. It is not surprising that David Steel could work with Roy Jenkins but could not be happy in close union with Owen. The bickering began. And disintegration followed when David Steel proposed that the courtship end and a marriage take place. It was a high-risk strategy and it failed. David Owen walked off in a huff with a handful of other SDP members; David Steel quit, leaving a very inexperienced Paddy Ashdown to hold the Social and Liberal Democrats together. The electorate is completely confused. Jokes are numerous. I doubt if you could find two dozen people outside the inner circle who could outline the difference between the SDP and the SLD. All they could say with certainty is that one of the two is headed by David Owen, but that they couldn't be sure which one. This muddle in the middle shows little sign of clearing. The two parties behave like a couple of divorcees out for the kill. They fight each other at by-elections, splitting the centre vote and allowing the Tories to remain victorious. There are talks of pacts, with Ashdown still arguing for merger and with Owen still arguing for a love-in lasting long enough to secure a non-Tory coalition government which would then introduce proportional representation. After that each would go its own way. The muddle in the middle continues. And aside from this confusion, there is a much more serious problem: while the two parties have been squabbling among themselves, the Labour party has been steadily moving to the right, until the middle ground, so empty in 1981, seems impossibly overcrowded. Not only is it difficult to tell the difference between the SDP and the SLD, but it is becoming increasingly difficult to tell the difference between them and the Labour party. On the main issues, the handling of the economy, defence and commitment to Europe, and the importance of local government and of devolution, there is little difference. There appears to be a genuine difference in the way the two regard trades unions, the Labour party with affection, the Democrats with scepticism. If the Labour party manages to loosen its ties to the unions and rid itself of the tyranny of the block vote, which just could happen, since the unions themselves are proposing such reforms, yet another division would disappear. By the time Labour has finished pruning and polishing, it could well have great appeal to the middle ground, provided the voter can take at face value the massive changes of heart in vital policy areas. This could be an easier task than accepting the Democrats, the bickering centre with its high-profile commitment to constitutional reforms, which always unnerves electorates. Huge majorities – the Thatcher experience – are rare, and the alternative, proportional representation, often leads to unstable government, a recipe for permanent pacts and deals done in back rooms. All in all then, two if not three parties will be chasing the anti-Tory vote, with nothing much to choose between them. The result could all too easily cause a splintering of that all-important vote, and the re-election of the Tories. And where does this leave David Owen? In a most precarious position, with enemies in the Labour party, which he deserted, and enemies in the SLD, which he also deserted. If he had allowed the Liberal-SDP merger to go through, the party would now be riding high, with by-election successes falling into the party's lap and Mrs Thatcher looking worried rather than amused. Instead, he's seen as a man who wants it all his own way; a man who won't compromise and who has promoted the biggest bout of bickering that politics has seen in years. That's exactly what he began by denouncing. Some argue that if any one person is responsible for the free ride the Tories have had in the eighties, that person is David Owen.

Plymouth Devonport, struggling with its own metamorphosis, may be fond of its maverick MP, but somehow it doesn't seem sophisticated enough to appreciate the discordant sounds that are accompanying the birth of a new political party.

Winchester, on the surface, looks as though it could cope with anything. It has a strength and security born of wealth. It was nomin-ated in a survey by Newcastle University as the richest place in Britain. A mere handful of factors were considered, including the unemploy-ment rate, employment growth – with special attention paid to the years between 1979–81, which signify the ability of places to weather the recession years – population growth, and the proportion of house-holds with access to two or more cars, which researchers considered to be one of the more reliable measures of material prosperity available from the population census. The university's research was concerned with something more than labels. It was trying to prove that there has been a major shift in economic fortunes away from the major cities towards relatively small towns situated in essentially rural surround-ings, whose traditional role has been one of serving the local area. In other words it demonstrated the reemergence of the market town; such places were booming, while the cities declined; at least, those with good access roads were. Winchester got the M3. Winchester's pros-perity is such that it now claims to be fighting off development plans, and saying no to newcomers: the town is full up. And the reasons why people chose to live there are simple enough – the back-to-a-real-community arguments hold good. Some become commuters; they ride daily by train into London and then write to the local paper complain-ing that they have had to stand all the way. But clearly they find it worth it for the enhanced 'quality of life' they have once off the train. Others not interested in commuting, fall in love with life in an eighteenth-century cottage and a six-minute car ride to the office. It is easy enough to settle in and start new businesses, they say, because the place is small, and that makes everyone friendly. Furthermore it is clean and green, the sea is thirteen miles away, there are banks and building societies galore, restaurants, delicatessens, wine bars and pubs, sports clubs. Crime is not a problem and there are good schools.

I settled myself in an hotel near the centre of town and thought I would visit the unemployment centre. Winchester Unemployed People's Centre was listed in the phone book. I dialled the number and got a weird sound. Directory inquiries said: 'They have ceased trading.' As a substitute I bought the local paper, the *Hampshire Chronicle*, and read it from cover to cover. It has advertisements on the front page, and inside there are items describing Mr Pat Fox's lecture on rabbit-catching, Mr R. Ballantyne's lecture on the life of a gamekeeper and Dr Carver talking to local farmers about linseed and lupins and other alternative crops. In between there are ads for pine kitchens, handmade sofas and independent schools. Dotted around are sad tales: £400 worth of salt had been stolen from a garden shed; a man of fifty pleaded guilty to stealing a sharpener for a rotary mower from Woolworths. He said he had been drinking heavily because his son had recently been shot in the leg with a shotgun. He was fined £50 and £5 costs. A fifty-two-year-old car-park attendant had pocketed £1.50 on four occasions instead of putting the money in the pay and display machine. The council's rent arrears had shot up to £146,000 and Mr John Taylor said that 'no hardship was involved, just sheer cussedness'. Tucked away at the bottom of a page, a correction stated that the paper was sorry for stating that a team of walkers the previous Saturday had raised money for boys' centres in Kenya. The walk had in fact taken place on Sunday; Saturday's efforts were in aid of the World Wildlife Fund.

To walk around Winchester, is a pleasure. The scale is human, the main shopping street has been pedestrianized, there are lots of trees, and one or two ugly buildings. The law courts built in the 1960s look out of place, not just in scale but in design and use of materials. The Job Centre was seeking the odd £2-an-hour cleaner: 'something to suit the hard up student'. The more I walked and the more I looked, the more I felt certain that Winchester was not wealthy, not Knightsbridge wealthy, at any rate. There were no overdressed women nor shops selling items without price tags. Winchester feels cosy and comfortable and solidly middle class. The people I watched seemed the sort to enjoy life through joining local societies to learn about the art of rabbit-catching. Winchester hates the 'wealthy town' label just as much as Consett hates the 'poor town' tag. Whenever I mentioned it people grimaced and said that it was inaccurate: Farnham or Guildford were much richer. I was told that there were far too many public-service employees working for the local authority, the law courts and the police headquarters, for the city to be considered wealthy. The kind of commuter who caught the 7.23 each morning was likely to be a BBC press officer rather than a merchant banker. There were far too many divorcees struggling on inadequate incomes and rather too many young people unable to afford a first home even on the Badger's Farm Estate, a controversial development on Church Commissioners' land, where prices start at £25,000 and you need a car to get into town. J. B. Priestley said of Winchester: 'I never pass through these smaller cathedral cities, on a fine day, without imagining I could spend a few happy years there, and never find myself compelled to spend a morning and afternoon in one without wishing the day was over and I was moving on.' Perhaps he didn't warm to cosiness any more than I did.

But I didn't feel like running away or rushing on. There was something I wanted to see. There was a part of Winchester I couldn't ignore. I'd sensed it within hours of my arrival. I was in a bookshop and over my shoulder I heard a most assured voice say: 'Hallo, sir.' Sir mumbled a reply as he leafed through a copy of Peter Ackroyd's *Hawksmoor*. The young man wore a huge overcoat, a size or two larger than he needed, as was the fashion. It was thrown on carelessly and the cuffs of the sleeves were frayed. He took from his pocket a Coutts bank chequebook to buy a £4 dictionary. I was close enough to him to see that the two previous cheques had been made out for under £3 and £5. Winchester College is an integral part of the city and the place is too compact for the college to take a back seat in one's mind. Both it and the cathedral made me very aware of how religion, learning and life were once not just linked, but closely and powerfully related. Nowadays, for the most part, religion, learning and life seem like strangers lashing out against each other. Life, the secular world, is a yappy little terrier, it wants religion to keep its distance and learning to know its place as a mere functionary to provide the means, the money to enjoy life.

I bought my two books, one Christopher Dilke's *A Study of Winchester College*, and returned to my hotel room to read it. It was published in 1965 when, not for the first time, the privileged position of public schools was under attack from a society still struggling with egalitarian notions. At that time public schools still had an awesome grip on the power structure in Britain. Reports showed that 80 per cent of judges and QCs, 77 per cent of the directors of the Bank of England and 70 per cent of directors of big companies came from public schools. No one could defend such a situation, not even the schools themselves and Dilke's answer was to demonstrate that Winchester had survived such attacks in the past by reforming itself and would do so again. Above all this book reminded me how *threatened* these schools felt by the Labour party's desire to reform them by allocating between 25 and 50 per cent of places to the state to fill, or be rid of them by, say, turning Winchester into a sixth-form college, thereby keeping its standards of academic excellence, but for all to share. Once again I wondered what would have happened if the Labour party had not lost its nerve and had absorbed such schools into the state system. It would certainly have speeded up the loosening of their grip on top jobs and influential areas of life. Instead changes elsewhere, particularly in the way universities select undergraduates, have dented the power of the public school. Oxbridge is still Britain's passport to positions of power and influence, but it no longer leans on public schools for its intake. The public school is no longer a toff's ticket to the top. None the less, some 10 per cent of the school-age population have parents who pay fees of up to £7,000 a year for a private education, justifying their actions – if they bother to justify them at all – by saying that if they lived in France or Germany it would be different, but in this country government after government has neglected state education and left them with no option but to pay for small classes, good teachers, a plentiful supply of books, discipline and a civilized and civilizing start in life.

They say that Winchester is a beautiful school; it is certainly imposing, all flint and stone and a confusing array of Middle Gates and Outer Gates and Chambers. As I waited for the door of Headmaster House to open, boys in blue caps and grey coats filed past, dwarfed by the buildings. Inside I was dwarfed by the size of the headmaster's study. The two shorter walls of the rectangular room were book-lined, one side was window-filled and a long wall was shared by a vast desk and a fireplace into which the gas-fire nestled, struggling in vain to take the chill off the December afternoon.

James Sebben Clare, a former pupil of the school and a member of staff since 1968, became headmaster in 1985. In thirty years the school has changed as much as the world outside. Science and arts, once scorned, are now a fixed part of every boy's studies up to O-level. Latin as a mind-trainer has given way to mathematics; 75 per cent of the boys take A-level mathematics, and the second most favoured subject is economics. The school, he said, is now friendly and caring and much less hierarchical than in his day. The practice of calling boys by their surnames has gone, and the silly privileges the boys used to acquire as they moved up the school have been dismantled. 'The number of buttons you could do up on a waistcoat was once a mark of distinction!' There is now less of a gap between the top of the school and the bottom. 'In the fifties, I moved up the school quite fast and was often being taught with boys three years older. Those boys somehow languished in the middle of the school and then left at eighteen and joined the army. That doesn't happen now.'

What surprised me was the fact that many of the boys now at the school were first-generation public school. That did not mean that working class boys were to be seen. They were not. James Sebben Clare said that his efforts to interest local schools had not been productive. He'd written to all Hampshire secondary schools, but they didn't seem interested. My second surprise was the fact that while 85 per cent head straight for university, only one third go to Oxford or Cambridge. In the past, the staff were mainly Oxbridge and now that ratio is fifty-fifty, but that's not the only reason. It is, he said, more difficult to get in to Oxbridge because of competition from girls and from state schools. 'In the 1950s it was an assumption that most of our boys went to Oxbridge, but no longer. Durham, Edinburgh, London, Bristol and Exeter are all popular.'

In the past the main aim of parents sending their children to Winchester was to enhance their chances of getting to Oxbridge. So what was behind parents' thinking today?

'We promote ourselves – and we promote ourselves actively these days – on high teacher-pupil ratios, a wide choice of subjects, discipline that is not based on a big book of rules, but in the work: teaching is designed to stimulate boys, to encourage them to investigate and explore, not stuff them full of facts.'

'But the state schools have also adopted the investigative approach with the GCSE examination.'

'Yes, and I much approve of the underlying principle, but here we believe in high-quality individual care. Much more than in the past we are concerned with the all-round development of the boys. And we have time to do this which cannot be found in a day school. Also, being at a boarding school enables you to learn about living with other people, not those you have chosen, but those imposed on you. And this teaches you about yourself too, how you are seen through the eyes of others. The boys get on well with each other; they have to, and this gives them confidence in dealing with others.'

The second master took me on a tour of the school, proudly showing me the science labs and the art rooms and the sports facilities, with which few state schools could compete. The dormitories were spartan, no curtains, no carpets, no heating and precious little space for personal possessions. Whatever else has changed in thirty years, the place remains as always – cold. 'The boys don't seem to mind, you know. They never complain. Come here, and look at this,' he said, as he walked towards a bed and lifted the cover. Under the cover was a teddy bear. 'That wouldn't have been allowed a few years ago! In rooms for older boys you'll find huge soft toys sitting on the beds.' I was much amused. We then went to look at the study area. 'We keep the scholars together. Then if they want to sit up most of the night reading, they can do so and find that others want to do the same occasionally and don't think it odd. But we do mix the ages. In this room there will be all ages from thirteen to eighteen. It's a bit hard on the eighteen-year-olds, but it's good for the thirteen-year-olds, who may come here thinking they are the cleverest thing for miles around and soon realize they are not when they are put with older boys.' The large room revealed a boy sitting in front of an open fire reading, a table laden with white bread and marmalade and coffee, and around the edges of the room cubicles where the boys studied. Peering in I saw computers, radios, family photographs, books. Most were untidy. The boys do not have their own studies. There is not a moment when the boys are alone. They didn't seem to mind.

Over lunch I joined a group of scholars, but there was little time for conversation: the meal was eaten with appalling speed. After lunch seven boys chose to stay behind and chat with me. They weren't pre-selected; they were asked at lunch to volunteer. Not one of the seven had a father who had been to Winchester, not one had a father who had been to boarding school. One said he had no idea where his father went to school. The seven claimed to love boarding-school life. They all assumed that they would go to university, preferably after taking a year off. They all assumed that Oxbridge was their goal, and one boy muttered something to the effect that they wouldn't be expected to favour Hull and then added, 'We are arrogant, aren't we?' Winchester boys used to be known for that, I replied. They seemed ill-at-ease with personal questions and at their best when I asked a general question and then left them to discuss it among themselves. They felt there was more emphasis on examination results than in the past; they echoed their headmaster in saying that it was not so easy to get to Oxbridge now that they had to compete with girls and with state schools. There was a surprising amount of uncertainty over future careers. Only one boy stated categorically that he was going into the City to make money. One said he thought he might be an academic, another that he was fed up with books and thought he'd live in the forest, one wanted to be a poet, another a journalist and another aspired to do 'something in pop music'. One said he hadn't decided. The money-seeker said he'd been influenced by his father, who had spent many years as a professor of engineering and then had become a consultant and doubled his income overnight. 'I want to do things the other way around. I want to earn money first and then at forty or forty-five find other priorities.' Why, what's so important about money, one of his colleagues asked. 'I want all the nice things that money can buy, a nice house and so on. If you become an academic you'll end up in a semi. You'll ruin the best years of your life.' Another suggested that if he sought money as a priority, he'd ruin the best years of his life. 'Just the opposite,' he replied. 'If I *don't* have money, I'll ruin the best years of my life!' This young man had the most pronounced views of the lot. He acted as a catalyst to the others. He'd throw out something provocative and the others would start to argue, but they'd never manage to demolish his views. The discussion on the value of money was sadly unresolved. I asked them about unemployment. They were not complacent, they didn't assume it was easy to get desirable jobs, but on the whole unemployment was something that happened to other people. They'd never met an un-employed person. One said he felt guilty because he didn't think about the unemployed very much or feel very concerned about them. They all agreed that high unemployment, figures as high as 3 million and now reduced to 2 million, had become part of our lives. No one was shocked by it any more, or talked about it much. The money-centred boy said that as far as he was concerned there were jobs for the unemployed – at least half a million – if only they were willing to move, and what a pity it was that the British were not more like the Japanese or the Koreans. Another boy reminded him that the job vacancies were in the south and that the unemployed couldn't afford to move. The conversation was lively enough, and the boys were charm-ing, but I was not excited by the school in the way I was excited by Longbenton Community High School.

I'm glad I peeped at Winchester. The short visit was reassuring. I came away convinced that there was nothing that Winchester offered that was impossible for a state school to supply if given the resources. Nothing. And it offers one thing that I consider to be of little worth: a boarding facility. I'll concede that there's a sustainable argument for weekly boarding schools, but the notion of taking children from their families and cutting them off from the rest of the world, the real world, for months on end, is something I find odd. It is odd. Nowhere outside Britain and her former empire is the boarding school much favoured. I doubt if it gives Winchester boys confidence in dealing with others: I suspect they'd have that in any event. It may just give them a superficial ability to get on with others, but it is only superficial and it is only *some* others. How can a Winchester boy learn anything about getting on with people from other backgrounds confined in that pretty place? He can't, and when he meets them in the workplace, he finds them different and they think he's odd. That would seem to me a lifelong handicap as well as spreading the loathsome seed of class-consciousness. And worse still, I would question the value of a boarder's ability to get on with those of his own kind. I think boarding schools are responsible for much of the conformity-tinged-with-dullness that bedevils the English. To exist in close confinement at Winchester, most boys will conform and survive by learning to be manipulative and devious; they learn how to get their own way without being direct and straightforward. They learn how to say one thing in order to fit in and have a quiet life; they learn not to fuss. In other words, they hone the skills of hypocrisy for which the English are famous. It's a well-known survival technique.

I seemed constantly to be surprised during my visit to the school, but the biggest surprise was that no one mentioned religion. Not once. Winchester was founded in 1382 to make sure that the brightest and the best headed for the Church. That is no longer its function, of course, but not so long ago boys still spent an inordinate amount of time on their knees. I thought this might have been drastically reduced, but not to the point where no one mentioned it. Winchester Cathedral is quite beautiful, one of the most ancient and majestic cathedrals in the world. The midweek evensong I attended attracted ten people. Inside the door I picked up a leaflet which invited me to 'find a seat and read this'. I did. It told me that Jesus Christ was reverenced as divine by over 1,000 million people throughout the world, and then told me why in a hundred words. It said: 'Jesus Christ was born in Bethlehem over 1,900 years ago. During his first thirty years he shared the daily life and work of an ordinary home. For the next three years he went about healing the sick and troubled people and teaching small groups in villages, in the fields and by the lakeside. He gathered twelve ordinary men to be his helpers. He had no money. He had no university degrees. He wrote no books. He commanded no army. He wielded no political power. During his ministry he never travelled more than 200 miles in any direction. He was executed by crucifixion at the age of thirty-three.' I sat back and wondered how long it had been necessary for Winchester Cathedral to explain in one hundred words the reasons for its existence. Once upon a time we'd have known who Jesus was, all of us, including tourists.

A mere 2 per cent of the population go to church. Although the

Church has little influence on our lives, it still has the power to command much media attention. Among the frivolous, this is because the goings on in the vicarage will raise a laugh anywhere, and among the serious-minded this is because the Church of England is the established Church, the Queen is still the head and the prime minister has the power to choose bishops, some of whom then sit in the House of Lords and criticize her. In recent years there has been much criticism. Church leaders have told Mrs Thatcher that they don't like some of her policies, which appear to ignore the poor and needy and promote the well-being of the greedy. In return Mrs Thatcher has told the Church to pay attention to man's spiritual and moral well-being and leave the rest to her. The Church has a point and Mrs Thatcher has a point. Most people do not know what morals are any more, and the churches are empty. This is beginning to concern some vicars. From the Essex village of Hawkwell, the Reverend Tony Higton is urging Church leaders to revere once more the Bible as God's word and let the Gospels guide men to an understanding of what is right and wrong. His church is full each Sunday, and since I first met him his flock has grown to such an extent that extra services have to be held in school halls. Tony Higton is giving his followers something clear and simple to believe in and he would like others to forsake the wishy-washy and do the same. To this end he put before the synod, the church's Parliament, a motion saying that practising homosexuals should no longer be allowed as clergy. The Bible doesn't advance the cause of homosexuals. Secular commentators suggested that AIDS was the trigger. At the time newspapers were full of articles on the new plague, which they claimed in an all too familiar sensational manner would kill one third of the population by the end of the century. The homosexual community became frightened of the virus and the more promiscuous forsook promiscuity in favour of stable relationships. The government found money to treat those with AIDS and to fund research into an anti-AIDS vaccine; the heterosexual community learned how to use condoms, and newspapers went in search of another story to sensationalize. Tony Higton denies that AIDS was the trigger. He says he has been worried by his Church's liberal attitude since it allowed the Bishop of Durham to be consecrated even though he said he had doubts about the Virgin birth and the Resurrection. He wants an end to the liberal ascendancy in the Church, which began in the sixties and has allowed all manner of free-range thought to dilute the Word. If it goes on any longer it will empty the churches completely. His motion and the little storm that came with it might have passed over; clever bishops reworked the wording so that the synod could happily say that homosexual tendencies were less than ideal, but not force practitioners out of the Church. The storm might have passed but for the death of Dr Gareth Bennett.

Dr Bennett wrote the – traditionally anonymous – preface in Crockford's, the Church's *Who's Who*. It contained a personal attack on the Archbishop of Canterbury as part of a general attack on the liberal ascendancy. Dr Bennett belonged to the opposite wing of the Church to Tony Higton. Tony Higton is a low-church Evangelical and Dr Bennett was a high-church Anglo-Catholic. The trigger for his outburst was the possibility of the ordination of women as priests – a possibility which seemed to be drawing ever closer, forced onwards by the American Episcopal Church, who were determined to consecrate the first woman bishop. The thought of a woman priest, let alone woman bishop, is to the Anglo-Catholics what the acceptance of homosexual clergy is to the Evangelicals: the awful summation of allowing liberal thinkers to head the Church. The press, focusing on a few words of critical comment on Dr Runcie, behaved like hunters after a fox, and Dr Bennett, having publicly denied authorship, committed suicide, fearing that he was about to be exposed.

Church politics are fascinating. It is more engrossing than any dog-fight between SLP and SDP. And at the end of the day, what does it all mean? That the churches are empty and we seem to live in a pagan country. Who is to blame? Is it the inevitable victory of a science-orientated world that makes it difficult for men to believe in the mystery of God? Or is the Church to blame? Has it brought upon itself the need to explain its existence in a hundred words in a leaflet? Should it go back to basics and offer people certainties? The liberals may consider this approach to be intellectually ridiculous, but the Evangelicals yearn for it. The sixties taught us how to question; how to question everything, including the role of religion in our lives. It allowed us to clobber the overbearing Church of England, which demanded too much of us. We sent it packing, and now we have no sense of direction. The last time the Church got into a mess, John Wesley appeared. Will the Evangelical wing revitalize the flock once again? In some ways the growth of environmental awareness, the growth of respect for the earth and the urge for men and governments to stop plundering, could well free even the most sophisticated mind to believe that there is a power, a force beyond man's grasp. A force that is warning us that man's unguided cleverness is a menace; that unless we find something else to worship besides material growth, we will find ourselves as empty shells on a derelict shore. Like the former pupils of Winchester, I had a very religious upbringing, attending a chilly Church of England school that gave me chilblains and a dislike of being on my knees. It also gave me a much-valued code of conduct, a set of simple and subtle, overt and covert rules by which my life is guided. Who now attempts to show others how to avoid being an empty shell on a derelict shore?

The Church, while it hesitates to turn men's minds to God, is at least beginning to champion family life. The Archbishop of Canterbury has said that family virtues, discipline, loyalty and vision are the four vital ingredients for a healthy community. 'Any community worthy of the name needs what I call family virtues – acceptance, tolerance, compassion and forgiveness. They provide companionship and they give a child anchorage in life. Without them no child will ever grow straight.'

The family has taken a bashing since the war. But its problems began long before that. Before the Industrial Revolution the home was the centre of all important economic and social activities; mother, father and children worked and played together with grandparents and other relatives close by. The coming of factories fractured all this, taking first the father and then children away from the home. Women's liberation took away the mother, and then the late fifties invented the teenager: the first generation to enjoy a gap between being a child and being an adult. Pop music started it; *Rock around the Clock* turned teenagers into consumers, to be wooed by marketing men into a lifestyle committed to chasing ever-changing fashion: a lifestyle based on self-expression and freedom. The generation-gap appeared. Those born since the war are arguably the most selfish generation. Their teenage years taught them that most things were disposable; one fashionable idea was succeeded by another fashionable idea. When the novelty wore off, another fad would appear. And that included marriage; discard it when it got boring, like clothes, or a disc – divorce could be bought as easily as a dishwasher. And if you don't fancy the compromises that marriage demands, don't bother with it in the first place. Don't ask too much of yourself and don't ask too much of others. Making demands is out; discipline is out. The unhappy fall-out is all around us. Mothers walk out on a 'bad scene', a child in each hand, knowing that the local authorities have a responsibility to house them. Was home and family life so awful that living in B. & B.s is a preferable alternative? Homeless teenagers talk into television cameras; they say they want hostels and money from the government to enable them to live away from their parents. But wouldn't a happy home be better; isn't that what they really need? Yes, of course there should be more low-rent accommodation for those in real need, more government support, but isn't that merely alleviating a symptom rather than attending to a cause? Family life has disintegrated; perhaps it needed to disintegrate. Shorn of its role as the centre of economic and social life, it ended up held together by a foul-smelling glue of duty and gratitude and guilt. But since no one has found an acceptable alternative, family life must be and will be resurrected. I'm glad the Church is plugging the family. When it is reborn it will be different; it will be better, less authoritarian, less restrictive; less of a burden for all parties. A shortage of labour is at last making employers and state consider crèches and nursery education, and that takes down one of family life's prison walls. The growth in part-time jobs could mean that parents *share* work and *share* responsibility for bringing up children. Small firms could mean that employees whatever their age and whatever their skills are no longer treated as cogs in the machine, with no initiative and no desire for responsibility. Those who are happy in their work make better wives, better husbands and better parents. I don't know about the churches; they may well remain empty. Perhaps it won't matter so long as basic Christian values filter through to us.

For instance: one shouldn't be greedy. My hotel had let my reserved room when I arrived. There was a muddle over dates. The room finally allotted to me was awaiting redecoration and its stained walls, tatty curtains and broken lampshades were dispiriting. The manager, who used to live in north London and sell insurance, was nice enough. 'If you'd have come yesterday, you'd have had a really nice room.' I accepted the alternative. What I couldn't accept was my colossal phone bill. The manager said it had to be correct because it was all done by computer. Fine, I said, show me the print-out. He said he couldn't; it had been thrown away. I said that if he couldn't produce the print-out, then I would pay only half the bill. The telephone calls made from the room were charged at double rate. It was, he said, the quickest way of recouping the cost of putting the phones in the rooms in the first place. I suggested he put a note in the room, by the phone, explaining his policy. No need, he said, most people just paid. They were expense-account travellers. Mrs Thatcher's sternest critics say that she has deified greed. This is nonsense. There are millions of us in this country and only the tiniest number are greedy. We have a choice.

Chapter 16

Chopping Down
the Cherry Trees

Waterloo is not the most depressing of London's mainline stations. As a nation we haven't paid much attention to our entrances and exits; we've not much cared what impression we make on visitors to our capital city. Indeed, during the years when travel has become commonplace, our aesthetic eye has become cataract covered. Waterloo is dully functional: the concourse is big, dotted with shops and stalls for coffee and newspapers. As I stood and watched, two men with buckets were making a half-hearted attempt to clean the tiled floor. They swirled dirty water across the surface, making no attempt to nudge muck that didn't flee as soon as it saw the mop descending. Outside, London looked grey. I headed for the taxi queue. For a while I watched the traffic and wondered how they do the sums that suggest traffic moves at eleven miles an hour through London. The wait plus the sight of sluggish traffic, lucky if it reaches half that speed, drove me underground and into the tube. It was full. Since the early 1980s the tube has become popular again, because the alternative is a lottery – the time needed to drive the same distance is so variable – and because the introduction of travel cards saves time and money. And the word is that an investment of £2–3 billion is to be made in the system, to include three new lines across London, east to west, north to south and from the centre to Docklands. It is much needed. Public transport that is cheap and pleasant to use could kill the car. I won't waste words on King's Cross underground. It is a nightmare of a junction: five underground and two overground routes. Everyone knows that it is a disgrace; it went up in flames one night because it is old and filthy and carelessly run: thirty-one people died, and many more were injured. I use the station almost daily when I'm in London. I hate the place.

Outside is little better. My bus stop is just round the corner, in York Way. This couple of hundred yards is most unappetizing. Long ago I nicknamed it Third World Corner: it both looks and feels as though it does not belong in a wealthy country. There are often drunks huddled together, hugging the walls. They are not aggressive and they don't beg; they sit there with their bottles, their loud talk punctuated by sad laughter. There are always ragged, punk-looking youngsters hanging around. Across the main road there's something called Family Leisure, an amusement arcade. Perhaps that is the attraction for them; the station supplies the nearest lager. There is often someone selling rubbish on the pavement; this being December, it is shirts at £3.99, gloves and scarves and a mountain of tinsel and seasonal decorations. Turning the corner, I lowered my eyes to the pavement. I have to. It is so uneven that every step is fraught with the possibility of tripping over. With eyes on the pavement, the gutter comes into focus; it is a mosaic of ring-pulls and cigarette butts, discarded bus tickets, the familiar debris of untidy lives. At the bus stop I can raise my eyes once more and take in the tacky scene.

The bookshop is boarded up and plastered with posters for pop concerts, but the Burger Express is open, the Indian restaurant awaits its evening trade and the two most prosperous-looking enterprises are Mecca bookmakers and a vast discount furniture warehouse. The bus queue is dull-eyed. Two thirds foreign and one half black, they skulk against the wall, beneath advertisements for whisky and vodka and a totally out-of-place plug for Jaguar. An elderly man spits into the gutter; another uses the grimy wall to steady himself. They don't look weary and cold, in need of a cup of tea to brighten a miserable day; they look detached, in need of a miracle to brighten miserable lives. I didn't have to travel all over the country to realize that the lucky and the luckless use the same bus stops but inhabit different worlds. I'd known that all along.

There are grand, grand plans for this area; 125 acres where the grass grows through abandoned tracks. It's the site of the biggest inner-city development in Europe. One day there will be offices, and shops to rival Regent Street, and houses and a park. The developers say they are striving for a balanced project; low-rent houses and blue-collar jobs to ease the problems in an area where one in nine is unemployed. London, egotistical, over-crowded, unlovable London, is, like other areas of Britain, in the middle of a building boom. It is growing again, for the first time since the war. I already find it huge, and constantly have to remind myself that, as capital cities go, it is smallish. In 1900, with a population of 6.5 million, it was the biggest city in the world;

2 million ahead of its nearest rival, New York. By 1990, Tokyo and
Mexico City will take the lead, with cities of 23 million people. New
York will be in third place and no European city will reach the top ten.
London is home to a mere 7 million. I must get used to thinking of it
as small. The building bug began in 1981 in the East End of London,
in an area known as Docklands. Eight square miles from Tower
Bridge, through Wapping and the Isle of Dogs into the Royal Docks
and including Rotherhithe and the Surrey Docks on the south bank.
For those who think of Wapping as the back of beyond, halfway to
Holland, there is another seven miles to go to the Royal Docks. This
huge expanse of waste land, of deserted docks, silent jetties, crumbling
buildings and boarded-up shops, is being transformed from a dying
fringe known to few, to a lively, born-again London inviting intense
curiosity. It is quite a remarkable achievement. Although much is
already in place, the Isle of Dogs still looks like a building site. It is not
the best moment to judge it; unfinished, it looks like a building mart,
where designs are put on display for the buyer to compare and contrast
styles and prices. One run on the toy-town Docklands Light Railway,
which is carried on stilts from Tower Gateway to Island Garden,
reveals much: it reveals an architectural zoo. There is no master plan;
companies enticed into the area by tax incentives and rate-free offers
can build more or less what they want, how they want. Coherence
there is none. Flashy-looking hi-tech units nestle against aluminium
sheds which, with their colourfully painted edges, are as flimsy-looking
as the Light Railway. When compared with the homemade, earthy,
honest world of brick warehouses built to last, they look off-the-peg
and ill-fitting, gimmicky high-fashion structures designed to be discarded after a season. A host of newspapers, ones that bang on about
architectural evils in our midst, have new homes amid this riot of
creativity. And the view from the little railway is as nothing compared
with the vision of Canary Wharf: a financial complex to rival the City
of London, containing a couple of outrageous potency symbols, the
tallest of tower blocks. It has plenty of defenders: Sir Roy Strong likes
the towers and says they are a focus in an area without focus and a
statement, an unapologetic statement: a raspberry blown at the cheap
compromise that has characterized British architecture since the war. A
less-than-convinced wit has suggested that the towers are a two-finger
sign to the City and that they bully everything around it. I'm loath to
join the naggers who see the whole enterprise as a lost opportunity in
architectural terms; who yearn for another Nash to create a watery
Regent's Park. I'm loath to think we have blown it again, but I do
have a sneaky feeling that speed and greed have goaded each other to

excess as least as far as commercial building is concerned. Domestic building has on the whole escaped the worst. The revamped warehouses with their river views are of course pleasing; and so are the Dutch canal houses, and so are the red-brick town-houses tumbling down to the water's edge. We certainly know how to adorn a waterfront.

My fears, tempered by admiration for the project, are as nothing compared with the screams from those who live close by. The rebirth of Docklands hasn't made everyone happy. Labour-controlled East End boroughs have nothing good to say about it; their wings were clipped, their powers usurped by the creation of an all powerful London Docklands Development Corporation, which expects to spend £800 million in the seven years up to the mid-nineties, to attract in excess of £6 billion of private development. Half the money, which is being spent on infrastructure, roads, sewers, bridges, comes from government grants, and the other half from buying land and reselling it at a nice profit. LDDC is a quango which illustrates the spirit of modern Britain and the methods of Thatcherism. It has shooed aside a certain breed of people and institutions: the stolid, stick in the mud, afraid of new ideas, it-will-never-work, we've-always-done-it-this-way breed of people. And in its place has encouraged a dynamic go-getting, pushy, I-can-do-it, confident, snappy, let's-get-things-done bunch of folk who have but a dozen years to burn brightly and achieve much before being disbanded. LDDC has a task and is in a hurry. It must be galling to be a local authority, watching all this and thinking of all the time wasted in the 1960s and 1970s, tut-tutting as the ships sailed away. In tune with councils came a chorus of other complaints from those who have lived in docklands for generations. Two hundred years ago, 4,000 ships a year used the Port of London and provided jobs for more than 100,000 men. At the beginning of the 1960s there were jobs for 28,000 men; today there might be work for 2,000. In between, bigger ships became more efficient as cargo became containerized. Jobs would have been lost even if the port had not dug its own grave with restrictive practices, overmanning and endless demarcation disputes which led to strikes.

Between 1949 and 1979, some 2,000 working days were lost each year in the Port of London because of some strike or other. Before the war dockers had a hard time, fighting each other for a day's work and dreading being left 'on the stones'. That ludicrous and cruel system was replaced in 1947 by a dock labour scheme which gave dockers tenure – guaranteed all-day jobs for life, whether there is work or not. Father followed son into a cushy number: the pendulum swung from one extreme to the other. Half our ports handling 70 per cent of our trade subscribe to this uncompetitive system. It is hardly surprising that after ten years in office, Mrs Thatcher's government intends to dismantle the scheme. It is hard to defend such a relic from a vanished era. And it is obvious that the government chose the moment for the confrontation carefully. With many of its policies under attack in mid-1989, and with the economy faltering, the government needed a fight that it knew most of the country would support; a fight that would embarrass the Labour party; a fight that would remind voters that the Tory party was committed to ridding Britain of restrictive practices. Jack Dash, one-time dockers' champion, considered that his men had been much maligned. Before he died he helped with the Museum of Labour, being built in Docklands as a memorial to times past. It is the story across Britain: a great industry diminished by a mixture of competition and modernization, ruined by the attitudes of management and men and finally reduced to a museum.

Needless to say, the regeneration of the Docklands has brought out some nastiness, a last fling from those who are locked into class warfare. A group who call themselves just that – Class War – have enjoyed a fair bit of Yuppie-bashing. They daub buildings: 'Yuppies Out', 'Mug a Yuppie', and write to the papers saying they are delighted at the sight of new trees being torn up and used to wallop incomers. They'd rather have weeds than wine bars. Others feel resentment because they see the present passing them by and have yet to see that their children will benefit from the future. The unemployed can only see that the new jobs are not for them: 'It's not for the likes of us,' they say, and resent the thought of ending their working days as doormen in fancy offices and porters in posh blocks; as servants to the new rich, when once with the cry, 'All Out,' they could prove that they were servants to no one. Some can see that their sons' and daughters' futures will be fine. The LDDC is offering courses to the un-employed under twenty-five to learn banking, computing, business studies, electronics – the skills of the future. And companies have signed contracts with schools in the area guaranteeing jobs for leavers who make the grade, who don't play truant, who are prepared to arrive on time and work for examinations and pass them. Real jobs with career prospects in exchange for real effort in acquiring the skills needed. I'm sure it isn't enough; I'm sure there are problems. It is inevitable in an age of transition. Like all times of transition it is full of opportunities for the active and the enterprising, and full of suffering for those who are neither, or who find themselves stranded with their acquired skills made valueless. And the suffering is made all the greater by the sense of being excluded from the benefits of an enormous increase of wealth. Change the tense in that sentence and you will find that it was said by Dorothy George in her *Social History of Britain, 1690 to 1815*. We have been here before. At least nineteenth-century Britain did not have television to magnify the divide. The unemployed and the poor in modern Britain have relentless reminders of other people's fortunes; the unemployed in the Docklands have reminders on their very doorsteps. They stare across the street and look down the road towards the City and shake their heads.

It is events down the road which have brought about the renaissance of the East End of London. Two worlds as far apart as any have been forced to meet through goings-on in the City of London. The goings-on go under the name Big Bang. Before the autumn of 1986, stock-brokers cocooned themselves in a large number of restrictive practices – something the neighbouring dockers can readily understand. But rather than face lengthy legal action over these practices, the chairman of the Stock Exchange and the government did a deal – Big Bang – which allowed outsiders to move into the City and break up the established cartel. This was made physically possible by advances in technology; dealers no longer had to be on the floor of the stock exchange. They could operate efficiently in front of a computer screen with a telephone or three clapped to their ears. There would be competition and a better deal for the punters buying and selling shares; something to be encouraged when Mrs Thatcher was also in the process of trying to turn each and every one of us into shareholders. With the doors open wide, there was no shortage of offers to clear away the remaining cobwebs. Folk rushed in; clearing banks became market makers, as did American, European and Japanese finance houses, either buying up jobbing and broking houses, or starting their own. The City of London, once the capital of the financial world, looks all set to become the centre of a sea of electronic information. For a while business soared. If you smiled at shares they rose in value. There were jobs galore at salaries that astonished the rest of us. And all these newcomers needed somewhere to live. They went to Docklands and bought penthouses and studios where they managed to catch a few hours sleep away from the world of wheeler-dealing, which demanded attention from 7 a.m. until 10 p.m., whether you were on the top rung in a penthouse or the bottom step in a studio. For a year stories of conspicuous consumption, particularly of champagne, poured out of the media and on to a public who, steeped in *Dallas* and *Dynasty*, seemed amused rather than sickened, envious rather than appalled. It ended in tears, of course. One year later, in October 1987, the stock market crashed, and crashed badly, badly enough to invite comparisons with events in the thirties. The City began shedding staff as quickly as it had hired them. None of this is to suggest that Big Bang was a bad idea; it was a good idea. Too many people rushed in, eager to expand, to get a foothold in the City and, once the bubbles have settled, the City will be a healthier place. For a start the toffs' hold on the City has been shaken. In the past, the place has been much criticized for its elitism and ridiculed as a damn great White's Club, run by public-school types for public-school types.

There is a story that one merchant bank said the reason for its success was the fact that it only lent money to people who had been at Eton. That sort of talk made the City much disliked. That sort of attitude hardly helped British industry. Labour-party research in the early 1980s showed that of the 150 directors of the ten main insurance companies, one third had gone to Eton and more than half had been at Oxbridge. Furthermore, the 150 directors held no fewer than 1,543 other directorships, linking them to clearing banks, merchant banks and a range of other institutions. In other words, economic power in Britain was in the hands of a small group of men from similar backgrounds and with similar likes and prejudices. And such people, the Labour party claims, gave them a hard time, again and again preventing them from doing what they wanted. In March 1977 Denis Healey introduced a budget that gave away to top earners ten times more than to an average wage-earning family, with the words: 'I would have liked to have done more for those at the bottom of the earnings scale, but I felt it necessary to concentrate relief where it was most needed.' Translators argued that this meant that the all-powerful City had leaned on him. It is an unconvincing excuse; the Labour party could have initiated Big Bang; it would have been to their advantage. It has unravelled the old, closely knit group of White's Clubbers, clobbered their supremacy by bringing in new blood, grammar-school boys who went to 'modern' universities and Americans and Japanese who laughed at City snobbery and forced the City Establishment to give way to the meritocracy. Suddenly it became more fashionable to be a barrow-boy than an old Etonian; fashionable enough for Caryl Churchill to write a play called *Serious Money*, fashionable enough for the play to move from the fringe into the West End and be a huge success. We are all City types now; we've all got shares, haven't we? In the early 1980s there were 2 million shareholders. There are now 9 million: privatization accounted for 4 million newcomers. But half the new shareholders have only bought one lot of shares. That figures; I'm one of them. I bought my Euro Tunnel shares, my only shares, to demonstrate my belief in a project that demonstrates that our future rests in closer ties with Europe. But I assure you that it takes more than a handful of shares to convert an agnostic into a popular capitalist. The City remains shrouded in mystery and myth, deliberately keeping the rest of us at arm's length and tempting us to take a dockers' view: 'It's not for the likes of us.'

It was with some trepidation then that I headed off in my City suit to spend the day exploring the London International Financial Futures Exchange. Four futures brokers, part of a much larger company, had agreed to my visit on the understanding that they were not identified. One of the four had previously succumbed to the ego-flattering notion of seeing himself quoted in print and had been teased mercilessly as a result: the article had referred to him lifting a glass of champagne with difficulty because of the weight of his Rolex watch. The City has become fair game for this style of reportage; since Big Bang and *Serious Money* it has become the target of Serious Teasing. I shall refer to my anonymous four, in the spirit of Serious Fun, as the Four Ms, in honour of money, mammon and Melmotte. M0 is female and, twenty-three, the youngest member of the team; M3 is the oldest, in his mid-forties, and the boss; M1 is mid-twenties and the closest to the popular image of the new city slicker; M2, also in his forties, kept something of a guard around himself and as a result seemed rather dull.

The two youngsters, M0 and M1, sat opposite their middle-aged colleagues, M2 and M3. When I arrived some time after 9 a.m., they'd been at their desks for well over an hour. They had, they said, just finished a discussion on sex. Sex is a regular topic of conversation and on this occasion they had been tossing around the difference in attitude between those in their twenties and single and those in their forties and married. They apologized for any four-letter words I might hear during the day. They were worried about the impact of their language on me. Odd that, how the City worries about bad language.

The futures market, I was warned, was dead; it had suffered from the crash. Burned fingers needed time to heal before they could play again. That day in October 1987 is one that none of them is likely to forget. Those who had lost on the stock market were desperately trying to recoup something, anything, and my four had worked flat-out for fourteen hours.

Since the crash, even though punters are in short supply, they haven't bothered with private clients; they had been left with one extremely bad debt, so private clients aren't welcome. Banks and institutions are their main clients; they have millions to back them, and millions to play with – particularly the French. My day, they said, was likely to be dull. We had chosen it because the trade figures were to be announced at 11.30 and could produce a little excitement, a little movement. The City expected that our balance-of-trade deficit, which had been worryingly large for some time, would reveal yet another set of bad figures, probably between £1.1 and £1.5 billion, and if such figures were announced, nothing much would happen. It had reached £2 billion a few months earlier. The interest rate stood at 12 per cent.

We talked at first of simple things like women in the city. They were welcome, but there were fears that they were being used as cheap labour. They could be hired for a lot less than a fellow, because they were so anxious for the chance to break into another male bastion. But cheap labour isn't all that cheap by non-City standards. Mo earns £14,000, but when the markets perk up she hopes that will be doubled at a stroke.

Mo fell in love with the City on the telephone. She was in the middle of her studies for a HND in business studies and determined to become a buyer in a department store. One day she learned it might take a while to reach the status of buyer and she had to be prepared to spend some time as an assistant buyer. The young in the eighties have no patience with this kind of time-serving attitude. They want it now. 'I knew I couldn't get stuck in a job with shit wages where you had to watch someone for ages before being allowed to do anything interesting.' She was nursing such thoughts when the phone rang. The caller happened to mention that a friend of his had become a yen dealer, and for the next hour she picked the caller dry of information. By the end of the hour she knew for certain that she had found the future. Her parents (her father works for an airline) were shocked. They thought the City immoral. Her careers adviser told her her ambition was pretty impossible. Some 120 letters and five interviews later she had her first job: she was to become a futures broker. Her first year was hard; the male voices on the phone treated her like a secretary. M3 told her to keep going; once she had broken through, the fact that she was female would be an advantage. Mo thinks her job is the bee's knees; her voice is loud, her movements quick, her energy and enthusiasm are enviable and exhausting, and she admirably conveys the sense of excitement she feels about her career. She quickly sensed my anxiety as I gazed at green writing on black screens and tried to make sense of what was going on. 'Just concentrate on the essentials and forget the rest. Financial futures are speculative contracts on interest rates of the four major currencies: the dollar, yen, D-mark and sterling. They are traded four months of the year, March, June, September and December. Banks and insurance companies – building societies are not allowed to speculate – try to make money out of predicting when and by how much interest rates are likely to move.'

We didn't have such a market in London until 1982. Then we copied the Americans, who had invented financial futures a decade before. The principle of futures trading is centuries old. It is an instrument used to protect producers and buyers of raw materials from price fluctuations. A futures contract enables a price to be set for a transaction at some point in the future. A farmer needing to iron out the highs and lows of producing coffee, sugar, oranges and so forth would sell a percentage of his crop in advance to buyers who also need a measure of price certainty. This principle was easily adapted to currencies: a buyer of Deutschmarks, dollars, yen or sterling locks in the cost of the currency, regardless of what happens on the currency markets. Banks and insurance companies have now gone one stage further and applied the principle to interest rates. They lend at one rate and try and recoup by speculating on that rate going up or down – a bit like a bookmaker laying off a bet.

The predictions are based on educated guesswork, making a pattern of umpteen people's opinions on things political, economic and psychological. There are no certainties, only hunches – one day a movement in oil prices can have an impact on the market and a month later a similar movement will be ignored. The skill is in taking a view and sticking to it. It sounds more of a lottery than reading the tea-leaves or following the stars; and since it is such a lottery, since it is so difficult, getting it right produces 'a buzz' – to use broker's language.

The phone rang from time to time. Most of the outward calls were made by M1, who was attempting to solve a serious problem. His lunch date had been cancelled. He'd been looking forward to Mario and Franco's spare-ribs all week, and now his main task was to find another rib-eater. Much of our talk was interlaced with 'ribbing' between the four and with anecdotes. There was no danger of this quartet taking itself too seriously.

At 11.20 a phone call delivered the rumour that the balance-of-trade deficit was going to be £800 million. That figure was batted around the room, offering the opportunity to regurgitate old stories of similar phone calls that had looked hopelessly inaccurate and then turned out to be spot-on.

I knew 11.30 had arrived because M3 stood up, prepared for action, his right hand planted in the waistband at the back of his trousers. 'Cor blimey,' he said. (He usually said struth.) The trade deficit was £2.43 billion; twice the figure the City had estimated; it was a colossal bill for imports, and our exports had dropped. The next five minutes were a blur of comments: 'What a shambles!' 'What a mess!' 'The base rate will have to move.' 'Why does that Chancellor keep lying? Why does he keep saying the economy is in a good state? Why does everyone believe him?' Mo and I left the office before we had time to digest all this; she had got me a place on the floor of the LIFFE. Not in the public gallery, but on the floor, and we had been allotted half an hour between 11.45 and 12.15.

My first impression of the floor was of a jumble of youthful figures, male, in lightweight jackets, the colour, like jockeys' caps, denoting the company for which they worked. They were milling around in two main pits and a couple of minor pits, and around the edges were stalls, where more young men and a number of young women yelled into telephones. A four-letter word floated by. 'I'm so sorry,' said its owner. He could spot an outsider: I was wearing a badge. I was trying to listen to Mo describing the scene: 'That's gilts. That's short term. That's Eurobonds ...' It wasn't easy to hear above the noise. As midday struck, I glanced at my watch. It was timely action and helped to cushion what happened next. It had been noisy; now it became frantic. Coloured jackets jostled for position, arms punched the air, grown men screamed, 'Watch me, for fuck's sake, watch me!' No one apologized. For a second I felt fear. I felt the mood of men out of control. My mind flashed to football crowds. Only Hogarth, or perhaps Hockney, could have done justice to this scene: these men were manic. My fear lasted only for a second, the time it took me to realize that interest rates had moved from 12 to 13 per cent. This was the sound of the City taken by surprise. I stood immobilized, catching mere fragments of the screams:

'100 at 08'; '350 aside Raz a small seller'; '100 at 18, we are the bid'; 'Done 39 working 11 at 00'. It didn't matter that I didn't understand the detail. I understood enough: I understood that this was the sound and these were the screams of money being made. I blinked at the scene, my mind able to focus only on tiny details; a 'No worries' button on a jacket; a host of bitten fingernails. I'd had enough before the half hour was up.

Back in the office M1 had secured a lunch partner and M3 was glancing at Garfield, the cartoon in the *Herald Tribune*. There was chat about the fast market and jokes about the quiet day I had chosen. I lapped up the humour. And then we settled down to discuss the deficit. Their view was that the trigger for the trade deficit could be traced back to the crash. Then the Chancellor and indeed everyone else in the City feared that a recession would follow and thus the obvious course was to stimulate the economy with tax cuts and lower interest rates in order to lessen the impact of a recession. What no one saw at the time was that the economy did not need stimulating; consumers armed with credit-cards were in the mood to spend and industry of all kinds also needed to go on spending. Bringing interest rates down to 7.5 per cent had given the economy an injection it did not need. They blamed the Chancellor for not realizing all this more quickly than he did and changing course sooner. The result was a whopping trade imbalance and the reasons for the size of this were the topic of conversation over steak sandwiches and glasses of wine at the neighbouring wine bar. The reasons place a question-mark over the strength of our so-called economic recovery. We buy from abroad because we can't find the products we want and need with a 'Made in Britain' label. M3 told me about his yew trees. He's been planting yew trees at his country home and his attempts to buy British yew trees were stymied; he'd tried to buy British, but incompetence and inefficiency had caused him to lose patience. He bought his trees from Belgium.

'The other day I bought a sesame-seed snack and noticed that it said "Made in Poland". Why? Surely someone in Bradford can make a sesame-seed bar!'

These may seem to be trivial examples, but they more than adequately make the point. The building boom is hampered by the shortage of British-produced building materials. Cement, bricks, doors, locks and structural steel are all being imported, adding billions to the balance-of-payment deficit. There are serious doubts about the underlying strength of the economy: doubts about levels of investment and of productivity and doubts about the extent of the entrepreneurial revolution. The conversation took me right back to the beginning of my journey, to Shetland and to thoughts that we had mismanaged our great gift of oil; that the government should have used at least some of the oil money to invest in research and development that would enable our manufacturing base to shoulder more responsibility for our economic health. What is going to happen once our oil begins to run out and we find ourselves importing once more? What are we going to do once privatization has run its course and there is nothing more to sell to boost the Exchequer? The appalling trade deficit shows that we are not only not making the things we need, we are not making things that other people need either. And we haven't done so for years. The government has poured money into defence products and aircraft and done far too little to ensure our survival in the more mundane market place of mechanical engineering, electronics, cars and motor-bikes and consumer durables. We can't even take comfort from the fact that we make the best aircraft or the best defence equipment, because we don't.

The Americans do. Of course, industry itself could and should do more research and development of its own but, since much research is hugely expensive, it is an area in which the government could be of assistance. Industry, all too often geared only to the short-term interests of shareholders, needs to be chivvied, cajoled and encouraged to think long term. The Japanese have achieved miracles by this kind of coordinated approach. The Ms are scathing about industry or, rather, about the way in which industry is managed in this country. We don't train people; we don't work with the spirit of common purpose; we don't make the right decisions; we are inefficient. Still. There is no economic miracle. There is pessimism. And what progress we have made to become more efficient is being jeopardized by inflationary wage demands. M3 was certain that the Chancellor intended his high interest rates to squeeze industry's profits so that they would not be tempted to give in to high wage claims and so help to undermine the all-important fight against inflation. Some argue that a glance at economic history shows that industry will respond to high interest rates and a strong pound – both of which make exports more expensive – by cutting the workforce. They predict a rise in unemployment. The Ms say that the workforce must break the habit of annual increases. It is hard to argue with them. They get bonuses when business is good, large bonuses that can double salaries *and* they get salary freezes and sometimes cuts and no bonuses when business is poor. Their earnings are geared to productivity.

I asked M3 why he didn't go into industry, didn't go off and make the sesame-seed bars. He paused and answered by justifying what he had chosen to do. 'Our service is needed. We help industry to run better and more smoothly. Without us it would be like driving a car with a gear-box without synchromesh. With us there are fewer bumps.'

Behind the justification lay the truth. All of them came into the City to make money and to make money while they were young. Industry could not compete with lifestyles that included planting yew trees in Somerset. I find it refreshing to hear people *admit* that they like to be well rewarded for what they do and that they enjoy spending the money they earn. For too long many people have simulated disdain of money. That is hypocritical. For too long people have scorned those who work hard – the English way was to pretend that success was effortless rather than hard graft. Successful public figures when interviewed are still prone to deny that they are competitive and try to suggest, in the old-fashioned public-school manner, that they never set out to 'win', to reach the heights. What hypocrites! In Mrs Thatcher's

Britain at least we are free – some of us – to admit that we are prepared to work hard and that success in whatever field is a struggle and not some kind of magic dust that settles upon the chosen few. And of course in just the same way as sex has run riot, released from its Victorian corset in the sixties, so now we are making hay with our new-found freedom to acknowledge the value of success and the importance of money. To unthinking ears, it can sound vulgar. Sometimes it is vulgar. I'd prefer that to hypocrisy.

None the less I told the Ms that if I had a magic wand I'd ensure that some of the highly motivated talent in the City – and for that matter in advertising too – found its way into industry and teaching. Then perhaps we could once and for all get the economic recipe right. They answered by saying that I ought not to underestimate the worth of the City. The export of financial services helps our balance of payments. As we were the first nation to industrialize, so we were the first nation to need complex financial structures. The arcane world of high finance, being something 'in the City', seems to suit our temperaments. We remain an important financial centre because of our expertise, and also because of the language we speak. America speaks English and America is important. And we are halfway between New York and Tokyo. For all that, I can't help but see financial futures as gambling, sophisticated gambling. It doesn't seem so different, in principle, from betting on horses: you study the form and take a punt. And what is wrong with that, you say? After all, we've always been seen as a nation of gamblers. The betting industry is huge and growing. The most prosperous-looking shop at King's Cross is Mecca.

Watching people making money is exhausting; watching people making money out of a situation that showed the country to be in poor economic health depressed me. I do not know – and nor does anybody else – whether our trade deficit, our ugly credit boom, is merely a highly visible cold sore or a cancerous growth. I do not know and nor does anyone else whether the prosperity of the late 1980s will be sustained or whether it will crack and crumble, taking Mrs Thatcher and all that she stands for diving to the bottom of the political pond. All I do know is that there is much doubt.

And I do know that as the next election draws near the government will be assessed first and foremost on its economic performance. There are two reasons for this. We have not yet reached the magic moment when citizens become disillusioned with material growth; voters are still overly wallet-conscious and if on election day they feel prosperous and if they feel the country is padding up the right economic path they, for the most part, are prepared to overlook other shortcomings. And secondly, the Conservative party has always been perceived as the party best able to manage, particularly the economy. It is the party that understands 'finance' and 'business'; it is the businessman's party. If then the Conservatives stumble on the economy, their unique selling-point disappears and they will be turned out of office in the decades-old seesaw between hard-nosed governments and soft-hearted governments. We know that the businessman's governments, instead of adding sweetness and warmth and grace to national life, add barrenness, and voters accept a touch of barrenness in order to promote material prosperity. But as soon as faith in the hard-nosed government's ability to deliver the pounds to our pocket begins to waver, voters start to focus on the barrenness and yearn for a touch of sweetness and warmth. The bottom line in the past has been that simple. However, when Mrs Thatcher won the 1979 election, there wasn't much sweet-ness and warmth emanating from the Labour party. The economy was sickly: the International Monetary Fund had been hauled in to help and it told the government to cut public spending. As a result, the govern-ment lost the support of its backbone, the trades unions, and the country was staggering under a series of public-sector strikes. And the party was full of left–right bickering. On its shelves were exciting plans for more democracy in the workplace and plans for revitalizing local government through a system of local income tax, but the party seemed incapable of doing anything, let alone anything exciting. As we floundered so we gained a reputation abroad both for our industrial militancy and for our national decline. The national psyche was sinking under a weight of both written and spoken words announcing and denouncing our decline.

In 1979 we needed Mrs Thatcher. We may not need her now; we may think that her reforms have gone far enough; we may wish that there had been another party fit to take the reins in 1987. But in 1979 we needed Mrs Thatcher. We needed someone who could take a cold, hard look at these ossified islands; someone not steeped in tradition and the old way of doing things. Someone who did not believe that politics was the art of the possible, but someone who was prepared to confront the impossible and who would kick us out of our fireside chairs, where we had grown complacent and unimaginative, melan-choly and increasingly shabby. The world was moving on; industries demanding muscle had decamped to other countries in search of cheaper sweat. Our industrial base was slowly vanishing and could no longer support us; the future threatened us rather than excited us and our response was to sink into debilitating drift. Our distinguished past and our reputation as a civilized country were not going to help us secure a place of significance in the new global economic order. For that we needed a strong leader with a vision. Mrs Thatcher's vision was to abandon the consensus which had shaped British politics since the war and replace it with a new, demanding credo based on individual responsibility that would flourish in a thrusting, more competitive, free-enterprise ethos. Public spending had to be cut; industries had to be privatized; taxes had to be cut; trades union power had to be curtailed; vested interests had to be dismantled; and institutions had to prove their worth. The state's role had to change from provider to enabler; citizens would cease to be passive workers who handed over money in the form of taxes and then expected the necessities to be provided. They would keep more of their money and become active, empowered to make their own decisions. And Mrs Thatcher had her own way of effecting this massive transition from pessimistic lethargy to optimistic, positive action. She may have been heading the party of tradition, but she was not shackled by history. Women are far less inclined to be sentimental about the past and far more irritated by tradition. The past for them has not been golden – it has been coloured grey by thankless, tiring work at home and tiresome, endless slog for recognition outside the home. Women whatever their lot are always more grounded in the present and more thoughtful about the future. Nature has made it this way and man has kept it this way: it is women who bear children and bring up children, therefore they have to be focused in the present and they have to worry more about the future: their children's future.

Mrs Thatcher, I think, shares much in common with Jeremy Bentham, a rare man who was not pickled in history nor ruled by tradition either, and whose mind was also free from professional and class feeling. Bentham too was inclined to apply the rigours of logic to the facts of society and he looked at institutions and asked them to justify their existence. His aim was the greatest good of the greatest number. Mrs Thatcher set about her reconstruction by looking at the institutions that are responsible for the prime needs of our lives: housing, health, education and jobs. Out went the nationalized industries; out went subsidies to firms who could not pay their way; in came small businesses and self-employment. She attacked the slumbering, lumbering, local authorities; out went their free-spending notions; out went their unquestioned control of housing and education. Their monopoly provision of rented houses was removed and in came self-managed estates and housing associations and private landlords. She formulated new patterns for education and freed schools, should they wish, from domination by local authorities. She attacked the universities and the health service and social security benefits. She has attacked the unskilled workforce and offered them the beginnings of training schemes. She has attacked the toffs in the City of London and in the legal profession. She has attacked us all by telling us to stop blaming society for our misfortunes and instead take responsibility for our own futures.

And in challenging received wisdom on all these fronts she was bound to be attacked herself. Some of those who attack her do so out of a mixture of prejudice and fear of change. They are the ones who concentrate their criticisms on style rather than content; they sneer at her voice and her manner and claim that she is an authoritarian when what they mean is that the men around her have little idea how to respond to a woman in authority; when what they mean is that their own ideas are in a mess. One of the great ironies of the Thatcher years, with their emphasis on giving the consumer a choice, is that in the most important area of all – politics – there has been no real choice. Both Thatcher supporters and non-supporters know this and find it frustrating and fear-making. We feel trapped: our supreme right, our ultimate weapon to oust one government in favour of another, has been removed. Our options are no longer clear.

We are fretful: this shows most clearly with the appearance of Charter 88, signed by 250 writers, academics, lawyers and show-business personalities. They warn us that the future could be grim. They are bothered by threats to our civil liberties: to the independence of broadcasting by the setting-up of a watchdog body to keep sex and violence in check and by refusing to allow Sinn Fein, the political wing of the IRA, to be interviewed on television and radio; by threats to academic freedom with the abolition of tenure; to the right to join a trades union by the abolition of that right at GCHQ, the government's listening post; threats to freedom of expression by the passing of Clause 28, which prohibits councils from promoting homosexual and lesbian lifestyles. To combat such threats the charter signatories argue for a bill of Rights to enshrine our civil liberties, and for proportional representation so that we are never again exposed to a government with a whopping majority able to force through whatever legislation it likes. The chartists are right to be vigilant, but their remedies have unpleasant side-effects: a Bill of Rights would give lawyers power over a democratically elected parliament and PR promotes backstage deals and insincere pacts. In any event, their list is alarmist; for each of their arguments there are, as always, counterarguments. I do not believe that the abolition of tenure is a threat to academic freedom; the banning of trades unions at GCHQ seems as nothing compared to the way in which civil liberties are infringed by union closed shops. The Sinn Fein ban is of dubious help in solving the Irish question, and has certainly made TV and radio hopping mad, but the threat of a watchdog has made television companies update their own guidelines to programme makers. We are a funny lot when it comes to words like freedom and notions of liberty. We feel attacked by the most sensible provisions. Remember all the fuss about seat-belts? If we'd had the sense to wear them there would have been no need for a law ordering us to do so. The thought of random breath-testing rightly upsets a good number of people, but then, if we had the sense to leave our cars at home when we feel inclined to drink, it would not be necessary. And now we are making the same fuss about ID cards at football matches. It would make a lot of sense, and life would be easier if we all had them all the time. Most countries in the EEC already do. As it is, I constantly have to get separate cards to enter this building, or attend that conference, or merely to get a railcard or a bus pass or to rent a video or cash a cheque. If one ID card could cover everything, I'd be delighted.

The truth about the last decade is that we have faced so many radical reforms we are unnerved. By 1989 we – and that includes a number of Conservative MPs – feel battered. The government is swirling in legislation; it is almost as though Mrs Thatcher, for all her utterances to the contrary, knows her days are numbered and is continuing her spring-clean of the nation at top speed. And as reforms are rained upon us we float in uncharted waters with the media as our compass. Television is a blunt instrument that makes the complex accessible by ironing out the wrinkles and inviting those with polarized views to appear on our screens to explain themselves in thirty seconds or ninety words. Such techniques foster an adversarial culture in which serious analytical debate is not encouraged. The so-called quality newspapers have the space and the time, but their efforts are often spoiled by lack of balance. Journalists get approval and an audience by exaggerating; their success is gauged by the size of their mailbag. They feed off each other's ideas, particularly in the political arena, and rarely leave the hothouse atmosphere of London. The result is information overload; we know, but we do not understand. The truth is that we cannot yet measure the success or otherwise of many of Mrs Thatcher's measures. If we are fair-minded and optimistic we wish them well; if we have closed minds and are pessimistic we wish them ill. If we are realists we know that some of these radical measures are bound to be for the best and some will turn out to be for the worst. Such is the nature of change. It is never all progress, even when it is essential.

The battle for the soul of the Victoria and Albert Museum can be used as a perfect cameo for the eighties. The V & A is an institution that prides itself on its devotion to our glorious industrial past. It is a vast and imposing building outside, dowdy and depressing inside. It has been kept short of money by successive governments who have had a hard enough time finding funds for the essentials from our sluggish economy. Now the museum's roof leaks after years of neglect and the old-era scholarly staff lack the will and the inclination to do much about the situation. The keeper barons of the various departments enjoy competing with each other but not with the outside world. And it is useless to argue that in a civilized country the state ought to fund the museums as part of its commitment to the arts. So it should; but it will never be a top priority and it will never favour places riddled with intellectual snobbery; places that do not help themselves and who make little effort to reach out to the people. On to the scene came a new director, Elizabeth Esteve-Coll, who had been the keeper of the V & A's art library. She did not belong to the art establishment; she didn't go to public school, or Oxbridge and the Courtauld Institute, and she had radical plans to put an end to the debilitating drift to ensure the museum's survival. It meant getting rid of nine employees, most of whom enjoyed a high reputation, but who were considered unwilling or unable to adapt to a new way of doing things. She was attacked by the old school as being a 'vulgar populist' and her plans were called 'asinine and uneconomical and destructive to scholarship'. She denies this; she says she is just as passionate about the museum as any of the old school and believes her plans will improve the V & A's reputation. We will not be able to judge the new V & A for some time. It won't be the same; but with luck it will appeal to a wider, if less discriminating, audience. It isn't philistine to be popular. 'Something' may well be lost; the place will be more egalitarian and above all it will survive.

Chekhov, the son of a strict, Church-going grocer, wrote *The Cherry Orchard*, a play in which a grand and famous estate is deeply in debt, and its decaying, genteel owners lament the fact but seem incapable of finding a way of retrieving the situation. Once the orchard yielded marvellous cherries that were dried and sent to Moscow and earned much money. But such prosperity became a memory, the recipe was lost. An outsider, the self-made Lopakhin, whose father had owned the village shop, and who has worked hard and saved money, comes along and buys the cherry orchard: the successful plebian ousts the upper-crust no-hopers. He is unmoved by the past, by the fact that the orchard is mentioned in the encyclopaedia, and decides to make the estate prosperous once more by chopping down the cherry trees and building summer cottages for rent. Chekhov insisted that Lopakhin was a subtle and sensitive businessman. The critics, at first, saw him as a vulgar son of a bitch.

If we are realists, we know that we needed Mrs Thatcher to curtail our decline; we needed her to find a way to renewed prosperity; we needed her to take the helm while the other parties regrouped and rearranged their thoughts. They have taken a long time, too long, to find the way forward. But when their time comes they will have a jolly task: it will be so much easier to ask us to pay more for the health service, for education, for measures to aid the environment. It will be so much easier for us to appreciate the case for having some essential industries in the public domain; it will be so much easier for us to see that while having money to spend is important, it is not all-important; it will be so much easier for us to look generously upon the poor and the unemployed. We will be yearning – when the time comes – to say a hearty farewell to hard noses and a warm welcome to soft hearts, who will offer us a kinder, gentler Britain. It will be so much easier to see the wood. We will undoubtedly find that too many cherry trees have been chopped down. The pendulum of change has a habit of going too far. But we can plant new cherry trees: it takes a mere dozen years for them to grow – strong and healthy, well pruned and groomed, this time, with care and understanding.

Bibliography

The Islands

Shetland, James R. Nicholson, David and Charles, 1972
Orkney and Shetland, Eric Linklater, Robert Hale, 1965
Orkney, Patrick Bailey, David and Charles, 1971

Scotland

Scottish Journey, Edwin Muir, Flamingo, 1985
Cobbett's Tour of Scotland, Aberdeen University Press, 1984
A History of the Scottish People, 1560–1830, T. C. Smout, Fontana, 1972
A History of Scotland, J. D. Mackie, Pelican, 1964
The Highland Clearances, John Prebble, Penguin, 1986
Scotland, The Real Divide: Poverty and Deprivation in Scotland, Gordon Brown and Robin Cook (eds.), Mainstream Publishing, 1983
No Gods and Precious Few Heroes, Scotland 1914–1980, Christopher Harvie, Edward Arnold, 1981
Scotland: The Case for Optimism, Jim Sillars, Polygon, 1986
Glasgow, David Daiches, Andre Deutsch, 1977
No Immediate Danger, Rosalie Bertell, Women's Press, 1985

Ireland

A Place Apart, Dervla Murphy, Penguin, 1979
Ireland: A History, Robert Kee, Weidenfeld and Nicolson, 1980
A History of Northern Ireland, Patrick Buckland, Gill and Macmillan, 1981
Them and Us: Britain-Ireland and the Northern Question, 1969–1982, James Downey, Ward River Press, 1983
Ireland: A Positive Proposal, Kevin Boyle and Tom Hadden, Penguin, 1985
Pig in the Middle, The Army in Northern Ireland, 1969–1985, Desmond Hamill, Methuen, 1986
Ireland: The Propaganda War, Liz Curtis, Pluto Press, 1984
Only the Rivers Run Free: Northern Ireland: The Women's War, Eileen

Fairweather, Roisin McDonough and Melanie McFadyean, Pluto Press, 1984

Wales

The Matter of Wales, Jan Morris, Penguin, 1986
Wales: Rebirth of a Nation, 1880–1980, Kenneth O. Morgan, Oxford University Press, 1982
The Welsh Extremist, Ned Thomas, Y Lolfa, 1973
The Celtic Revolution, Peter Berresford Ellis, Y Lolfa, 1985
Wild Wales, George Borrow, Fontana, 1982
Gerald of Wales, The Journey through Wales, Penguin, 1987
The Miners' Strike 1984–5: Loss without Limit, Martin Adeney and John Lloyd, Routledge and Kegan Paul, 1986
Digging Deeper: Issues in the Miners' Strike, Huw Beynon (ed.), Verso, 1985
Scargill and the Miners, Michael Crick, Penguin, 1985
The Great Strike, Alex Callinicos and Mike Simons, a Socialist Worker Publication, 1985
A History of British Trade Unionism, Henry Pelling, Pelican, 1984

England

A Social History of England, Asa Briggs, Penguin, 1987
English Social History, A Survey of Six Centuries, G. M. Trevelyan, Penguin, 1986
British Society Since 1945, Arthur Marwick, Penguin, 1986
England in the Twentieth Century, David Thomson, Penguin, 1986
Post-War Britain, Alan Sked and Chris Cook, Penguin, 1986
Change in British Society, A. H. Halsey, Oxford University Press, 1986
England in Transition, Dorothy George, Penguin, 1962
English Culture and the Decline of the Industrial Spirit, 1850–1980, Martin J. Wiener, Penguin, 1985
The Uses of Literacy, Richard Hoggart, Penguin, 1986
The Oxford History of Britain, Kenneth O. Morgan (ed.), Oxford University Press, 1988
The Making of the English Working Class, E. P. Thompson, Penguin, 1968
English Journey, J. B. Priestley, Penguin, 1984
Kingdom by the Sea, Paul Theroux, Penguin, 1986
The Return of a Native Reporter, Robert Chesshyre, Viking, 1987
The Road to Wigan Pier, George Orwell, Penguin, 1986

Wigan Pier Revisited, Beatrix Campbell, Virago, 1985
A Writer's Britain, Margaret Drabble, Thames and Hudson, 1984

The Conservative Party from Peel to Thatcher, Robert Blake, Fontana, 1985
The Politics of Thatcherism, Stuart Hall and Martin Jacques (eds.), Lawrence and Wishart, 1983
Mrs Thatcher's Economic Experiment, William Keegan, Penguin, 1985
The Politics of Hope, Trevor Blackwell and Jeremy Seabrook, Faber and Faber, 1988
Manifesto, A Radical Strategy for Britain's Future, Francis Cripps, et al., Pan, 1981
The Strange Rebirth of Liberal Britain, Ian Bradley, Chatto & Windus, 1985
Claret and Chips, The Rise of the SDP, Hugh Stephenson, Michael Joseph, 1982
Partnership of Principle, Roy Jenkins, Secker and Warburg, 1985
Militant, Michael Crick, Faber and Faber, 1984

Liverpool on the Brink, Michael Parkinson, Policy Journals, 1985
Inside Left, Derek Hatton, Bloomsbury, 1987
The Scarman Report, Lord Scarman, Penguin, 1986
Report of the Broadwater Farm Inquiry, chaired by Lord Gifford, Karia Press, 1986
Tales from Two Cities, Dervla Murphy, John Murray, 1987

Unofficial Secrets: Child Sexual Abuse, The Cleveland Case, Beatrix Campbell, Virago Press, 1988
The Public School Phenomenon, Jonathan Gathorne-Hardy, Penguin, 1979
The Coming of the Greens, Jonathan Porritt, Fontana, 1988

Index

INDEX

INDEX